THE HOW AND WHY OF

MECHANICAL MOVEMENTS

The HOW and WHY of

A POPULAR SCIENCE BOOK

MECHANICAL MOVEMENTS

Exactly How Machines Work:
Engines, Turbines, Transmissions,
Brakes, Clutches, Rockets,
Atomic Generators, Gyroscopes,
Guidance Systems

by Harry Walton

Illustrated by Ray Pioch

POPULAR SCIENCE PUBLISHING COMPANY • E. P. DUTTON & CO., INC.
NEW YORK

Library of Congress Catalog Card Number: 68-31227

DESIGNED BY CHRISTIAN OHSER

Manufactured in the United States of America

DEDICATED TO MY PATIENT WIFE

Contents

THE HOW AND WHY OF

MECHANICAL MOVEMENTS

The Basic Facts
about Things Mechanical

In the physical world, mankind's climb from the primitive has from the first depended upon the beneficent application of power. It was of course only the power of human muscle to begin with. The harnessing of animal power came long after the caveman era, and the first use of natural forces such as wind and water much later still.

Today we are far more dependent on the development and use of power than ever before in the world's history. The great Northeast electrical blackout of 1965 was a dramatic demonstration of this. A nation's wealth and standard of living can be gauged by the amount of power it generates and uses. The total amount of power available has multiplied astronomically in the last hundred years, or since the end of the Civil War, although the steam engine was already then powering ships, trains and factories.

A surprising amount of power stands ready for your personal use. In your car, the throttle may command from 50 to 400 horsepower. The electric toaster on your table may consume up to a horsepower and a half for brief periods. A single-room air conditioner will draw that much power for much longer periods. Oil and gas heating represent power too, though in a different form than electricity. Refrigeration, laundry equipment, communication and entertainment all consume growing amounts of power, and in addition there are the vast power needs of industry.

1

Power means machines, both to generate it and to use it. Webster defines a machine as "Any device consisting of two or more ... parts, which may serve to transmit and modify force and motion so as to do some desired kind of work." The alternator that supplies the current for your toaster is a machine. So is the prime mover that turns the alternator. (A prime mover, says Webster, is "A natural agency applied by man to the production of power [from] some natural source.")

Muscles, windmills, waterwheels, gasoline, steam and diesel engines, nuclear power plants, and electric motors driven by flashlight cells all qualify as prime movers. They convert the natural forces of the body, wind, moving water, fuels, nuclear fission, and chemical action into mechanical energy. A pneumatic jack hammer, a subway-train motor and an electric shaver are not prime movers, because their power sources are secondhand, or synthetic. You don't find compressed air or alternating current in nature. They have to be produced by machines, which are in turn driven by prime movers.

Future electrical generators may not be whirring machines. It is possible to generate electricity by the direct combustion of gases in what are called fuel cells. An even more recent development is the generation of electricity in gases piped through magnetic fields, instead of by spinning coils inside such fields. But the accessories necessary to such systems, such as pumps, will still be machines, and so will most of the devices that make use of the power generated.

Automation has already multiplied the development of highly sophisticated machines, and will continue to do so. Yet every machine, new or old, can be resolved into a combination of no more than six basic mechanical elements, known to the Greeks—and perhaps others—a couple of centuries before Christ. These are the lever, the pulley, the wheel and axle, the inclined plane, the wedge, and the screw. Some prefer to consider the inclined plane and wedge as two phases of the same thing, reducing the number of basic elements to five.

EARLY AUTOMATION

The seeds of ingenuity, always present in the human makeup, have sometimes borne strangely premature fruit. Automation itself, for example, began some time in the Middle Ages with an unkown miller who wanted to grind grain as rapidly as the wind allowed. Grain was fed to the millstone through a hole in the bottom of a hopper, but when the wind dropped and the wheel turned more slowly, unground grain would pile up and cause trouble. If

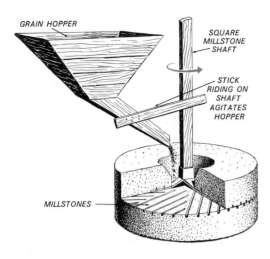

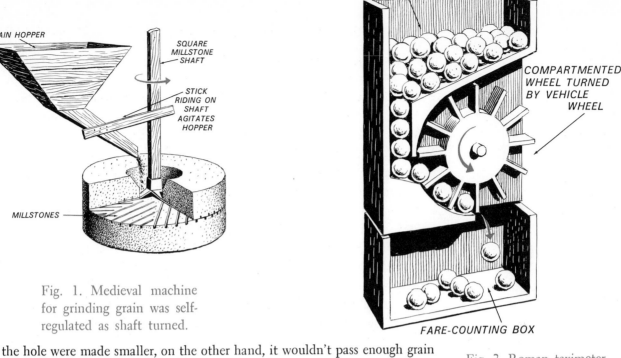

GRAIN HOPPER

SQUARE
MILLSTONE
SHAFT

STICK
RIDING ON
SHAFT
AGITATES
HOPPER

MILLSTONES

COMPARTMENTED
WHEEL TURNED
BY VEHICLE
WHEEL

FARE-COUNTING BOX

Fig. 1. Medieval machine for grinding grain was self-regulated as shaft turned.

Fig. 2. Roman taximeter.

the hole were made smaller, on the other hand, it wouldn't pass enough grain to keep the stone working at full capacity when the wind was brisk.

The millstone shaft was square in those days, being rounded only where it ran in the bearings. The miller fastened a stick to the hopper so that its outer end lay against the square shaft, which in turning operated like a four-lobed cam (Figure 1). The faster the millstone turned, the more often it jiggled the stick. The more rapidly this agitated the hopper, the more grain fell onto the stone. When the wind dropped and the shaft slowed down, the stick and hopper were jiggled less and the flow of grain diminished. The system regulated itself according to need, which is a fair definition of automation.

If asked to guess when the notion of a taximeter dawned on human thought, you might reasonably suggest that such a device might have appeared on hired carriages in the 18th or 19th century. You'd be wrong, for a Roman engineer named Vitruvius described a crude taximeter in the first century B.C. Credited to an Alexandrian named Hero (or Heron) the gadget had a compartmented wheel somehow connected to revolve slowly as the vehicle wheels turned (Figure 2). Above this paddle-like wheel was a hopper full of smooth pebbles. As the wheel turned, it received one pebble at a time and, as the filled compartment came to the bottom, dropped it into a box below. At the end of the ride, the driver counted the pebbles in the box and charged accordingly.

Hero, a mathematician and mechanic living about 150 B.C., also built slot machines that vended holy water, rigged temple doors so that they would open of themselves when a fire was kindled on the altar, and invented a simple steam turbine that did nothing but spin—and amaze the onlookers.

3

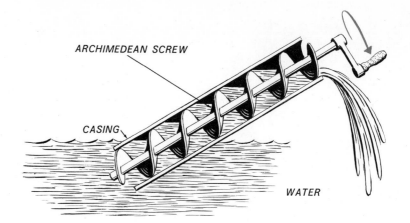

ARCHIMEDEAN SCREW

CASING

WATER

Fig. 3. Archimedean screw.

Another Alexandrian, Otesibius, invented the force pump and was probably therefore the first man to make practical use of the cylinder and piston idea that propels our automobiles today. He had a competitor named Archimedes who had a different scheme for raising water. It was a long screw or spiral—a sort of continuous one-bladed propeller—enclosed in a casing with one end under water (Figure 3). When turned, the Archimedean screw (or cochlea, as it is also called) raised water continuously. Used in ancient Egypt, it still serves for irrigation in some Mediterranean countries.

A very considerable mastery of the six basic machine elements must have been necessary to build the pyramids, in addition to a knowledge of geometry and surveying.

BATTERIES IN BAGDAD

Nonmechanical wonders of past ages included the dread Greek fire, ancestor of today's flame thrower and quite as unpleasant. This was a concoction of combustible chemicals that could not be extinguished with water.

Still more astonishing is the discovery, on the site of ancient Bagdad, of electrical batteries 2,000 years old. These are pots with cylinders of sheet copper in them, and an iron rod inside each cylinder, the two elements being insulated from each other with pitch. Mr. W. M. F. Gray, of the General Electric Transformer Division at Pittsburgh, has rebuilt some of these pots, added an electrolyte, and found that they generate current. It is believed that they were originally used for electroplating. Confirming this, archeologists have found electroplated objects not merely 2,000, but 4,000 years old, in the same area where the batteries were discovered.

War has always lent tremendous impetus to invention. Huge multi-leveled battle towers that could be shoved up against fortress walls were the forerunners of today's tanks. Giant machines that could hurl bolts, spears and stones were powered by weights, the torsion of twisted hair or sinews, or the resilience of wood, horn and iron.

The ideas left by Leonardo da Vinci, that 15th century genius—artist, civil and military engineer, mathematician, and architect—foreshadowed a number of "modern" inventions. A builder of canals, bridges, fortresses, cannons and water wheels, da Vinci leaped far ahead of his day. He fired a gun with steam, sketched plans for a helicopter, submarine, airplane and parachute, and suggested interchangeable gears.

FORCE, WORK AND POWER

These seem to be familiar, everyday words. But they have special meanings in physics and mechanics.

Force, a word derived from the Greek one for tendon, is a directed effort tending to change the motion of a body—by making it move, speeding it up, or slowing it down. Force can exist only if it has a physical object to act on, but it may exist without producing any change in motion, if opposed by an equal counterforce. In fact, the object acted upon by a force always exerts one of its own, so forces can be said to exist always in pairs, and unless the body is being accelerated or decelerated, these forces are equal and opposite.

If you push on a wrench, the wrench pushes back on you with the same amount of force. Your weight exerts a force on the floor, and the floor exerts an equal upward force to support you. This second pair of forces is so great in comparison to that of the wrench, that it effectively anchors you; so the backward push of the wrench isn't noticeable. But if an astronaut in free space tries to loosen a nut with a wrench, he will be propelled away from it by that reaction force, a problem recognized by the recent development of a tool for astronauts that will absorb reaction forces.

If you were to anchor two spring balances inside a rigid frame and tie the two together, the two scales would read the same. One force would exactly balance the other, and the balances would be motionless. Should you cut them loose, the unbalanced forces would produce violent action.

Work, the second important word with a precise meaning in physics, is the result of a force overcoming resistance—a larger force overcoming a lesser. Work is therefore force acting over a distance. If you lift a 50-pound weight off the floor to a shelf 6 feet high, you have performed 300 foot-pounds

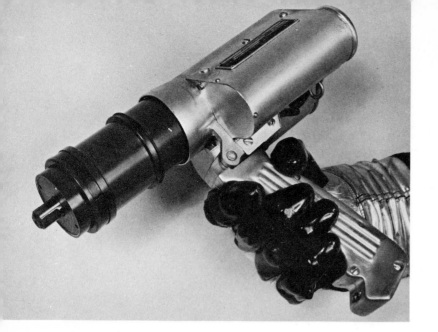
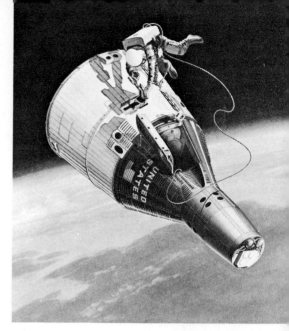

A "zero-reaction" tool used by astronauts to prevent their work from spinning them away from the spacecraft. The armature and motor casing turn freely in opposite directions, winding a spring which delivers reactive kick to the tool's shaft. *Courtesy of Black and Decker Manufacturing Company.*

of work, having exerted a force of 50 pounds over a distance of 6 feet.

But if you were to take that same weight off the shelf and simply hold it at the same height, getting more tired every minute, you wouldn't be doing a lick of work in the technical sense. Though you must exert force to keep the weight from falling, that force isn't acting through a distance. Your fatigue may seem all too real, but it isn't admissible evidence in the court of physics. That's not so unreasonable, when you stop to think that you could be replaced by a tripod or a pedestal, which wouldn't tire at all.

Energy is the capacity to do work, and can be measured in the same terms (such as foot-pounds) as work itself. In lifting that 50-pound weight to a height of 6 feet, you have given it the 300 foot-pounds of energy you expended. This could be recovered (minus certain small losses) by letting the weight drive a clock, or hooking it to a pulley system so that it raises something else.

The raised weight therefore has *potential* energy. So has a rock some receding glacier left on a hilltop, a wound-up spring, a mountain lake, or a stick of dynamite, though the last's is purely chemical in nature. The coiled spring could drive a clock, an instrument or a toy. If water from the high lake is allowed to fall on a water wheel, it can yield useful power. Utility companies take advantage of this to develop extra electrical power for peak-use periods. On the other hand, during the off-load periods, electricity generated by steam or nuclear plants is sent to waterside installations. Here it spins motors that turn centrifugal pumps, which lift water from a low level (such as a river) to a higher one, perhaps a lake impounded by dams.

When extra generating power is needed, valves are opened to let the water flow back through the pumps. But now they act as turbines, spinning the motors. These now become alternators, generating current that is sent back where it is required. There is of course considerable loss involved in the process, but alternating current cannot be stored, and this roundabout system has been found worth while to provide much-needed extra capacity.

If that weight you lifted rolls off the shelf, it will briefly have *kinetic* energy (energy of motion), which it will dissipate in a split second when it hits the floor. In the scientific sense, that energy isn't lost. It has been transformed partly into heat at the point of impact, and partly into work by deforming the substance of the weight and the floor.

An automobile in motion has a tremendous store of kinetic energy, which becomes dramatically visible in the results of a crash. To slow down a speeding car quickly, that kinetic energy must be dispersed by the brakes, which convert it rapidly into heat. Brake fade, or loss of braking effort, results when the heat cannot be dispersed quickly enough.

Power. You can do the same amount of work quickly or slowly. Whether you lift 50 pounds of sand 6 feet high a shovelful at a time, or grab the whole sack and hoist it up in two seconds, you are doing exactly 300 foot-pounds of work. But you are expending a great deal more *power* in the second case. Power involves the rate at which work is done. The more time the same amount of work takes, the less power is being applied. How long it takes an automobile to accelerate from zero to 60 miles per hour at full throttle depends chiefly on the horsepower of its engine.

When the steam engine began to do the work of horses in English mines, the engine maker's customers invariably asked how many horses a given engine would replace. To answer that, manufacturers began to rate their machines' output in "horsepower," and this obsolete, often awkward term is still very much with us.

James Watt, the most famous of the engine makers, conscientiously measured the capability of a husky draft horse. He found that it could exert a 150-pound pull while walking at 2½ miles per hour, which works out to 33,000 foot-pounds per minute, or 550 per second. Watt was in fact overly conscientious, and weighted the figures against his engines, for a horse cannot maintain that power output continuously.

If you weigh 165 pounds and climb a hill or a building 200 feet high, you too will have done 33,000 foot-pounds of work. How much *power* you have expended will depend on the time in which you did it. Had you made the

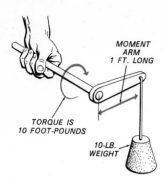

MOMENT ARM 1 FT. LONG

TORQUE IS 10 FOOT-POUNDS

10-LB. WEIGHT

Fig. 4. Amount of torque is calculated by multiplying the weight by its distance from center of shaft.

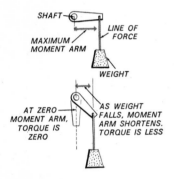

SHAFT

MAXIMUM MOMENT ARM

LINE OF FORCE

WEIGHT

AT ZERO MOMENT ARM, TORQUE IS ZERO

AS WEIGHT FALLS, MOMENT ARM SHORTENS. TORQUE IS LESS

Fig. 5. Example of an arrangement that would not maintain contant torque. Moment arm diminishes in length and approaches zero as it nears the bottom.

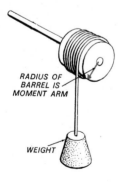

RADIUS OF BARREL IS MOMENT ARM

WEIGHT

Fig. 6. Rope wound around barrel on a shaft, then hung with a weight, produces constant torque as the moment arm is the radius of the barrel.

climb in one minute, you would have been expending a full horsepower (which isn't likely). Taking five minutes, you would have put out .2 (or one-fifth) horsepower, which is hard work but possible. A man's average working rate is nearer one-tenth horsepower, though he can surpass that for short periods.

Torque involves the idea of rotary motion, or action around a central point. Webster defines torque as "that which produces or tends to produce rotation or torsion." You may remember it more easily as what it takes to unscrew a jar lid. Torque is twisting effort.

As Webster's definition implies, torque can exist without movement just as force can. Torque is simply a force applied in such a way that it *could* produce rotary movement. In Figure 4 a shaft is held firmly in one hand. A lever or crank arm is affixed firmly to one end of the shaft, and at the end of the one-foot arm is hung a 10-pound weight.

This puts a torque or twisting effort of 10 foot-pounds on the shaft, which will turn unless the hand holds it firmly. The torque figure is found by multiplying the weight (force) by its distance from the center of the shaft. The same torque would be produced by a 5-pound weight hanging on an arm 2 feet long, or by a 20-pound weight on an arm a half foot long. (Foot-pounds of torque are sometimes called pound-feet, instead, which avoids risk of confusing them with foot-pounds of energy or work.)

If the weight were hung on the shaft itself, it obviously wouldn't tend to turn it at all. The greater the distance between the line on which the force acts (a vertical one in the case of a weight) and the axis of the shaft, the greater the torque effort.

Torque is also called *moment* and the distance between the force line and the fulcrum (axis) may be called *moment arm.* The amount of torque may be expressed in any convenient unit. For car engines, it is commonly given in foot-pounds. But small motors and such powered devices as electric drills may have torque expressed more exactly in inch-pounds or even inch-ounces.

If allowed to move, the arrangement in Figure 5 would not maintain constant torque. As the arm nears the bottom, the moment arm shortens and eventually becomes zero. Although the weight (force) remains constant, when it is multiplied by zero the product (torque) is zero. You can do better by mounting a barrel on the shaft as in Figure 6, wrapping a rope around it, and hanging the weight on the rope. The moment arm is now the radius of the barrel, and the weight will maintain a constant torque as long as it is free to drop. This is of course the way a grandfather clock operates.

A piston engine that develops torque only during the firing stroke is "helped over" the rest of its cycle by the flywheel. This stores some of the energy imparted during the firing stroke and then gives it back to keep the shaft turning at other times. For even greater smoothness, we multiply the number of cylinders, a practice culminating in the grand old 16-cylinder Pierce Arrow automobile. But an engine develops no torque at all standing still, so if we want to measure engine torque and power, it must be done on the run.

MEASURING HORSEPOWER

Figure 7 shows in diagram form what is called a Prony brake. The Prony brake is an absorption dynamometer, a device for measuring power. The block type shown is only suitable for outputs up to about 10 horsepower. A rope type is applicable to outputs five times that, and for industrial testing the electric dynamometer is commonly used. In this, the engine under test is made to drive an electric generator, and the electrical "load" or amount of current generated is measured and mathematically converted into horsepower.

The two blocks of the Prony brake shown are clamped around a drum or pulley keyed to the engine shaft and tightened so that the engine is working at its full capacity. The work being done is transformed into heat by the friction between the drum and the blocks. Meanwhile, the spring balance shows a force being exerted downward. This reading, from which should be subtracted the weight of the arm, is multiplied by the length of the arm to get a torque figure. All we now need to calculate horsepower is a tachometer (for reading the speed at which the shaft turns) and a pencil.

The indicated torque is being developed through the full 360-degree circle of rotation, even though the arm doesn't turn. Therefore the work being

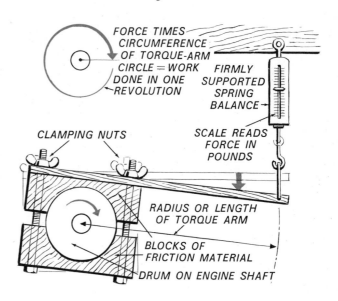

Fig. 7. Prony brake is a device for measuring horsepower, called an absorption dynamometer.

done is the product of the force (scale reading less weight of arm) times the circumference of a circle whose radius is the length of the arm. To find the *power* output, we must know in what length of time this amount of work is done. But since Watt's horsepower is 33,000 foot-pounds per *minute*, we may as well use the number of revolutions per minute the shaft makes, rather than a single turn. With the time factor thus included, it's now almost as easy to calculate horsepower as to add up a grocery bill. We get:

$$\text{Horsepower} = \frac{\text{Force times 2 Pi times Radius times RPM}}{33,000}$$

The horizontal line means "divided by." But first we can divide 2 Pi into both terms and simplify the equation to:

$$\text{Horsepower} = \frac{\text{Force times Radius times RPM}}{5,250}$$

With this formula and a home-rigged Prony brake, you could calculate the horsepower of a small gas engine, a model engine, or a motor. Auto makers specify the maximum torque of their engines, but if you multiply this figure by the speed given and divide by 5,250, your answer won't jibe with the maximum horsepower they claim. That's because top torque occurs well below top speed, while maximum horsepower is developed at very high revs even though torque is then lower. This fall-off in torque is a characteristic of the gasoline engine. If the specifications gave the torque reading at the point where horsepower is calculated, you would find that the above formula holds.

Force, work and power can of course be expressed in other units than pound, foot-pound and horsepower. Scientists prefer metric units, and in scientific circles the unit of work is one *joule* per second. (A joule is roughly three-fourths of one foot-pound.) The name given to this one-joule-per-second unit is the *watt*, in honor of James Watt.

The term is so often applied to electricity that it is often supposed to be an electrical measurement only. But this isn't so; in the grand concept of physics, energy is interchangeable. The watt is really a mechanical power unit, though a much smaller one than horsepower. One horsepower is the equivalent of 746 watts. The kilowatt (1,000 watts) is the more commonly used commercial unit. It is just a little shy of 1½ horsepower, or what it takes to heat your wife's steam iron.

Now let's go on to take a closer look at the six basic machine elements and see what man has managed to do with them.

II

The Lever—

Simplest Machine of All

If monkeys came before men, it's possible one of them put the first lever to work. Lending credence to this is the case of an untrained orangutan reported years ago by Dr. Raymond L. Ditmars. Given an old chisel, the animal used it to pry up a floor board in its cage.

It can be argued that the orangutan may sometime, somewhere, have seen a man use a wrecking bar or a crowbar, and only imitated his action. But whoever or whatever first made it, the discovery of the lever was both important and inevitable. The first man (or monkey) to see a desirable beetle scuttle out of reach between two rocks, and poke a stick after it, was on the brink of invention. A little prying added to the poking made that stick a lever, and was the first glimmer in the dawning of the machine age.

It isn't stretching truth to call that stick a lever. One definition of the term is a rigid piece, capable of turning about a point or fulcrum, by which force applied at another point is transmitted or modified at a third point. To put it otherwise, when one end goes down, the other end goes up, as shown by the seesaw.

In Figure 1 the fulcrum is that point where the stick bears against the smaller stone. When force is applied at the upper end, it is amplified to move or lift the load represented by the larger stone.

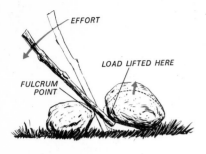

Fig. 1. Primitive man used a lever when he lifted a heavy rock with a long stick.

The word lever comes from the Latin verb *levare*, meaning to raise (we get *elevate* from the same root). Evidence of the use of levers goes back beyond recorded history. Some of the most astounding examples are the great stone erections found in parts of England and France, Stonehenge being perhaps the most famous. A huge monolith, or natural pillar of stone, could be moved along the ground with levers—probably the trunks of small trees (Figure 2). The task could have been done more easily with rollers, but extra logs may have served as rude skids instead.

A hole was dug for the monument, and perhaps earth was packed into a ramp leading up to it. Pried to the brow of the excavation, the stone was finally levered over until it dropped in, then set erect with more muscle power applied to levers and perhaps ropes or their Stone Age equivalent.

In this example the lever was used to gain mechanical advantage, so multiplying the force muscles could apply. But a lever can also be used to gain speed instead, to change direction, to weigh or balance, or to reduce or increase motion in a precise ratio.

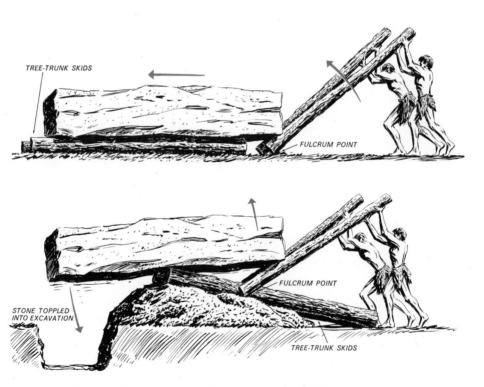

Fig. 2. Stonehenge's pillars were probably moved into place by using the trunks of small trees as levers.

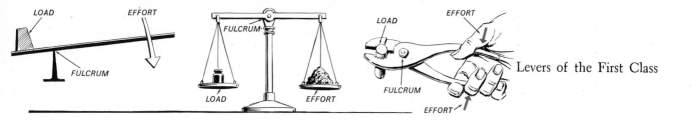

Levers of the First Class

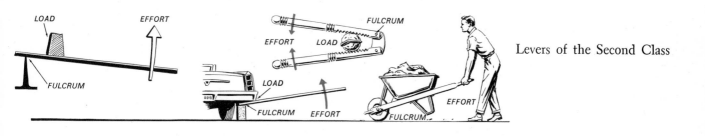

Levers of the Second Class

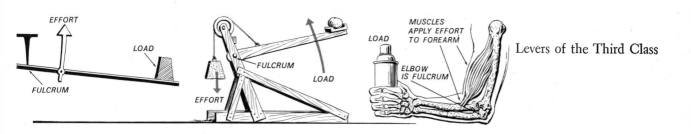

Levers of the Third Class

Fig. 3. The three classes of levers.

THE THREE CLASSES OF LEVERS

All the levers ever applied can be classified in three groups (Figure 3). The seesaw, pan scales and common pliers are all levers of the first class, in which the fulcrum is between the effort and the load.

But the fulcrum can be at one end, the effort at the other, and the load somewhere between. This is a lever of the second class. An important difference between it and one of the first class is that the effort is applied in the same direction as it is desired to move the load, whereas a lever of the first class reverses the direction of the effort.

The same crowbar can be employed as a lever of the second class if we put the brick fulcrum *under* the car and then *lift* the outer end of the crowbar instead of pushing it down. (Since we can't lean our weight on it to help matters out, we'd probably be smart to switch back to the class-one setup shown before.) But mechanically both levers offer the same mechanical advantage. Familiar examples of the lever of the second class are the wheelbarrow and nutcracker.

A lever of the third class has its fulcrum at one end, the load at the other, and the effort between. As this means the effort arm *must* be shorter than the load arm, this lever loses mechanical advantage. Its user gains, however, by having to apply effort through a shorter distance than the load moves. This gain in distance also means a gain in speed. If the load arm is four times

Fig. 4. Sixteenth-century toy illustrates the convertibility of the lever principle. Moving either the upper or the lower bar brings the hammers down on the spike.

as long as the effort arm, for instance, the load will move four times as fast. A weight-powered catapult rigged as a lever of the third class could hurl a rock more swiftly than its weight fell.

The human forearm is a lever of the third class. The throwing stick used by some aborigines, and the baseball bat, both extend the arm's length, so multiplying its distance and speed still more. Thus the aborigine could hurl a stone with great force, and the batter can hope to hit the ball out of the field, feats impossible to the human arm alone.

As already shown, the same crowbar may be used as a lever of the first or of the second class. The toy shown in Figure 4 is another example of this convertibility. If the upper stick is held and the lower one is moved, the pivots in the upper bar and the hips of the figures act as fulcrums, and the figures are levers of the first class. If the upper bar is moved and the lower one is held, the figures act as levers of the third class. In either case, the length of the effort arm is the same. The greater length of the load arm—the torsos, heads and arms of the figures—moves the hammers through a greater distance, bringing them down on the "spike" with a satisfying smack. This toy has a secondary claim on our interest because it is a true antique. It appears in the hands of a child in a 17th century painting by Jan Havicksz Steen. Plans for it were recently published in a national magazine, so presumably this old-timer experienced a brief rebirth.

Appropos of the seesaw, the scale, and the law of the lever, there is a venerable puzzle worth a thought. It is the lever paradox (Figure 5). Two levers are mounted on fulcrums, one above the other, but joined at their ends to move as one. Rigidly attached to each of the vertical links that join them is a horizontal bar, on which a weight may be slid to vary its distance from the fulcrum line, an arrangement used on some scales.

If made so that the levers balance, and if the two adjustable weights are equal, it would seem that moving one weight out farther than the other should certainly tip the beams down on that side. But the fact is that this contraption will stay in balance no matter where you move either weight. At first this seems to contradict the law of the lever, but in fact it does not. You may want to try to figure out this teaser before reading the answer at the end of this chapter.

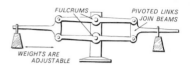

Fig. 5. The lever paradox. Which end goes down? See answer at end of chapter, page 26.

THE LAW OF THE LEVER

Archimedes, the same Greek philosopher who invented the spiral water pump, sensed the law of the lever. He once said, rather grandiosely, "Give me a lever and a place to stand, and I will move the world." But it remained for Leonardo da Vinci to formulate the law 1,700 years later. In effect, he said that a certain force at a given distance from the fulcrum would support a weight at the other end as much greater as its distance from the fulcrum was smaller.

In other words, the product of the acting force and its distance from the fulcrum is equal to the resisting force (or load) times *its* distance from the fulcrum. On a seesaw (Figure 6) a 75-pound child 6 feet from the fulcrum will

150-LB. MAN
3 FT. FROM
FULCRUM

75-LB. BOY
6 FT. FROM
FULCRUM

150 X 3 = 450

75 X 6 = 450

Fig. 6. Seesaw offers a typical illustration of da Vinci's law of the lever.

balance a 150-pound adult 3 feet from the fulcrum. But if they seesaw, the child will move a vertical distance twice as great as the adult will. To balance the greater weight, the child must move farther, just as to move the stone in Figure 1 a little way, the user must swing the other end of the lever much farther.

The more mechanical advantage we need, the greater must be the ratio between the effort and load arms. Suppose a car is to be levered out of a mudhole (Figure 7) and that the force necessary will be 800 pounds. We can place bricks on a board to provide a fulcrum, and position a 6-foot long crowbar so that it lifts the car frame 8 inches from the fulcrum. That leaves 64

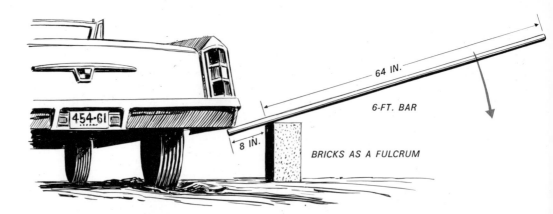

Fig. 7. To increase mechanical advantage, the ratio between the effort and load arms of a lever must be increased. In this situation, the effort arm is eight times the length of the load arm, enough to do the job.

inches of the crowbar for our effort arm, which is eight times the length of the load arm. We should be able to lift the car's 800-pound load with 100 pounds of force on the crowbar (plus whatever it takes to overcome mud suction). Mathematically stated, the product of the 800-pound load and the 8-inch load arm is 6,400. Dividing this by the 64-inch length of the effort arm, we get 100 pounds as the force required.

Two things are worth noting: the fulcrum has to exert an UP force equal to the two down forces on the lever (800 pounds plus our 100-pound effort). If the bricks break or if the board is driven into the soft ground, the fulcrum can't do that.

The other thing to note is that we'll have to swing our end of the crowbar through a distance of several feet in order to lift the car a few inches. We swap our smaller force through a greater distance for a larger force through a shorter distance.

COMPOUNDING THE LEVER

Archimedes notwithstanding, there is a practical limit to the length of the lever we can use and the distance through which we can move it. To weigh a truck, for example, with balance weights light enough to handle, we'd need an outsize lever arm (Figure 8) and a ladder to reach the weights pan.

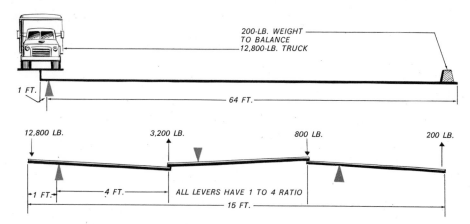

Fig. 8. Breaking a lever into short segments enables us to weigh extremely heavy objects while maintaining the same ratio between effort and load arms.

Instead, we can break that long lever up into three short ones and interconnect them to do the same job. The three levers shown schematically in Figure 8, each with a 1 to 4 ratio of load and effort arms, multiply that ratio not merely by three, but by the third power, or cube, of 4. The total ratio is 1 to 64, the same as for the single long lever, and we have saved a lot of space, for instead of 65 feet, the total length is 15 feet.

By using one class-one and two class-three levers, we can achieve a more compact grouping as in Figure 9. The levers are connected with links, a more reliable means than letting them ride on each other. Such compound lever

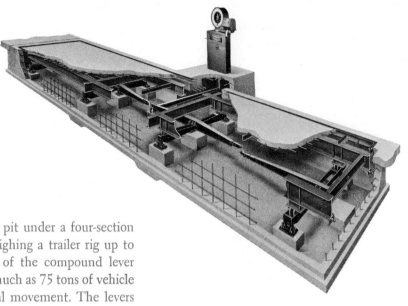

This cutaway view of the pit under a four-section truck scale, capable of weighing a trailer rig up to 70 feet long, shows part of the compound lever system that translates as much as 75 tons of vehicle weight into calibrated dial movement. The levers of the Toledo Truckmaster are of steel. Locating surfaces of the self-aligning pivots are accurate within two-thousandths of an inch. *Courtesy of Toledo Scale Corporation.*

Fig. 9. Platform scales employ compound levers.

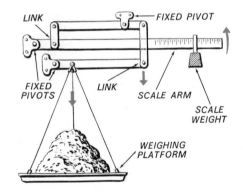

arrangements are used in platform scales. Compound levers are also used where vernier action is desired, or where great force must be exerted over a short distance. Bolt cutters are a good example of this (Figure 10). The two long handle levers are linked, by short load arms, to two shorter levers whose own load arms are the cutting jaws. The handle ends must be moved several inches to close the jaws, but the mechanical advantage is so great that an iron bolt can be cut through.

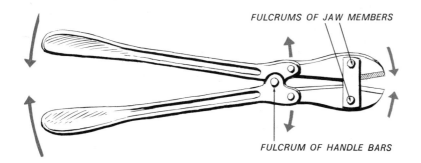

FULCRUMS OF JAW MEMBERS

FULCRUM OF HANDLE BARS

Fig. 10. Compound levers give bolt cutters tremendous mechanical advantage.

LEVERS AROUND A CORNER

A simple lever changes direction by 180 degrees—pull one end down, and the other end goes up. A bent lever can change direction by almost any amount less than this. (Though bent, the lever must of course still be rigid.) An everyday example is the hammer (Figure 11), which in pulling a nail acts as a bent lever of the first class. A rolling (rather than a knife-edged or pivoted) fulcrum is provided by the curved surface of the claw.

A lever with its arms 90 degrees apart and its fulcrum at the corner or elbow is commonly called a bell crank. This name is a hangover from the days before electric bells, when cords or wires were used to ring distant gongs mechanically. The wire might have to travel around several corners from the place where it was pulled, so small bell cranks (Figure 12) were used to change direction. A combination or double bell crank (Figure 13, left) not only changed direction 90 degrees, but split the signal two ways. By making the effort arm longer than the load arm (right), you can gain mechanical advantage in addition to a change in direction.

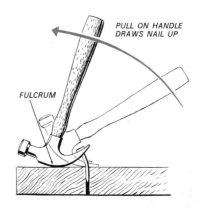

PULL ON HANDLE DRAWS NAIL UP

FULCRUM

Fig. 11. In pulling a nail, a hammer acts as a bent lever of the first class.

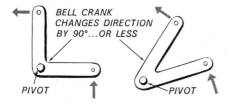

BELL CRANK CHANGES DIRECTION BY 90°...OR LESS

PIVOT

PIVOT

Fig. 12. Bell cranks changed direction of applied force, enabling men to ring gongs with wires or ropes traveling around corners.

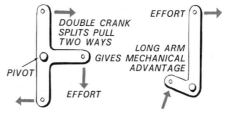

DOUBLE CRANK SPLITS PULL TWO WAYS

EFFORT

LONG ARM GIVES MECHANICAL ADVANTAGE

PIVOT

EFFORT

Fig. 13. Combination bell crank (left). In bell crank at right, effort arm is longer than load arm, giving mechanical advantage.

19

LINKAGES AND LAZY TONGS

Some useful devices are made of levers ingeniously linked together. A linkage of four bars (strictly speaking not levers at all) converts up-and-down motion into right-and-left motion or vice versa (Figure 14). This simple action becomes more interesting and useful if we lengthen the bars past their pivots (so converting them into levers) and connect several units, with one of them on a fixed pivot, as shown in Figure 15. Force applied at one end (to the single linkage) will be translated into a longer and speedier movement of the other units.

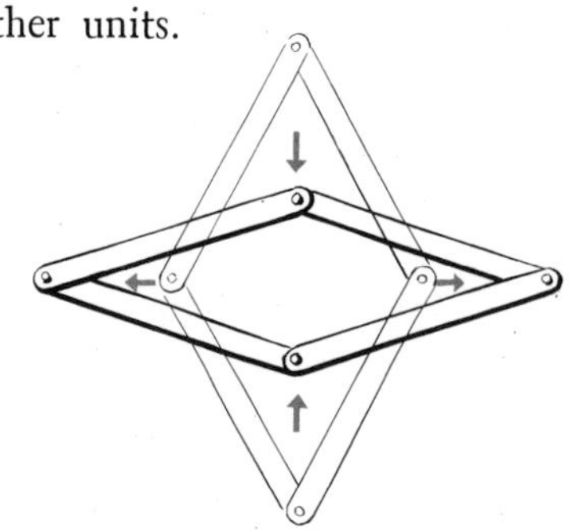

Fig. 14. Linkage of four bars converts up-and-down motion into right-and-left motion, called parallelogram action.

Fig. 15. Connecting several sets of four-bar linkages together translates force at one end into a longer and faster movement of other units.

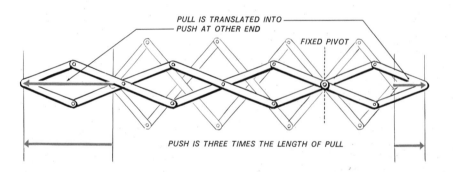

PULL IS TRANSLATED INTO
PUSH AT OTHER END
FIXED PIVOT
PUSH IS THREE TIMES THE LENGTH OF PULL

STRAIGHT-LINE MOTIONS

The steam engine and its developers brought about some weird and wonderful works in mechanical geometry. Usually some of the parts involved (such as piston rods) had to move in a straight line. Therefore the point of attachment of valve and pump linkages also had to travel in a straight line, and the name straight-line motions was given them. Figure 16 shows four of these, with the names of their originators. In all of them, the point P travels in a straight (or almost straight) line. Obviously if this point is attached by a pivot to some reciprocating member, motion can be taken from some other link to open or close valves, power pumps, and so forth.

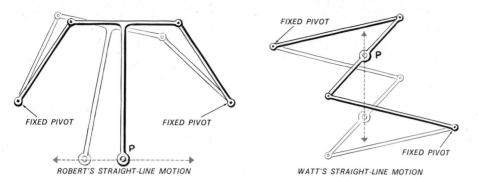

FIXED PIVOT

P

FIXED PIVOT   FIXED PIVOT

P

ROBERT'S STRAIGHT-LINE MOTION

WATT'S STRAIGHT-LINE MOTION

FIXED PIVOT

Fig. 16. Four types of straight-line motions.

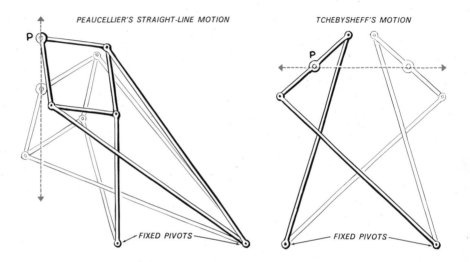

PEAUCELLIER'S STRAIGHT-LINE MOTION

TCHEBYSHEFF'S MOTION

P

P

FIXED PIVOTS   FIXED PIVOTS

MECHANICAL DRAWING APPLIANCES

If two plain bars are joined by identical links as in Figure 17, top, the bars will remain parallel at any separation. Such a device can be used for drawing parallel lines at various spacings. A somewhat more complex parallel ruler, shown in Figure 17, bottom, makes use of two levers pivoted at their centers and at one end. The other ends have pivots that slide in slots in the two horizontal parts. These crossed levers keep the bars parallel whether they are close together or pulled apart.

Fig. 17. Mechanical drawing appliances make use of lever principle to keep edges of rulers always parallel.

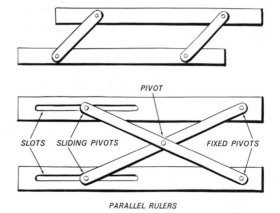

PIVOT

SLOTS   SLIDING PIVOTS   FIXED PIVOTS

PARALLEL RULERS

21

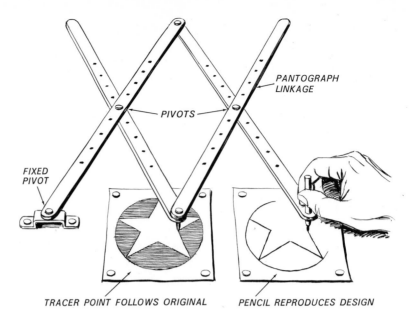

Fig. 18. More involved link-age in the pantograph can copy, enlarge or reduce a drawing in exact proportion.

PANTOGRAPH LINKAGE

PIVOTS

FIXED PIVOT

TRACER POINT FOLLOWS ORIGINAL

PENCIL REPRODUCES DESIGN

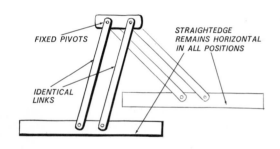

FIXED PIVOTS

STRAIGHTEDGE REMAINS HORIZONTAL IN ALL POSITIONS

IDENTICAL LINKS

Fig. 19. Straightedge on swinging links is a satisfactory T-square.

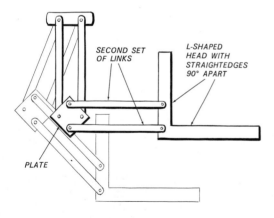

SECOND SET OF LINKS

L-SHAPED HEAD WITH STRAIGHTEDGES 90° APART

PLATE

Fig. 20. Substituting plate for straightedge, and adding another set of links and a right-angled piece, produces a T-square and a 90-degree edge in one instrument.

22

The pantograph is a more intriguing linkage, which can copy, enlarge or reduce a drawing in exact proportion. It consists of four bars linked as in Figure 18. The outboard pivot A simply rides on the drawing board. A tracing point attached to pivot B is caused to follow the drawing to be copied, while a pencil fixed at C reproduces the material, the user moving the pencil while watching the tracing point. The pivot points are usually interchangeable, there being a number of holes in which they may be set, to alter the ratio of reduction or enlargement.

Using the principle of the parallel ruler, we could fasten a straightedge to two swinging links as in Figure 19. The straightedge would always remain horizontal, and would be a fair substitute for a T-square, though the links limit its useful length.

But we can carry the idea a bit further. We can substitute a plate for the straightedge, add a second set of links, and at their outer end fix a straightedge—or better still a right-angled piece as shown in Figure 20. Now the links allow us to move the right-angled head anywhere on the drawing board, and they are no longer in the way. We have in one instrument both a T-square and a 90-degree edge.

Drawing ellipses hardly seems a job for a linkage of straight bars, but it is. Geometrically speaking, an ellipse is a plane curve in which the sum of the distances from any point to its two foci is the same. In Figure 21 for example, the total length of the solid line is the same as that of either pair of dotted lines.

The fact is easily proven by drawing an ellipse with two nails, a piece of string and a pencil. Drive the two nails in some distance apart; these are the foci of the ellipse-to-be. The line through them will be the major (or longer) axis of the ellipse. Knot the string into a loop somewhat longer, place it around both nails, and hook the pencil into the far end of the loop. Now if you swing the pencil around, keeping the loop taut, you can draw a clean ellipse—and prove the definition given. The distance between the nails being fixed, the

A simplified ellipsograph, made of a block of wood with pivot bars sliding at right angles in slots, draws a perfect ellipse.

length of loop left outside them is always the same. When you hook the pencil inside the loop and swing it around, the slack in the loop becomes "the sum of the distances from any point" to the two foci.

The ellipsograph produces the same result mechanically. Its base is a plate with two slots at right angles, one parallel to the major and one to the minor axis of the ellipse to be drawn. A bar with a pencil at one end has two pivot pins that can slide closely in the slots; the pin settings are usually adjustable to permit drawing different sizes and shapes of ellipses.

As the pencil end of the bar is swung about, the pins move out of one slot into another. The distance from the pencil to the farthest pin is one half the length of the major axis; that from the pencil to the inner pin is half the length of the minor axis. As the pins pivot first in one slot and then in the other, the pencil reach gradually lengthens or shortens to draw a perfect ellipse.

TOGGLE ACTION

This is a lever mechanism that exchanges effort distance for high mechanical advantage. Figure 21 shows a simple form. One arm is mounted on a fixed pivot and joined to a second arm by another pivot. The lower end of the second arm is pivoted to a sliding member. If we apply force to the midjoint, or elbow, to straighten out the links, we'll move the sliding block down a lesser distance but with greater force.

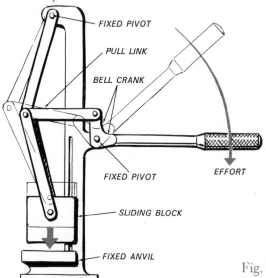

Fig. 21. Toggle action applied to a machine press.

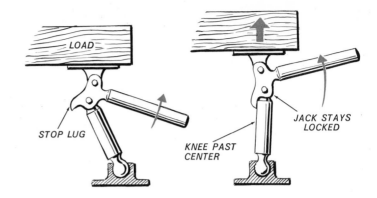

Fig. 22. Toggle action enables knee jack to lift heavy loads and remain locked.

If we want to apply this principle to a machine punch or press, we won't push directly on the elbow. We might instead add a pull link to the elbow joint, and connect this link to the short end of a bell crank having a long handle. This further multiplies mechanical advantage. A modest down pull on the long handle will move the sliding block down with immense force.

The toggle action also applies to the knee jack shown in Figure 22. Here one arm and the long handle are combined. As the handle is raised, the two parts are straightened out and the load is raised. If the parts are properly proportioned, with a stop lug to prevent further movement when the knee joint is slightly past the vertical line, the jack will remain locked in that position by the pressure of the load.

The powerful straightening-out action of the toggle came into play a long time ago in ancient wine and printing presses. A husky round member or capstan was made free to turn on a heavy shaft fixed in the top crossbar of the press (Figure 23). The platen was free to slide on or between the two vertical columns, so squeezing the typeface (or the grapes) between the platen and a bed plate below it.

Fig. 23. Ancient wine press relied on toggle action.

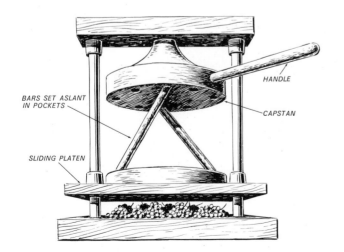

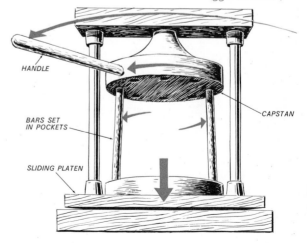

In the bottom of the capstan, and in the top of a plate on the platen, was a circle of holes or pockets. The platen being set over the work to be pressed, two or more strong bars were set obliquely with one end in a capstan hole, the other in a platen hole slightly around the circle. A long handle was socketed firmly in the capstan, and the pressman leaned against it to turn the capstan. This straightened the bars, which in turn forced the platen down. The long handle added considerable mechanical advantage, and the toggle action of the capstan and bars still more. Thus levers plus rotary motion did the work of that more sophisticated machine element, the screw.

ANSWER TO THE LEVER PARADOX

You can't cheat the laws of nature. If the weight rods were fastened to either of the two scale beams, a weight farther from the fulcrum would be able to move through a greater distance than one nearer it, and would overbalance the other, as in the first drawing of Figure 24.

But rods mounted on the links remain horizontal when you tilt the beams, as shown in the second drawing. Weights on these rods therefore move up and down through precisely the same distance as the scale's two links themselves do, no matter where on the rods the weights are set. As it is impossible for either weight to move through a greater distance than the other, neither has an advantage and the scale must remain in balance. To put it another way, since by mounting the weights this way we have refused to exchange a greater distance of movement for a larger moment or torque, nature turns down the deal and the equal weights will have equal effect no matter where they are moved.

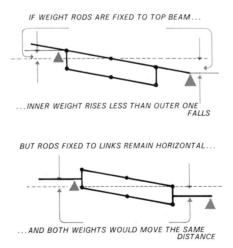

IF WEIGHT RODS ARE FIXED TO TOP BEAM...

...INNER WEIGHT RISES LESS THAN OUTER ONE FALLS

BUT RODS FIXED TO LINKS REMAIN HORIZONTAL...

...AND BOTH WEIGHTS WOULD MOVE THE SAME DISTANCE

Fig. 24. Answer to the lever paradox.

Rotary Power and the Wheel

It is a safe bet that the patent office would be much less busy if the wheel had never been invented, because it has in turn spawned inventions by the hundreds of thousands. There is just no substitute for the wheel, prototype ancestor of the gear, the pulley, the turbine and the jet engine.

Yet the wheel itself is a true old-timer—it dates back over 5,000 years to the New Stone Age. This is the era (3,500 to 3,000 B.C.) when in the Near East migrating tribes gave way to tillers of the soil, when the hoe, stick plow and irrigation planted the first seeds of practical agriculture and men could grow their food instead of wandering about in search of it.

But in its most primitive form—the roller—the wheel was probably used even earlier, in the Stone Age. Surely some hairy genius among the men who erected Stonehenge and similar monoliths discovered that stones could be moved more easily if logs were placed under them crosswise to the direction of travel—as rollers instead of skids. Dead trees, with the branches lopped off them, made passable rollers. By removing the rearmost one as the load slipped off it, and placing it under the front end, these early engineers could have moved gigantic stone blocks on what amounted to a primitive conveyor belt, forward movement being maintained by levers (Figure 1).

27

Fig. 1. Most primitive form of wheel, the roller, was probably used, in conjunction with the lever, by Stone Age men to move large stones.

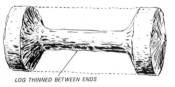

Fig. 2. Early wagons used a wheel-and-axle combination carved from a log.

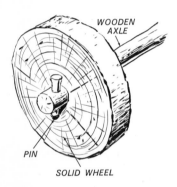

Fig. 3. Solid wheel made of wood used in early Egypt and Mesopotamia.

Fig. 4. Wheel built up from a number of small pieces.

There is some reason to think that very early wagons were made with one-piece wheels and axles. These were logs whittled down between two outer sections (Figure 2). The axle turned with the wheels, of course, an arrangement on which some millions of railroad-car wheels are still operating.

But the next inspired idea was the wheel and separate axle, a tremendous step. Nothing like it—a circular member free to turn (but not fall off) a central rigid one—appears in nature. Nobody knows who thought this one up, but the idea wasn't slow to catch on. Egyptian and Mesopotamian picture relics show wagons with clumsy solid wheels (Figure 3). As logs of large diameter would be hard to cut up into suitably thin slices, somebody soon learned to build big wheels of little pieces (Figure 4).

About 4,000 years ago, nomads from the northern steppes introduced the horse into the Near East. Soon it was hitched to war chariots having two *spoked* wheels. About 500 years later (1,500 B.C.) the Hittites forged themselves a highly successful war machine with such vehicles. Pictures of these have been found on Egyptian and Assyrian temple walls.

HUB, SPOKES AND FELLY

It was a long way from the built-up solid wheel of Figure 5 to a spoked wheel such as the Hittites used. The first step was a wheel having two spokes set between a central member pierced for the axle (the hub) and an outer rim (the felly), probably made up of segments. The two spokes proving pretty shaky, they were braced by two extra members. These braces weren't radial and so weren't true spokes, but apparently the wheel proved practical, because

28

it was later translated into metal. Bronze wheels of this design, 20 inches in diameter, have been found among Bronze Age artifacts. The Greeks decided to go all the way and substitute a pair of cross spokes for the braces. The Assyrians went them two better and adopted six-spoke wheels.

Wooden axles were all the rage at first, chiefly because there was nothing better. To retain the wheel, a peg was driven into a hole in the axle. Brass was probably used in its turn for axles, and iron still later. The wheel felly was at first only wood, the iron tire being a later development that greatly increased its durability. Made as a solid ring, expanded by heat and dropped around the felly, the iron shrank on cooling, pulling the wheel members into one tightly bound entity far stronger than ever before. Iron hubs turning on well-greased iron axles gave us wheels that opened the West and have been rolling on TV screens ever since.

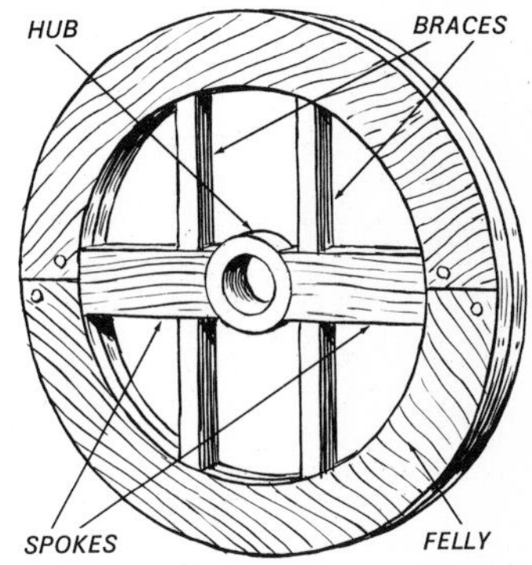

Fig. 5. Spoked wheel used by the Hittites.

OTHER WHEELS

The potter's wheel, on which clay can be spun to a round shape inside and out, also began to turn before recorded history began. It could have stemmed from the wood slab on which the potter placed his clay, and which he swung around as he shaped the vessel. To make a bearing for the slab, with the idea of using rotary motion as well as his fingers to round the material, was a logical improvement that may have been centuries appearing.

Another early wheel served for irrigation. This was the wheel of pots (Figure 6), placed over a stream. A primitive water wheel, it was turned by the

Fig. 6. Early adaptation of the wheel for irrigation—sometimes called the wheel of pots.

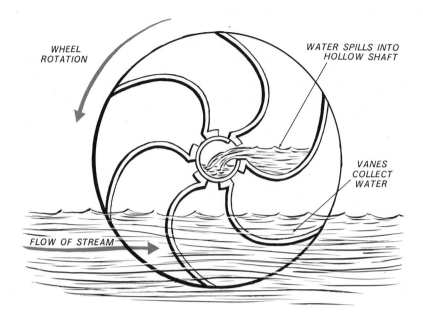

WHEEL
ROTATION

WATER SPILLS INTO
HOLLOW SHAFT

VANES
COLLECT
WATER

FLOW OF STREAM

Fig. 7. Persian wheel scooped water up in curved vanes and carried it away through hollow, tilted axle.

AXLE

ANIMAL PUSHES
SWEEP AROUND

MILLSTONES

Fig. 8. Horse-powered millstone was another wheel-and-axle device.

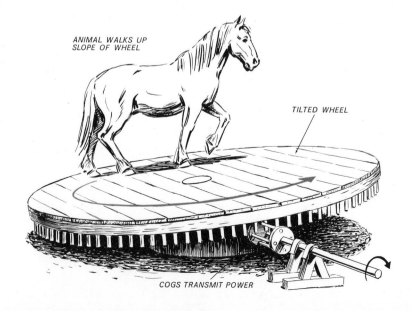

ANIMAL WALKS UP
SLOPE OF WHEEL

TILTED WHEEL

Fig. 9. Inclined animal wheel transferred power to a simple geared axle.

COGS TRANSMIT POWER

30

current, causing each pot to pick up water as it emerged. On approaching the top, the pots spilled their burden into a trough, from which the water could flow to the fields. This was of course a very primitive and inefficient water raiser. Somewhat better was the Archimedean screw shown in Chapter 1 with a paddle wheel mounted at the bottom. The flowing stream turned the wheel, and thus the screw, which lifted water to its upper end.

Equally ingenious was a Persian wheel having deeply curved vanelike buckets (Figure 7) and a hollow shaft. The current, acting on the backs or convex surfaces of the vanes, turned the wheel. The rising buckets scooped up water, and on going past the axis spilled it into the hollow shaft, which was set at enough of an angle to lead it away. In addition, tubs hung on the periphery of the wheel lifted water to its top, where they were tripped to spill it.

The millstone was another early wheel. One method of powering it was to fit a rude axle with one or more long arms that could be pulled or pushed by man or beast (Figure 8). Of later origin was a wheel in the shape of a cage, in which a small animal could run along the inside of the rim. Known now as the squirrel cage, such wheels were used in medieval times with dogs running inside to turn meat-roasting spits—a tantalizing chore for an animal with a nose attuned to a high-protein diet. Bigger wheels of this kind, in which a horse could trot, are said to have been used for powering paddle wheels on small ferryboats.

Of later origin, and a bit more ingenious, was the inclined animal wheel (Figure 9). Suitably restrained so that it couldn't walk off the job, the beast trudged endlessly uphill, its weight turning the wheel. This device was in use in American Colonial times, and examples of it still exist.

Man-powered wheels had treads on the outside of the rim, being turned by the weight of a man trudging up these endlessly sinking steps. Some such wheels were used for punitive purposes, the power they produced being merely a by-product. In many lands man-powered wheels were used for irrigation, and it is possible some still survive for that purpose.

THE WHEEL COMES OF AGE

Fine as a loose wheel on a fixed axle is for reducing friction, there is a special virtue in a wheel fixed to an axle, especially if we rig the latter in bearings so that wheel and axle can turn as one. This is one of our basic machines. It is, in fact, a rotary lever system that can exchange distance for mechanical advantage, or the reverse.

Figure 10 shows a flat-rimmed wheel rigidly fixed on a rather oversize axle (which we might therefore call a barrel), the whole turning in two bear-

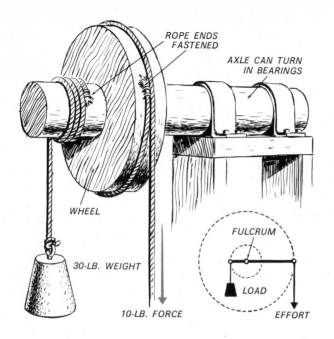

Fig. 10. Wheel on axle, with rope wound around each, is actually a class-one lever.

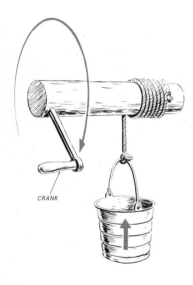

Fig. 11. Replacing the wheel with a handle turns the machine in Figure 10 into a simple windlass.

ings. A rope fastened to the wheel rim is wound around it before the end is left to hang free. Another rope is fastened to the axle, or barrel, and wound around it in the *opposite* direction. If we now hang weights on the rope, we have in effect a continuous class-one lever, as the smaller diagram shows. The pivot or fulcrum is the very center of the axle; the short side of the lever is the radius of the axle, and its long side is the radius of the wheel.

The law of the lever holds too. If the wheel radius is three times the axle radius, a 10-pound force on the wheel rope will balance a 30-pound weight on the axle rope. In other words, there is a three-to-one mechanical advantage. But in compensation, the 10-pound force must be exerted through three times the distance you wish to raise the weight.

This is the principle of the windlass, in which the wheel rope is replaced—for greater convenience—with a handle stuck in the wheel. On second thought, we may as well omit the wheel and fix the handle to an arm stuck directly into the axle (or windlass barrel) as in Figure 11, so reinventing the *crank*. The earliest record of this familiar device is in a 9th century Utrecht Psalter, where it is shown turning a grindstone. But even though our wheel has vanished, the windlass uses the principle of the wheel and axle, the length of the crank arm being the wheel radius.

If you apply the effort to the axle radius and hitch your load to the wheel radius, you'll gain speed in lifting the load, but at the expenditure of proportionately greater effort. One of the few applications of this to a practical purpose was the old high-wheel bicycle. It wasn't built that way just to orna-

32

Fig. 12. Early bicycles had large wheels for maximum mechanical advantage.

HALF TURN OF PEDAL
MOVES BIKE HALF OF THE WHEEL'S CIRCUMFERENCE

ment Currier and Ives prints. You try to figure a better way to make a bike run speedily, in an age before cheap and durable chains and sprockets (not to say ball bearings) were around. If, lacking such means of power transmission, you had to mount the foot pedals directly on the wheel shaft, the simple answer was to make the wheel as big as a rider could straddle (Figure 12).

The ratio of the pedal arm (or crank throw) to the wheel diameter exchanged force for distance in the same ratio. A half turn of the pedal moved the bike a distance equal to half the circumference of the big wheel. When what was first called the safety bicycle appeared—a name presumably based on the fact that one had less far to fall, the wheels being smaller—it achieved the necessary speed step-up with the now familiar chain transmission. A big sprocket on the pedal shaft driving a much smaller one on the wheel did the trick.

Nor were the great ship's wheels helmsmen struggled with designed for drama on the late late show. They were an adaptation of the windlass to a special purpose. The plain wheel was fitted with outer spokes that not only served as handles, but further increased the length of the force arm, giving the helmsman still more mechanical advantage (Figure 13).

Fig. 13. Connection between ship's wheel and tiller bar was a simple but effective one. Spokes on the wheel gave the helmsman an additional mechanical advantage.

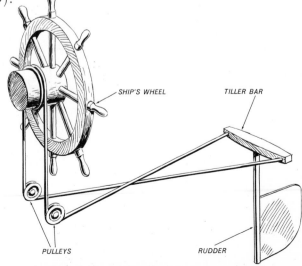

SHIP'S WHEEL   TILLER BAR

PULLEYS   RUDDER

WHEEL, ROPES AND TREADLES

Almost as soon as man began putting the wheel to work, he was faced with the problem of converting its rotary motion to back-and-forth movement, or the converse. How do you make a water wheel saw wood, crush ore or hammer metal? These tasks all demand a powerful reciprocating action, not a rotary one. (The circular saws and rotary crushers of our day were still undreamed of then.) Or how, if you haven't a water wheel, do you run a lathe with hand or foot power?

Various solutions were reached by adding cranks, levers, ropes and cams to the wheel. That Greek gadgeteer Hero powered an organ pump by a windmill. The windmill shaft had a disk (or wheel) at the end opposite the vanes (Figure 14). Fixed in the disk were rigid pegs like wheel spokes without a rim.

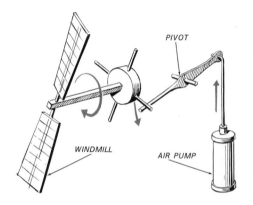

Fig. 14. Organ pump powered by windmill was devised by early Greek inventor.

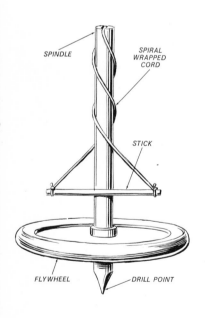

Fig. 15. Cord-powered drill.

A lever pivoted on an upright nearby was connected to the pump rod at one end. The other end of the lever was in the path of the rotating pegs. One at a time, these pressed down that end of the lever, raising the pump piston. As a peg slipped off the lever, the piston dropped back ready for the next stroke.

The opposite problem—that of getting rotary motion from hand movement—was probably solved much earlier for fire making and hole drilling. One simple means was the bow drill. The bowstring was looped once around the stick or spindle to be spun. As the bow was swung back and forth, the string rotated the spindle.

Somewhat more sophisticated was the drill shown in Figure 15. The middle of the cord was wrapped spirally around the drill spindle. What was remarkable, though, was a heavy wheel or disk mounted on the spindle as a flywheel. As the user pulled down the stick to which the spiral-wound cord was connected, the spindle turned. When the string was unwound, the operator slackened off and allowed the momentum of the flywheel-weighted shaft to wind the cord up again, whereupon it was ready for another downward yank. This would turn the spindle in the opposite direction. Presumably the drill bits of that time weren't as choosy as ours about their direction of rotation.

Not until the 12th century did French and German turners invent a similar device to drive their lathes, though turned artifacts dating back to the 2nd century B.C. prove the wood-turning lathe was known even then. The "new" drive, which enabled the turner to supply power for the work himself instead of having a slave or apprentice do so, consisted in part of a rope wound once around the lathe spindle. A foot treadle, hinged at one end, was fastened to the bottom end of the rope. But what made the rig work well was a spring pole, to which the upper end of the rope was tied (Figure 16).

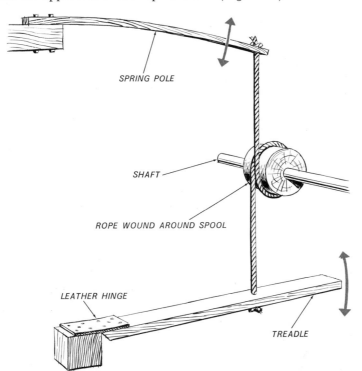

SPRING POLE

SHAFT

ROPE WOUND AROUND SPOOL

LEATHER HINGE

TREADLE

Fig. 16. Early foot treadle for turning a lathe.

Pressing down the treadle caused the rope to turn the lathe spindle, at the same time pulling down the spring pole. As the turner lifted his foot, the rebound of the pole pulled rope and treadle up again, turning the lathe spindle backwards. This half-backwards motion would be annoying to us today, but it was no great detriment in hand turning and the treadle drive freed a second man to do other work.

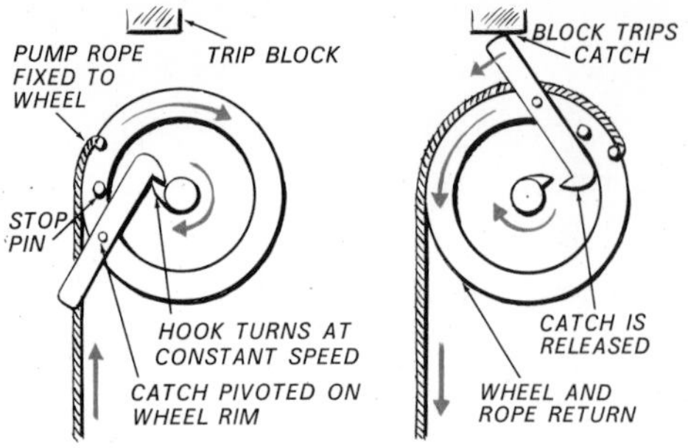

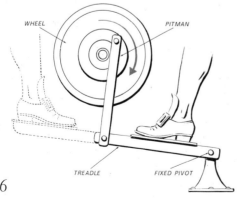

PUMP ROPE
FIXED TO
WHEEL

TRIP BLOCK

BLOCK TRIPS
CATCH

STOP
PIN

HOOK TURNS AT
CONSTANT SPEED

CATCH PIVOTED ON
WHEEL RIM

CATCH IS
RELEASED

WHEEL AND
ROPE RETURN

Fig. 17. Rope-and-wheel device for converting rotary to reciprocating motion.

Another rope-and-wheel device, this one for converting the constant rotary motion of a windmill or waterwheel into a reciprocating action, is shown in Figure 17. The problem here was to alternately raise and lower a rope attached to a water-pump piston.

A hook fixed to the shaft turned constantly with it. In swinging to the first position shown, the hook engaged a catch fastened to a wheel, this wheel being loose on the shaft and therefore not turning with it. But as the hook engaged the catch, the wheel was yanked into motion, raising the pump rope and swinging the catch arm to the second position shown.

As the outer end of the arm struck the trip block, the catch was freed from the hook on the shaft. Though the shaft kept right on turning, the loose wheel was at once pulled back by the weight of the pump rope and its piston. When the hook came around again, it once more picked up the catch and repeated the cycle.

LEVERS THAT TURN WHEELS

Being sure to stretch and deteriorate under stress, rope was hardly an ideal material for transmitting power. The human arm that turned a crank suggested a mechanical arm to do the same thing. Connecting this arm to a treadle was only a short step, and this device (Figure 18) eventually replaced

WHEEL

PITMAN

TREADLE

FIXED PIVOT

Fig. 18. Improved foot treadle replaced rope with a mechanical arm.

36

rope motions for powering lathes, spinning wheels and other light machines. Sometimes the treadle fulcrum was in the middle instead of at one end, or for greater mechanical advantage the treadle was lengthened the other side of the pitman, or connecting rod, as shown by the dotted lines. Working at the far end, the foot had to move through a greater distance than the crank arm, with a proportionate gain in torque. The rotary action was continuous instead of alternating in direction as the spring-pole drive did.

But it was in the steam engine that the *crank* attained its zenith of power and majesty. Whirling crank webs the size of a small car, giant cross-heads smashing up and down through a stroke to be measured in yards rather than inches, were a sight now become so rare you are unlikely to see it. The familiar crank movement of the steam engine (Figure 19) translated the back

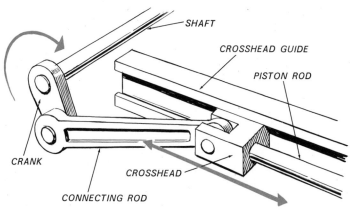

Fig. 19. In the steam engine, reciprocating motion was converted to rotary motion by this device.

Fig. 20. Modern automobile engine converts reciprocating power of the pistons into rotary power by means of a connecting rod attached to a crankshaft.

and forth push of the piston into shaft rotation. It is an elegantly simple arrangement, ideal for its purpose. Yet at one time the crank was so closely controlled by a patent that James Watt was forced to invent a far more complex action for his engineers.

Multiplied to match the number of cylinders, the crank is still universal in reciprocating engines, including practically all of today's automotive and outboard engines. The crosshead is dropped in favor of the *trunk piston* (Figure 20) but otherwise the action is the same.

Quite different is the *Scotch yoke* action of Figure 21. By dispensing with the con rod, this made steam engines much more compact. The crosshead is replaced with a slotted yoke, in which the crankpin both turns and slides. For greater durability a sliding block was sometimes used, the crankpin turning in this instead of directly in the slot.

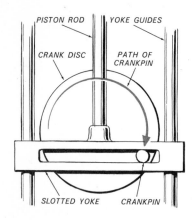

Another effort to reduce engine height—which the huge cylinders and long strokes necessary to low-pressure steam made especially desirable in boats —was the beam action. The beam was an immense lever, rocking on a center fulcrum. One end was linked to the crank by a connecting rod; the other to the piston rod. Even in the twenties one could still see paddle-driven river boats "walking" on the water, as the action of the great rocker beams strongly suggested.

All these single-crank movements had a "dead center"—that is, they could stop at a point where, when steam was again applied, neither push nor pull could cause rotation. In foot and hand-driven machines it was a simple matter to turn the shaft a little past this point. In big engines the engineer sometimes had to sweat mightily with a crowbar to do so, and would use all his skill in stopping to get the crank past center before it stilled. (Once turning, the momentum of crankshaft and flywheel constantly carried the crank over dead center.)

Two-cylinder steam engines with pistons phased 90 degrees apart (Figure 22) were self-starting in any position. Locomotives and the engines used on steam power shovels and derricks were examples of these.

Fig. 21. Scotch yoke action, used in steam engines, dispenses with the connecting rod of the automobile engine and gains compactness.

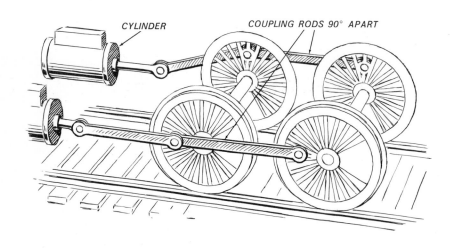

Fig. 22. Two-cylinder steam engine with couplings 90 degrees apart, designed to overcome "dead center" problem.

A lever could also be used to couple two wheels so that one would drive the other. But a single set of coupled wheels would stick badly at dead center —they had to have a second coupling rod at a suitable phase angle (usually 90 degrees) connected to a third wheel. The wheels of steam (and of some electric) locomotives were cases in point. They are shown schematically in Figure

23. Sturdy rods, with a bearing working on a crankpin at each end, were simpler to make and easier to maintain than the train of gears that would otherwise have been necessary.

ODD CRANKPIN MECHANISMS

Even without a con rod, a crankpin can translate rotary motion into back-and-forth movement. Figure 24 shows an intermittent action. The bell crank will be tripped by each of the three pins as it comes around, providing three lever movements per revolution. There could be fewer pins or more, of course.

An intriguing action for converting rotary into reciprocating movement is shown in Figure 25. The horizontal bar is first moved to the right as crankpin A engages the lug on the bar. While this pin slides off the lug, crankpin B is approaching the bottom end of the bell crank. As it swings this up, the upper part of the bell crank thrusts back pin C, which is fixed in the sliding bar, and returns it to the left. Having done this, pin B contacts the returned lug and begins pushing the bar to the right. It will then be pin A's turn to hit the bell crank.

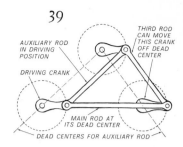

Fig. 23. Schematic drawing of locomotive wheel couplings, showing second coupling rod for moving wheels off dead center.

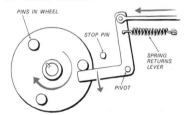

Fig. 24. Rotary motion is converted to reciprocating motion by crankpins on wheel hitting bell crank intermittently.

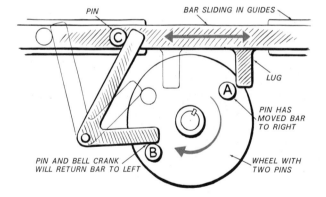

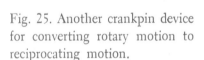

Fig. 25. Another crankpin device for converting rotary motion to reciprocating motion.

A slotted yoke working on a crankpin can produce some peculiar motions. One of these is used in the metal-working shaper, which has a heavy ram that slides back and forth, with a tool at one end. On the return stroke, the tool does no work, so it is desirable to make this part of the movement quickly. Forward ram action, on the other hand, is heavily loaded as the tool shaves away metal, so it requires more energy and may sensibly sacrifice speed for greater mechanical advantage.

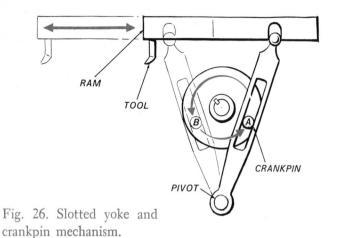

RAM

TOOL

CRANKPIN

PIVOT

Fig. 26. Slotted yoke and crankpin mechanism.

Geneva stop motion, shown in a model made by the author, has a drive disk turned by the hand, and a slotted wheel. As the drive disk is turned, pin enters slot in the wheel, rotating it the distance between slots, then wheel stops until pin engages the next slot.

Can you figure out a simple mechanism, driven by a single shaft running at constant speed, that meets these conditions?

The one in Figure 26 does so very well. A slotted arm is pivoted at the bottom. Its upper end works in a socket in the ram, moving it back and forth. A crankpin works in the slot, and at first glance it would seem that back-and-forth movements would take place in the same time. But look again. The secret of the action is that each end of the ram stroke is reached when the crankpin is *below* the shaft center.

In going counterclockwise from A to B and so moving the ram forward on the cutting stroke, the crankpin describes an arc of considerably more than 180 degrees. But in returning the ram as it goes from B to A, the crankpin covers a much shorter path. Crank speed and torque being constant, it's easy to see that more energy is being expended on the forward stroke, since an equal force is being applied over a greater distance.

Or consider the leverage involved. In going from A to B, the crankpin is exerting force farther from the fulcrum and nearer the end of the load arm. But in moving from B to A the crankpin's force is applied nearer the fulcrum, which makes the effort arm shorter in proportion to the load arm than in the first case, and so sacrifices mechanical advantage for speed.

GENEVA STOP MOTION

One of the most fascinating pin-and-slot movements, this device imparts an intermittent move-and-hold action to its slotted wheel. As the driving member continuously rotates, its locking disk turns inside an arced notch of equal radius in the edge of the driven wheel, so holding it motionless. But the locking disk is partially cut away on the side nearest the drive pin. As the pin enters a slot in the wheel, the cutaway passes the center of the notch, releasing the wheel.

The pin now quickly sweeps the notch around, moving the wheel the distance between slots. As the pin leaves the one it has driven, the locking disk is engaging the next notch. Again it holds the wheel, while the pin swings around to the other side, until the pin enters the next notch to repeat the action. The Geneva movement can be designed for various numbers of slots.

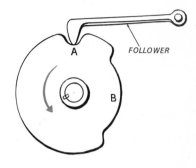

Fig. 27. Example of a notch-in-wheel mechanism for translating rotary motion of wheel into small up-and-down motion of arm.

FROM NOTCHES TO CAMS

An idea that is just the opposite of a peg set into a wheel is a notch cut into its edge. Such notches can produce small radial movements of a suitable follower. The arm in Figure 27, for example, will drop and rise again almost at once in notch A, but remain dropped for a longer interval in notch B. This idea has been used for centuries in clocks with strike movements, and this very morning woke millions of people as their alarm clocks went off.

Fig. 28. Pegged wheel used in the 18th-century European forges was forerunner of the cam.

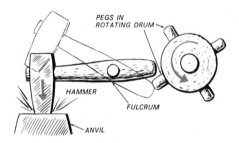

Hero's spoked or pegged wheel was put to sturdier purpose in European forges about the 18th century. An old print shows a long cylindrical barrel, presumably turned by a water wheel, that was fitted with three rings of pegs. As the barrel turned, the pegs swung down against the ends of three pivoted levers. The opposite ends of these carried heavy hammers (Figure 28). Raised by the turning pegs, the hammers dropped as the pegs slipped off the levers, only to rise again as the next peg pressed down the lever in turn. These pegged wheels may well be considered the forerunner of cams.

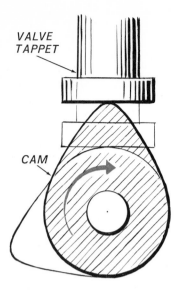

VALVE TAPPET

CAM

Fig. 29. This type of cam raises and lowers the valves in a gasoline engine.

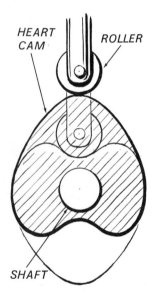

HEART CAM

ROLLER

SHAFT

Fig. 30. Heart-shaped cam is used to lay thread evenly on sewing-machine bobbins.

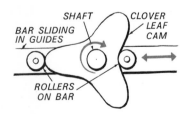

SHAFT

BAR SLIDING IN GUIDES

CLOVER LEAF CAM

ROLLERS ON BAR

Fig. 31. This cam imparts reciprocating motion to the bar by means of the two rollers which are in constant contact with the cam.

True cams are specially shaped wheels or disks, often quite thick in proportion to their diameter. They can impart accurately timed and even complicated movements to other parts—the needle of a sewing machine or the valves of a gasoline engine, for example. Tripping the ignition points in your car as much as two or three thousand times a minute is a little steel cam on the distributor shaft. It has as many lobes (high spots) as your engine has cylinders.

Many cams are far more complex, providing movements of different lengths at specific times. Followers may be simple rods or levers, or they may be fitted with rollers to lessen friction against the cam. In place of a follower, there may be a yoke that completely surrounds the cam, so generating other than simple back-and-forth movements.

The gas-engine cam is one of the simpler kinds. It is circular around most of its circumference, then rises steeply. The follower or tappet is motionless during the dwell period, then rises swiftly, is held up briefly, and as rapidly snapped shut (Figure 29).

A heart-shaped cam lifts the follower fairly slowly at first, then during almost half a revolution more rapidly, and returns it in the reverse order (Figure 30). A familiar use for such cams is the tracker that lays thread evenly on sewing-machine bobbins.

With these cams, the follower must be held in contact by a spring, weight or other device. A positive-motion cam may be a groove in the face of a disk, with the follower in guides that keep it inside the groove, as shown in an accompanying photograph.

Another kind of positive-action cam requires two rollers on the follower, these bearing on opposite sides of the cam. To keep both rollers in constant contact, the cam must be designed so that its maximum dimension is equal at all points across its shaft center. The cam in Figure 31, which imparts reciprocating motion to the bar, is an example.

Face cams have their contour formed on the ringlike face or edge of a recessed wheel (Figure 32). The follower must be held against it by a spring or other means. Follower movement is parallel to the shaft of the cam.

Positive axial motion can be imparted to the follower by a cylindrical cam. Figure 33 shows such a cam as it might be arranged to drive a sabre saw. The groove runs all the way around the cylinder. A roller on the end of a bell crank tracks in the groove as it turns, being rapidly traversed from the foremost to the rearmost part of the groove and back again. Such cylindrical cams may be longer in proportion to their diameter where greater follower travel is desired, and the groove may be formed to impart other actions than a simple reciprocating one.

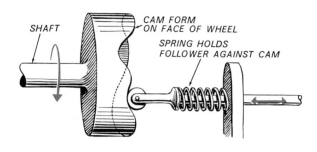

Fig. 32. Contoured face of this cam imparts motion to spring-held follower.

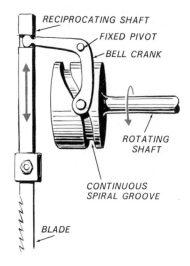

Fig. 33. Reciprocating action as it might be used in a sabre saw is imparted by a cylindrical cam.

An unusual cam action once used in French railroad engines is shown in Figure 34. A triangular cam is mounted on a disk and rotates with it, working in a rectangular yoke. In the position shown, the cam swings by without at first producing any yoke action. But as soon as the left-hand lobe rolls against the bottom of the yoke opening, the yoke begins to move down. When the end of this lobe passes off the yoke surface, a second dwell period begins, continuing until the lobe at the right impinges on the top of the yoke opening, which starts the delayed return stroke.

ECCENTRICS

Perfectly circular disks, mounted off center on their shafts, are called eccentrics. Typically the follower, called an eccentric strap, is a ring that fits it closely (Figure 35). As the shaft turns, the eccentric and its follower sweep around it in a circular path, the effect of their off-center mounting being to generate a reciprocating motion like that of a crank. An eccentric is in fact a better substitute for a crank than is generally supposed. Its action is even reversible—that is, pushing and pulling on the eccentric strap can rotate the shaft.

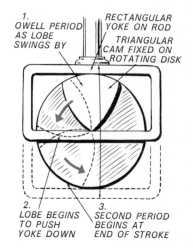

Fig. 34. Triangular cam inside rectangular yoke was once used in French railroad engines.

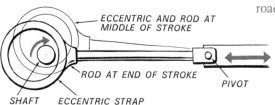

Fig. 35. Example of an eccentric and eccentric strap.

43

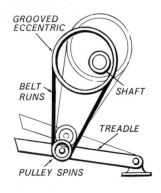

Fig. 36. Early treadle movement made use of a big eccentric on the shaft.

This action was adapted to a small high-speed steam engine built from a twin-cylinder refrigerator compressor. The compressor had pistons driven by large eccentrics, not cranks. Fitted with a suitable valve, which admitted steam alternately to the two cylinders, the pistons drove the eccentrics around as readily as if they had been cranks, powering an automobile generator to supply electricity aboard a boat.

This function of the eccentric dates back a long time. One of the early treadle movements made use of a big eccentric on the shaft (Figure 36). Instead of a ringlike strap, there was a rope or belt, and to allow this to travel freely as the eccentric swung around, it was run over a sheave or pulley fastened to the treadle. An advantage of this rig was that it required only a straight shaft, not a crank, and the treadle could be located anywhere between the shaft bearings.

Figure 37 shows an eccentric movement once used on toy film projectors. The eccentric rotates inside a close-fitting yoke, which has several distinct movements. It first advances almost horizontally, pushing the claw into a sprocket hole. Once fully entered, it starts pulling the film down, doing so in little more than a quarter of a turn. The claw is then withdrawn, leaving the picture on the screen for a longer period.

The swash plate might be considered a type of face cam. It is nothing more than a flat disk fixed obliquely on a shaft. As the shaft turns, the disk will impart to a follower a reciprocating movement parallel to the shaft. The follower may be a simple rod or tappet, but the swash plate is well adapted to a positive-action drive. All this takes is a jaw-like follower embracing the edge of the disk, or a roller on each side. The swash plate mechanism has been applied to a number of steam, gasoline and hot-gas engines, most of them experimental.

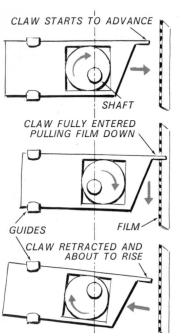

Fig. 37. Eccentric movement typical of that once used on toy film projectors.

IV

Flexible Levers—
Rope and Pulley Systems

Rope is wonderful material, even though it stretches in time, often displays a remarkable cussedness, and eventually wears out. Rope can transmit force to a distance (the top of a flagpole, for instance), direct it around a corner, even reverse it. The usefulness of rope is increased when the rope is combined with a pulley, and a combination of pulleys becomes a block and tackle that multiplies muscular force. Combinations of movable and fixed pulleys add up to the powerful mechanisms we have today in the modern Spanish Burton, in giant hoists and cranes, and in the familiar differential hoist in the auto repair garage, all of which are explained in this chapter.

Once rope was invented, it was almost sure to spark the invention of the pulley—a special adaptation of the wheel. Hoisting sails up a mast, a problem that appeared with the first sailing vessels, called for a single simple pulley. This seagoing application was probably one of the earliest. It was surely known long before Christ, for Aristotle about 350 years earlier left a record of a sophisticated pulley arrangement that halved the effort required to lift the load. Probably the pulley and its rigging systems date back still further, to civilizations of which we have little or no record. Given enough rope, inventive man must have devised and used such systems in other ages. The pulley, one of the six basic machine elements, may have been in use before historians began scribbling.

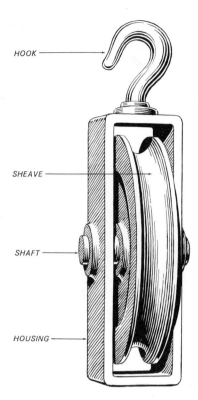

HOOK

SHEAVE

SHAFT

HOUSING

Fig. 1. A pulley mounted in a housing with a hook is called a block.

GROOVED WHEEL IN A BOX

A pulley, more properly called a sheave, is a wheel grooved on its periphery so that a rope, belt or chain will ride securely on it. Mount a sheave in a housing, add an eye or a hook by which the unit can be fastened to a load or a support, and you have a block (Figure 1). A combination of blocks is usually called a tackle, and it is in combination that pulleys best work their mechanical miracle of exchanging distance for effort.

One of the oldest applications of a single fixed pulley is shown in Figure 2. Like one fixed to the top of a ship's mast for hoisting up a sail, this single sheave merely reverses the pull applied to the downcoming end of the rope, and so hoists the bucket of water up. In the drawing, the rope is wound around a small windlass barrel fitted with long spokes, which multiply the force applied. But the pulley affords no mechanical advantage. The load is raised by a like force on the other side of the rope, and this force moves the same distance as the bucket rises. (The hands on the spokes, however, move through a greater distance, and this does afford some mechanical advantage.)

THE MOVABLE PULLEY

Now let's put the pulley on the load instead, as in Figure 3. Since the load is to move, the pulley is no longer fixed but movable. This makes a tremendous difference, for now we have to pull the rope up only half as hard to lift the same load.

Fig. 2. Single fixed pulley merely reverses direction of rope. Windlass multiplies force applied.

FIXED PULLEY

LOAD

You'd rather pull down than up? Okay, let's add a second pulley—a fixed one this time—and haul the rope over it as shown by dotted lines. This fixed pulley adds no further mechanical advantage, but by reversing the direction in which we have to apply force it lets us pull down, and so add our weight to the effort if necessary.

What's the bill for the mechanical advantage we gain from a movable pulley? The usual one of exchanging distance for effort. We have to pull our side of the rope twice as far as we wish to raise the load. As this enables us to move weights much greater than we otherwise could, it's a fair deal.

PULLEYS AS ROUND LEVERS

To see exactly why a pulley rigged this way gives us a mechanical advantage of two, we can equate it with our old friend the lever. As Figure 4 shows, a

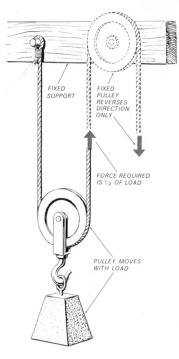

Fig. 3. Putting the pulley on the load halves the work required to lift the load.

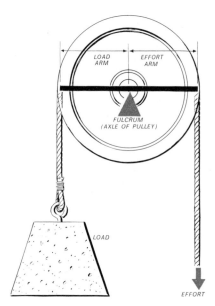

Fig. 4. Fixed pulley acts as lever of the first class.

fixed pulley acts as a simple lever of the first class. The fulcrum is the axle (the point at which the pulley is supported). The effort arm is the radius of the sheave—that is, the distance from the fulcrum-axle to the side of the rope we pull on. The load arm is also the radius of the sheave—the distance from the fulcrum-axle to the load-carrying side of the rope. The two arms being equal, the force will lift an equal weight, and move through the same distance as the weight is raised. Nothing is changed except the direction of the applied force.

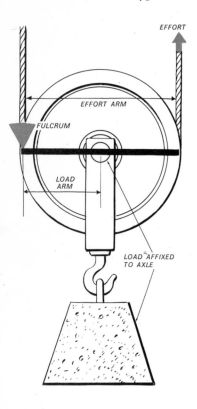

But the movable pulley in Figure 3 acts as a lever of the second class. The fulcrum is the fixed side of the rope. The load, being fixed to the axle or axle strap, is between the fulcrum and the force side of the rope—the one we pull up (Figure 5). Since the length of the load arm is the radius of the pulley, and the length of the effort arm the *diameter* of the pulley (that is, twice the radius) the lever has a mechanical advantage of two. Our effort will lift twice as much of a load, though we must expend it over twice the distance the load moves.

In reality, we don't gain quite that much. Since the movable pulley becomes part of the load to be raised, the extra effort needed to lift it must be accounted a loss. Also, the inevitable friction of the sheave or sheaves on their axles, and the effort necessary to flex the rope around them continuously, all require some extra output on our part. Nevertheless, there is a big net gain that makes pulley rigs well worth while.

PULLEYS THAT PULL PULLEYS

If the pulley is comparable to a lever, how about compounding it for still greater gain? Figure 6 shows one way of doing this. We can use three

Fig. 5. Movable pulley acts as lever of the second class.

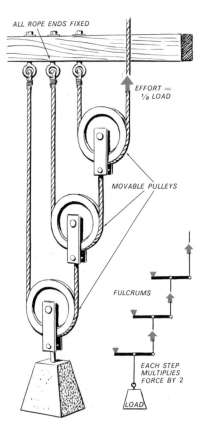

Fig. 6. Compound pulleys, like compound levers, greatly increase mechanical advantage as each step is added.

pulleys and as many separate ropes. The ropes are all fixed to a common over-head support, and all the pulleys are movable ones. What do we gain?

The diagram shows the same rig in the form of compound levers. Each step multiplies the force applied by two. Our total mechanical advantage is two times two times two, or eight—the cube of two. With four steps, we could increase the mechanical advantage to sixteen. And again, if we prefer to pull down rather than up, it's permissible to add a fixed pulley at the top to reverse direction. We'll pay for the mechanical advantage gained by hauling the rope a greater distance—eight times as far as the load rises with three movable pulleys, or sixteen times as far with four pulleys.

The rig shown in Figure 6 would work, but it isn't particularly conven-ient. Installation would require at least three anchor points, and the free-swing-ing ropes would be prone to tangle. Somewhat better is the tackle shown in Figure 7. It calls for three fixed pulleys, the topmost of which merely reverses direction. But these require only one anchorage, and the fixed end of the rope is fastened to the axle strap, so the whole affair can be handled as a unit.

The movable pulleys are also in tandem, with the weight depending from their axle strap, a quite different arrangement from the one in Figure 6. Because of this difference, the 1-to-2 gain of each movable pulley is not cubed, but merely added. The total mechanical advantage is six, not eight. You can determine the gain for most pulley tackle of this kind by counting the number of strands that support the load (the rope you pull on doesn't count).

To minimize tangling and make tackle easier to handle and install, the three pulleys in each set can be mounted side by side in a single block, all the sheaves being the same size and turning individually on a common axle. Figure 8 shows a five-pulley tackle. Five strands support the load, and the rig has a mechanical advantage of five.

So long as the sheaves are free to turn independently of each other, their size isn't critical. Of course they must be large enough to let the bight of the rope run around them freely. Pulleys of too small a radius will impose extra bending loads, besides wearing the rope unduly. But with smaller rope, you can scale down pulley action as far as you like; the principle and mathematics apply to any size tackle.

Surprisingly, it's possible to build a pulley system—of sorts—without pulleys. It wouldn't be efficient, nor practicable in large sizes or with heavy loads. But you could grease the rope well, and run it around smooth, grooved collars in place of pulleys. It's the configuration of the rope that really does the trick, the free turning of the sheave that makes it practical.

Want proof? You can make a model of any of the pulley systems shown by running strong thread around pins or thumbtacks. Small as the diameter of

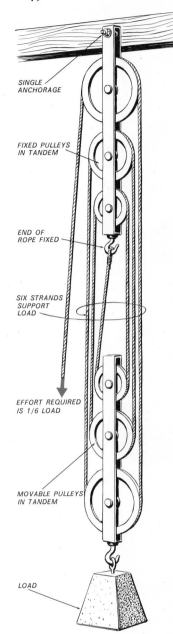

SINGLE
ANCHORAGE

FIXED PULLEYS
IN TANDEM

END OF
ROPE FIXED

SIX STRANDS
SUPPORT
LOAD

EFFORT REQUIRED
IS 1/6 LOAD

MOVABLE PULLEYS
IN TANDEM

LOAD

Fig. 7. Three fixed and three movable pulleys, all in tan-dem with a single anchorage, is an improvement over ar-rangement shown in Fig. 6.

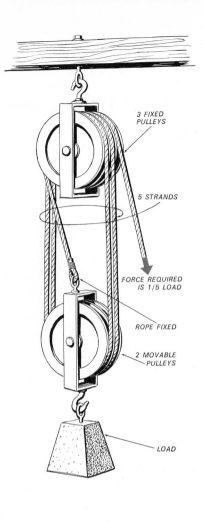

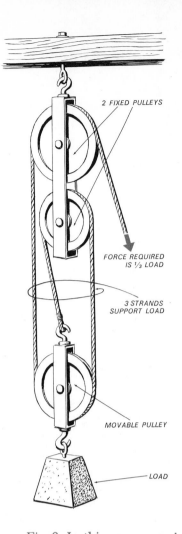

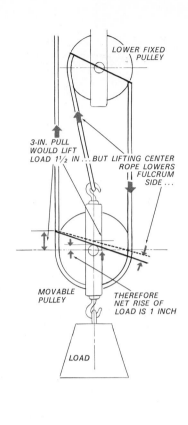

Fig. 8. More compact arrangement puts pulleys side by side in a single block, minimizing tangling.

Fig. 9. In this arrangement, upper fixed pulley only changes rope's direction; the one below it multiplies by half again the effect of the movable pulley.

Fig. 10. Analysis of a typical pulley arrangement.

a pin is, it will act like a pulley and demonstrate the same exchange of distance for mechanical advantage. Though friction is high, such models do work.

The role of fixed pulleys is sometimes a peculiar one. To understand better how such tackle as the ones in Figures 7 and 8 work, have a look at the simpler one in Figure 9. Remember that the upper fixed pulley only changes direction. But the one below it multiplies the effect of the movable pulley by half again. Here's how:

In the adjacent diagram (Figure 10) note that a 3-inch pull on the rope would normally lift the load half that far, or 1½ inches. But raising the load

FIXED PULLEY

MOVABLE PULLEY

FORCE REQUIRED IS ⅓ LOAD

Fig. 11. Two-pulley rig gives mechanical advantage of three. Both pulleys act as levers of first class.

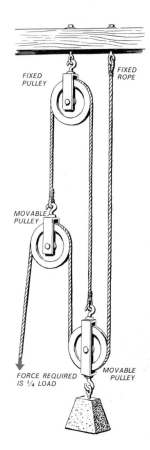

FIXED PULLEY

FIXED ROPE

MOVABLE PULLEY

FORCE REQUIRED IS ¼ LOAD

MOVABLE PULLEY

Fig. 12. Single Spanish Burton gives mechanical advantage of four with one fixed and two movable pulleys.

also raises (or shortens) the rope directly above it. As this rope section passes around the lower fixed pulley, it comes down on the other side and so lowers the right-hand side—the fulcrum side—of the movable pulley. This partially negates the lift; while the left-hand rope is raising the load 1½ inches, the lowering of the fulcrum lets it down a half inch, leaving a *net* rise of only 1 inch. Of course this curious give-and-take continues so long as we're pulling on the rope, and not in the steplike sequence described, but simultaneously and smoothly.

What do we gain by giving back a half inch of load rise? We get its equivalent in mechanical advantage; since we exert force through 3 inches while the load moves only 1 inch, the laws of physics repay us with a mechanical advantage of three instead of two.

This principle also applies to the two-pulley rig in Figure 11. As you raise the load, shortening the right-hand side of the rope that goes around the fixed pulley, the left-hand side lengthens and lowers the movable pulley. This counteracts part of your pull (in other words, it makes you pull through a greater distance by feeding the pull rope toward you). You get a mechanical advantage of three even though individually both pulleys act as simple levers of the first class!

Another example of this curious give-and-take action is the rig in Figure 12, sometimes called a single Spanish Burton. Here you get a mechanical advantage of four with one fixed and two movable pulleys. The separate rope that runs over the fixed pulley keeps lowering the movable pulley on the left, so that you have to pull four times the distance the load moves. Note, incidentally, that the strand count doesn't give the mechanical advantage correctly in these two cases.

THE CHINESE WINDLASS

An old name for what is better called the differential windlass, this astonishing contraption (Figure 13) will give you almost any degree of mechanical advantage you wish (at the usual rate—distance in exchange for force) with a single movable pulley! Instead of pulling a rope, you turn a crank. The length of the crank arm is an important factor but needn't concern us at the moment.

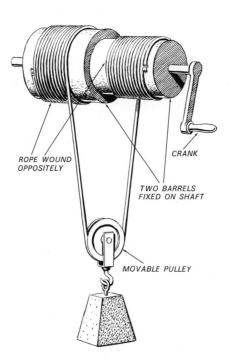

ROPE WOUND
OPPOSITELY

CRANK

TWO BARRELS
FIXED ON SHAFT

MOVABLE PULLEY

Fig. 13. Chinese windlass gains mechanical advantage by stepped barrel, single strand of rope.

The windlass barrel is stepped—that is, it has two different diameters, and the ends of a single length of rope are wound on these two diameters in opposite directions. As the shaft is turned, one end of the rope will wind up while the other unwinds.

Sounds frustrating, doesn't it? But there is a differential action. If you crank the rope on the bigger part of the barrel up, you gain a little each turn because the smaller diameter doesn't let dawn quite as much rope as the larger pulls up. For every turn of the crank, you gain an upward distance equal to the *difference* in the circumferences of the two barrel diameters. But this is halved at the center of the movable pulley, where the load is attached. So to move the weight up half the difference between the two barrel circumferences, you have to swing the crank in a comparatively large arc—which results in a correspondingly great mechanical advantage.

The *smaller* the difference between the two barrels, the more oomph this rig will have (and the longer you'll have to crank to inch the load upward). But the barrels must never be the *same* diameter; if they were, you wouldn't be lifting the load at all.

THE DIFFERENTIAL HOIST

By now you've probably recognized the Chinese windlass for what it is —the forerunner of the handy differential hoist you see in auto repair shops and factories (Figure 14).

Instead of a crank and windlass, this device has two fixed sheaves rigidly joined together to turn as one (in fact, they may be made as one piece). Both sheaves have notches in their grooves to give a chain nonslip traction. The continuous chain runs around the two fixed pulleys and a movable one to which the load is hitched. Pull the side of the chain loop that runs to the bigger sheave, and you lift the load. But the smaller sheave turns with the big one, and lets down that side of the chain running to the movable pulley. In other words, we are pulling up one side and letting down at the other. The net rise per revolution of the upper two sheaves is the difference in their circumference, halved by the action of the movable pulley. As you raise a load, the chain loop becomes longer. Pulling the other side of the loop lowers the load.

If the diameters of the top sheaves are almost the same, the mechanical advantage can be so great that the action is irreversible; that is, the load will hold at any height to which it is hoisted. The reason is that, with the *reverse* ratio of the mechanical advantage working against it, the load is simply not great enough to overcome sheave, shaft and chain friction and spin the wheels backward.

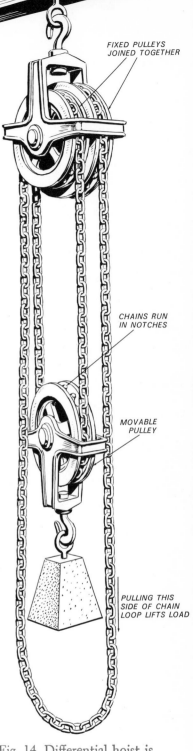

FIXED PULLEYS
JOINED TOGETHER

CHAINS RUN
IN NOTCHES

MOVABLE
PULLEY

PULLING THIS
SIDE OF CHAIN
LOOP LIFTS LOAD

Fig. 14. Differential hoist is used in auto repair shops and factories.

V

The other three simple machines—

Inclines, Wedges
and Screws

Only recently have scientists dared dream of antigravity—some yet unguessed means of nullifying earth's pull on all material objects. Yet even primitive man used a device that sliced the force of gravity into conquerable parts—a device that has no moving parts and indeed doesn't seem to be a machine at all. It is the inclined plane—in prehistoric terms merely a ramp of packed earth or the natural slope of a hill, up which a monolith could be muscled to an eminence worthy of its purpose.

Of course those early builders didn't think of that slope as an inclined plane. It was there and taken for granted. The suburbanite who slants a couple of planks up to his station wagon to load a power mower hardly thinks of them as a machine element. Yet the inclined plane is just that, and it is the basis of the final two basic machine elements—the wedge and the screw.

Undoubtedly the builders of the Egyptian pyramids (about the 29th century B.C.) knew and used the inclined plane. But even Archimedes (250 B.C.), though he was familiar with the screw, didn't formulate any theories on the properties of the inclined plane. It wasn't until the early part of the 16th century that Jerome Cardan, a mathematician, made an effort to do so. His analysis involved a small-order error that was set straight in 1586 by Simon Stevin, of Belgium.

54

SPLITTING 20 INTO 12 AND 16

Would you believe that a 20-pound force can at one and the same time exert two other forces, one of 12 and one of 16 pounds? Or that a sled weighs less when you're pulling it than when at rest? Or that a rope tested to 1,000 pounds will break if a 700-pound load is fastened to it in a certain way?

All three are true, part of the weird world of vectors, as the inclined plane is too. A vector is really less forbidding than the word itself—it simply means a directed quantity. If you speak of a 20-pound force, you have defined a magnitude only, for the force may be exerted in any direction. But a 20-pound weight is a force exerted in just one direction—downward.

On paper, a vector is represented by a straight line drawn in some definite relation to a base line, the center of a circle, or some other reference so that it indicates the direction of a force. The line must also be drawn to a definite length that will represent the strength or magnitude of the force.

For example, Figure 1 shows a boy pulling a loaded sled. The pull is evidently along the line of the rope, so it can be represented by a line A–B

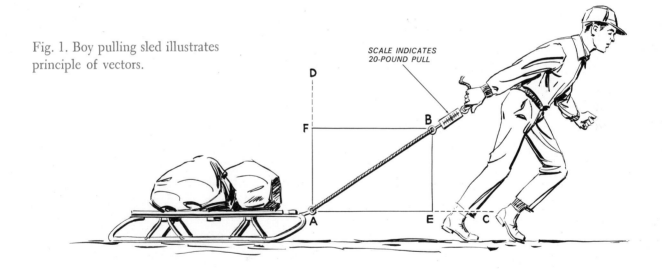

Fig. 1. Boy pulling sled illustrates principle of vectors.

SCALE INDICATES 20-POUND PULL

drawn at the same angle—in our diagram, we will let it be the rope. A spring scale between the boy's hand and the rope indicates a pull of 20 pounds. We choose a convenient scale unit—say ⅛ inch to the pound—and draw the line 20 units long, or 2½ inches.

If the boy could pull along the actual level of the sled—along the horizontal line A–C—all his effort would result in forward movement. If he were to pull straight up along the vertical line A–D, *none* of his effort would move the sled forward. The actual line of pull A–B represents a sensible compromise with the geometry of the human frame, enabling the boy to lean into the load to best advantage.

Nevertheless, since that vector lies between the line of maximum advantage A–C and that of minimum advantage A–D, some of his effort is evidently lost. How much of his 20-pound pull moves the sled? To find out, we can complete a simple vector diagram. We drop a vertical line from B to meet A–C at E, and a horizontal line from B to cross A–D at F.

The resulting rectangle is a graphic presentation of the forces at work. Measuring A–E to our ⅛ inch scale, we find it is 2 inches long and so represents a horizontal pull of 16 pounds. Similarly measured to scale, the vertical A–F, being 1½ inches high, gives the vertical component as 12 pounds. In other words, the 20-pound pull produces 16 pounds of horizontal force that moves the sled, and 12 pounds toward trying to lift the sled. If the sled were weighed while at rest, and then hauled across a platform scale with a rope at the angle shown, it would actually weigh 12 pounds less while in motion!

ZANY ARITHMETIC?

No, we haven't subverted the rules of addition. The 12- and 16-pound components are at right angles to each other (they're vector forces too, of course) and though both are produced by the single 20-pound pull, they can no more be added than apples and oranges. They do, however, obey the rule of the hypotenuse—the sum of the squares of the two sides is equal to the square of the hypotenuse. (144 plus 256 equals 400).

This sort of analysis is called the resolution of forces—we've resolved the pull along the rope into two components. This is a sample of vector mechanics. Another—though it isn't pertinent to the inclined plane—is that a weight on the middle of a tightly stretched horizontal rope will stress both sides of the rope with vector forces much greater than the weight itself. If on the other hand the rope is allowed to sag, the stresses are less; if the sag angle is 120 degrees, each side of the rope will be stressed by a force equal to the weight. If the sag be greater, the stress is smaller, until when the rope hangs straight down in two strands, each strand will bear only half the load.

It is because of the vector forces imposed on a tightly stretched rope that it is almost impossible to pull a long one taut. It will break under its own weight. This too is the reason you always see a sag in the tow cable between a tug and the liner or barge it is pulling. When drawn taut by sea action, it is in danger of snapping.

ROLL UP THE BARREL

To see how vector forces work on an inclined plane, imagine you are rolling a 200-pound barrel up a plank 16 feet long, with its upper end 4 feet above the ground (Figure 2).

As the force of gravity acts straight down, we draw a vertical line from the center of the barrel A to a convenient scale—say ⅛ inch shall represent

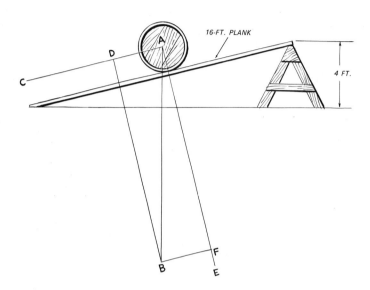

Fig. 2. Vector forces at work on an inclined plane.

10 pounds. This gravity vector is therefore 2½ inches long. The force we must put forth to hold the barrel on the plank can be shown on the line A–C parallel to the plank. To establish its length we draw a line from B at right angles to the plank, crossing A–C at D. When measured, A–D proves to be ⅝ inch long which scales to 50 pounds. This is the force necessary to hold the barrel motionless while you catch your breath; it will take a bit extra to overcome inertia, friction and chewing gum on the plank when you start it moving again.

Let's finish the vector diagram by drawing A–E also at right angles to the plank, and cross it with B–F parallel to the plank. A–F now represents the second component of the 200-pound force of gravity, namely the force with which the barrel bears against the plank. On measurement, it scales off to about 194 pounds.

(Oh yes, the barrel puts less weight on a sloping plane than on a horizontal one! On a level surface, it would exert 200 pounds. If the plank were vertical, the barrel would put no weight at all on it. But as the plank is swung farther under the barrel, more and more weight would come on it.)

That simple machine, the inclined plane, has resolved the force of gravity into two lesser components of 50 pounds and 194 pounds. Since the plank supports all of the latter, we have to tussle only with the 50 pounds (or as much more as necessary to overcome inertia and friction) and can raise the 200-pound barrel with comparative ease.

WHAT A DIFFERENCE AN ANGLE MAKES

Of course the steepness of the inclined plane is a key factor. The faster it rises, the more of the barrel's weight we have to shove up the slope. A gentle incline gives us greater mechanical advantage.

The effort we must put forth is the same proportion of the load as the total rise is to the length of the slope. With a 16-foot plank and a 4-foot rise, a 1 to 4 ratio, we need exert only one fourth as much force as the barrel's weight (Figure 3). If the rise is one in three, we'll have to push on a 200-pound barrel with 66⅔ pounds of force. A 1 to 2 incline calls for heroic effort—100 pounds of uphill push.

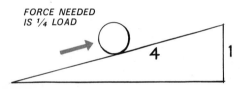
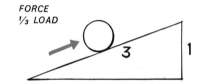
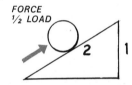

Fig. 3. Mechanical advantage depends on steepness of inclined plane.

In actual practice it always takes somewhat more to overcome inertia and friction, though the latter can be reduced with wheels, rollers or lubrication.

Mathematically, the ideal mechanical advantage can be found without knowing the length or height of the slope, for both are implicit in the angle of the inclined plane to the horizontal. The force necessary to hold a frictionless load on it is the weight of the load times the sine of the angle, a quantity that can be found in trigonometric tables.

What do we pay for the mechanical advantage gained? The same as in the cases of the lever, the wheel and axle, and the compound pulley. We have to exert our smaller effort through a greater distance than the load is moved.

If our 200-pound barrel is raised to the top of the 16-foot plank, its height has been changed by 4 feet, and we have done 800 foot-pounds of work. In the process, we will have exerted a 50-pound effort (neglecting friction) over the 16-foot length of the plank, which also multiplies to 800 foot-pounds of work. Fair enough?

A CURIOUS BALANCE

Galileo arrived at the law of the inclined plane by pondering the law of the lever. The inclined plane is in fact a strange sort of scale or balance, without fulcrum or lever. Suppose we push a shaft through our 200-pound barrel, on which it can turn freely, and rig a harness from the ends of the shaft to a rope, then carry the rope over a pulley at the top of the incline and fasten a 50-pound weight on the down side of it (Figure 4).

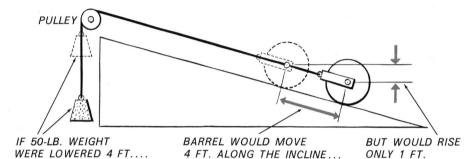

PULLEY

IF 50-LB. WEIGHT
WERE LOWERED 4 FT....

BARREL WOULD MOVE
4 FT. ALONG THE INCLINE...

BUT WOULD RISE
ONLY 1 FT.

Fig. 4. Inclined plane is a strange sort of scale without fulcrum or lever.

That 50-pound weight will balance the 200-pound barrel anywhere on the incline, for in the direction of the plane (which is the same as the rope runs) the barrel has an effective weight of only 50 pounds. Though the barrel and weight are free to move, neither can move without the other, and the presence of the plane will allow the barrel to rise or fall vertically only one-fourth the distance the weight does.

Tilt the plane upward toward the horizontal, and the weight will fall, drawing the barrel higher, for you will have increased the mechanical advantage of the weight. But yank the inclined plane out from under the barrel, and it will assume all the authority of its greater weight, and snap the 50-pound weight upward.

Aside from using planks to haul loads up into a station wagon, or up cellar stairs, you encounter inclined planes every time you take out your car. Every sloping road—perhaps your own driveway—is one. Your car lifts itself from one elevation to another by traveling on inclined planes. Highway engineers measure grades in percent; a rise of 1 foot in 100 feet of length is a 1 percent grade. But such a slope as the 1-in-4 of our barrel-loading plank (a 25 percent grade) is unthinkable in road construction. So mountain roads are built in switchback fashion, weaving back and forth through a greater distance to reduce the grade to a reasonable figure.

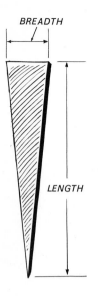

BREADTH

LENGTH

Fig. 5. Determine mechanical advantage of a wedge by dividing its length by its thickest breadth.

The inclined plane is sometimes applied to machinery. You'll find it on some woodworking jointers, for example. The tables of these slide on inclined ramps, being positioned on them by screws, to adjust table height in relation to the cutter head.

THE MANY FACES OF THE WEDGE

Make a solid inclined plane small enough to move about, and you have a wedge. Whereas the inclined plane is stationary, and the load moved on it, the wedge is moved inside the material it is to split or push apart in some way. In effect, the incline is pushed under the load instead of the load being pushed up the incline.

The classic application of the wedge, of course, is to split wood or stone. The Greeks used wedges to crush olives between boards for extracting the oil, and the Romans put them to work on their astonishing engineering feats. The wedge principle is also involved in driving a nail, plowing soil, using an axe, plane, chisel or air hammer. It is even behind the success of the "flying wedge" formation in football and hand combat.

The ideal mechanical advantage of a wedge is found by dividing its length by its thickest breadth (Figure 5). Thus a 10-inch-long wedge 2 inches thick has a theroretical advantage of five, and a 50-pound blow on its head should produce a splitting strain across the wedge of 250 pounds. But the actual advantage is much less because of friction, which varies with different materials, their surface smoothness, and the area of the wedge in contact at any time.

This considerable friction tends to keep a driven wedge firmly in place, which is why nails hold and wedges fasten hammer and axe heads securely to their handles. Wedges can also provide fine or venier adjustments, such as the tilt setting of a power-sander table (Figure 6) or raise a building (Figure 7). In these cases the wedge movement is irreversible—that is, the load cannot move the wedge because of friction, the wedge angle, and in some cases the screw or other adjusting device.

Fig. 6. Wedge used to provide fine tilt setting of a power-sander table.

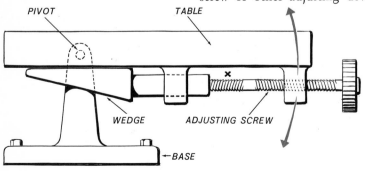

PIVOT   TABLE

WEDGE   ADJUSTING SCREW

←BASE

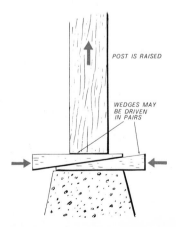

POST IS RAISED

WEDGES MAY BE DRIVEN IN PAIRS

Fig. 7. Wedges used to raise a building.

But as anyone who has ever shot a watermelon seed out of his fingers knows, the reverse action can occur under some conditions. Generally, however, the angle chosen for the wedge is such that it will remain in position. The Morse taper shanks on lathe centers, big drills, milling cutters and other machine-tool accessories are a good example (Figure 8). Such a taper shank need only to be rammed with moderate force into a tapered socket to hold firmly. Yet the least outward movement will free it instantly and completely.

THE SPIRAL INCLINED PLANE

If you cut out the profile of an inclined plane and wrap it around into the form of a cylinder (Figure 9), you have the basis of the screw. In actual practice, the slope of the plane must be made a spiral ridge, rather like a stepless spiral staircase. The screw can convert rotary motion into axial (lengthwise) motion, as it does in the screwjack (Figure 10), as well as in the wood and machine screw, the auger bit, corkscrew and meat grinder.

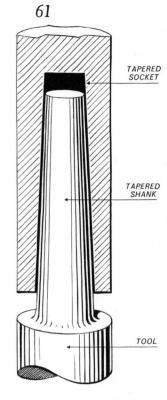

Fig. 8. Tapered shank holds firmly in tapered socket, but it can be freed instantly by slight outward movement.

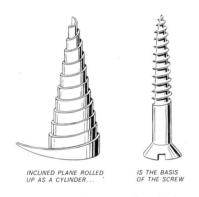

INCLINED PLANE ROLLED UP AS A CYLINDER...   IS THE BASIS OF THE SCREW

Fig. 9. Screw is an inclined plane wrapped into form of a cylinder.

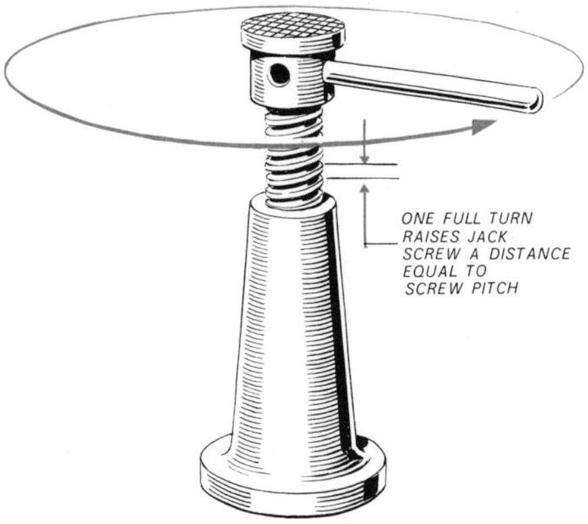

ONE FULL TURN RAISES JACK SCREW A DISTANCE EQUAL TO SCREW PITCH

Fig. 10. Screw can convert rotary motion into axial motion, as in the screwjack.

The geometry of the spiral helix was set forth by another Greek mathematician, Apollonius, who lived about 200 B.C. Greeks and Romans both used screw presses to squeeze grapes and crush olives. A Pompeiian mural shows a screw press for linen. At a later date such presses were used for paper making and printing, and the thumbscrew for grimmer purposes. The 19th-century copying press, invented by the same James Watt of steam-engine fame, was a small one in which a letter, written with special ink, could be squeezed against moistened copy sheets to make several duplicates. (Before the day of the typewriter and carbon paper, such copy presses were standard office fixtures.)

GEOMETRY OF A SCREW

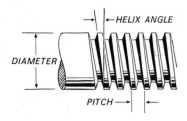

Fig. 11. Determining the pitch of a screw.

The helix angle (equivalent to the slope angle of an inclined plane) determines how many ridges or threads can be accommodated on a given length. A screw having 20 threads per inch has a *pitch* of $\frac{1}{20}$ inch, which is the distance between like parts of two adjacent threads (Figure 11). It is also the distance the screw will move axially if turned one revolution. (Or the distance a nut on it will travel in one turn.)

Old woodcuts of early printing presses often show the pressman straining against a long bar socketed in the screw, much like the one in the screw jack (Figure 10). The effort is therefore exerted through a distance equal to the circumference of a circle swept by the bar. As all this effort-movement results in an axial movement equal to the screw pitch, the mechanical advantage can be high. Ideally, it is the circumference divided by the pitch, or

$$\frac{2\ Pi\ R}{P}$$

where R is the length of the bar and P the pitch.

GENERATING A SCREW THREAD

Wooden screws for presses, carpenter's clamps and such Colonial delights as adjustable candleholders were probably made first by hand, then with a die consisting of a cutter fixed in a hardwood block, with a follower or indexing pin that rode in the thread to maintain the correct pitch as the tool proceeded.

But real precision came only with the screw-cutting lathe invented by Henry Maudslay in 1797. He didn't even design it for its own sake, but to help him build a hydraulic press. In a modern screw-cutting lathe, the workpiece is turned while the carriage carrying the tool is traversed along it. Tool movement must be precisely correlated with spindle movement, and of course a screw is ideal for the job. This is the lead screw, running almost the full length of the lathe and driven by gears from the spindle so that it moves "in step" to produce the desired screw pitch. Carriage movement is started and stopped by a split nut that can be closed around the rotating lead screw or opened to release it.

Later, Maudslay was in part responsible for the automatic manufacture of bolts and nuts, which today's home mechanic would find it difficult to be without. Machine screws are designated by body diameter and pitch. A $\frac{5}{16}$-18 machine bolt, for example, has a $\frac{5}{16}$-inch shank or body with 18 threads per inch on it. The bolt may, of course, be shorter than an inch, or much longer.

Below $\frac{3}{16}$ inch, body size is designated by a number instead of the actual dimension, No. 10 being $\frac{3}{16}$-inch diameter and No. 5 being $\frac{1}{8}$-inch. A 4-40 screw, for example, has a No. 4 body (which is .112 inch in diameter, or about $\frac{7}{64}$ inch) and 40 threads per inch.

Depending on the direction of the helix angle, a thread may be right-handed or left-handed. Standard threads are right-handed, which means that turning a bolt clockwise moves it into the nut or threaded hole. Turning a right-handed nut clockwise tightens it on the bolt. Left-hand threads are readily cut on a lathe by reversing the direction of the lead screw, so moving the carriage from left to right instead of from right to left. Left-hand threads are found on the wheel studs and nuts on the left side of many cars.

For special purposes, screws are sometimes made with two or three distinct threads instead of one. Though the pitch remains the distance between adjacent threads, the distance the screw moves in one turn (called the lead of a multiple thread screw) is the distance between the nearest two turns of the same thread (Figure 12). This gives the effect of a "fast" thread (a single thread of large pitch) while keeping more threads in engagement. A thin nut that would perhaps have only one thread of a coarse-pitch single thread in it would have two or three threads if multiple threads are used.

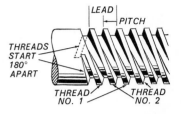

Fig. 12. Example of a "fast" thread on a screw.

WORM GEARS AND PROPELLERS

The worm used in high-ratio speed reducers is a special kind of screw. Its thread is tangent to a gear having teeth cut at the same angle (Figure 13) and often cut to a concave radius matching the worm's. One revolution of a single-thread worm rotates the gear a distance equal to the pitch of its teeth. The mechanical advantage or speed-reduction ratio is therefore the same as the number of teeth on the worm gear.

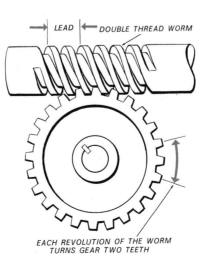

Fig. 13. Worm gear meshed with a common spur gear.

Worm drives are commonly used in the swivel action of oscillating fans, the worm being on the fan shaft and the gear on a crankshaft that produces oscillation. These and most other worm drives are irreversible—the worm has to be the driving element, while torque applied to the gear will not turn the worm. But what happened when a Stutz coasted downhill? That classic car had a worm on the propeller shaft driving a gear on the differential cage, and obviously it had to be reversible whenever car momentum overran engine revs.

It worked fine, and does today in the French Peugeot automobile and some trucks with similar worm drives. To be reversible, the worm has to have a helix or pressure angle acute enough to permit the sliding contact of the gear teeth to turn it freely. One difficulty, however, is that a sufficiently steep helix angle results in a coarse thread with insufficient tooth engagement on the gear for heavy service. The answer is a multiple-thread worm. Each individual thread has a "fast" angle, but the intermediate ones provide plenty of tooth engagement.

Since the lead of a four-thread screw is four times the pitch between adjacent threads, the ratio of a four-thread worm is only one-fourth the number of teeth on the gear. For a double-thread worm it is one-half the number of teeth on the gear. Thus a double-thread worm driving a 40-tooth gear will have a speed-reduction ratio (or mechanical advantage) not of 40 to 1, but of 20 to 1.

Air and boat propellers (and the blades of household fans) may seem to have little kinship to the screw at first glance. But imagine each blade as the start of a thread on a multiple-thread screw (though chopped short soon after it starts) and the likeness emerges. When turned so rapidly that the inertia of the air or water will not allow that medium to get out of the way fast enough, the propeller actually does screw itself through that medium (Figure 14). Its trail, if visible, would further resemble a screw.

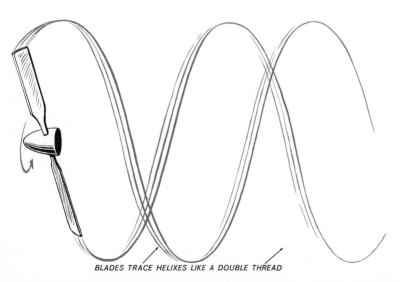

BLADES TRACE HELIXES LIKE A DOUBLE THREAD

Fig. 14. Propeller actually screws itself through air or water, leaving a trail that would resemble a screw.

Archimedes' water-pump screw plays a new role in a weird vehicle called the Marsh Screw Amphibian. Designed and built by the Chrysler Corporation for the U.S. Navy Bureau of Ships in 1963, it rides on two cylindrical pontoons fitted with spiral blades, or helixes. As the pontoons are turned by the engine, they literally screw the 2,300-pound craft along through water, swamp, deep snow or hip-deep muck.

Just as a right-hand thread remains right-handed even if turned end for end, a fan or propeller will blow air or produce thrust in the same direction if reversed on its shaft. The only way to change the direction in which the blades act is to bend them the other way, or turn the shaft in the opposite direction.

SOME SCREW MECHANISMS

Screws are highly useful for making fine adjustments—for setting calipers or a drafting compass, for instance. The machinist's micrometer, which can measure to a ten-thousandth of an inch (.0001) has a 40-pitch screw that moves in or out $\frac{1}{40}$ inch (.025) per revolution.

Suppose you had means of making only relatively coarse threads—none finer than $\frac{1}{20}$ pitch—but wanted to make a device that will move a block or an anvil a much smaller distance per turn—say $\frac{1}{80}$ inch. Hopeless? No, it can be done with a differential screw. Figure 15 shows how. The screw has two coarse threads of almost the same pitch—say 16 threads per inch on the larger diameter and 20 threads per inch on the smaller. The blocks are of course threaded to match.

Fig. 15. Differential screw can make fine adjustments.

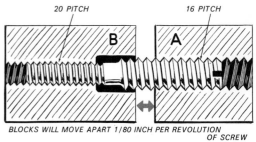

20 PITCH   B   A   16 PITCH

BLOCKS WILL MOVE APART 1/80 INCH PER REVOLUTION
OF SCREW

When the screw is turned clockwise, it moves block A to the right $\frac{1}{16}$ inch per revolution, but block B only $\frac{1}{20}$ inch. As B is losing ground the two blocks are pushed apart by the difference ($\frac{5}{80}$ minus $\frac{4}{80}$, or $\frac{1}{80}$ inch) at every turn. Rotating the screw counterclockwise pulls the blocks together at the same rate, with great force. We have created a vernier action twice as sensitive as that of a good micrometer with coarser threads.

Feeling that adjustments would be too slow with a single thread, the makers of the sanding table in Figure 6 added a *left-hand* thread at the inner end (x) of the same screw. This engages a like thread in the sleeve at the end of the wedge. As the knob is turned clockwise, the right-hand thread in the table edge moves the whole screw inward, pushing the wedge forward. But the left-hand thread turns itself out of the sleeve, rejecting the wedge and therefore also moving it forward. This dual action moves the wedge (assuming both threads are the same pitch) at double speed.

Just the opposite—a very slow vernier movement—could be achieved with two right-hand threads, the one in the wedge sleeve slightly finer than the other. As the coarser one in the table edge moves the screw inward, pushing the wedge forward, the finer thread would draw into the sleeve, pulling the wedge back a slightly lesser distance. The net effect would be that the wedge would advance only by the difference between the two thread pitches.

A sequence timer of a kind used on a certain washing machine can be built with a screw as its actuating element. The long threaded shaft is turned by a timer motor at relatively slow speed (Figure 16). In turning, the screw

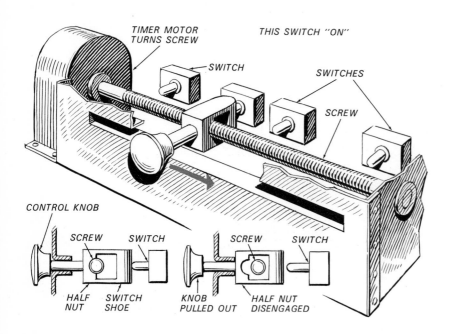

Fig. 16. Screw used as actuating element for sequence timer on a washing machine.

moves a half-nut along its length. At suitably spaced intervals are mounted switches that control various operations. As the half-nut, with the knob and switch shoe it carries, moves along the screw, it opens and closes the switches in the ordered sequence. Pulling out the knob at any point disengages the half nut from the screw, permitting the switch shoe to be slid by hand to repeat any operation, skip some, or start over again.

Surely one of the strangest applications of a screw is an old one for tightening bearing brasses, or liners, in the big ends of connecting rods. A hollow space was provided behind one brass (Figure 17) and this space was filled with steel balls. A pointed screw in a threaded hole, when turned into the balls, so compressed them that they exerted force in every direction much like a fluid. As only the brass could move, it was pressed tighter against the crankpin.

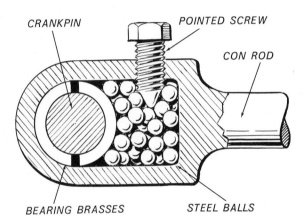

Fig. 17. Screw used to tighten bearing brass in connecting rod.

A RUSSIAN PUZZLE

Published in a magazine for technical students in the Soviet Union, this puzzle shows two identical bolts held together as in Figure 18. If you swing one around the other without letting the bolts turn in your fingers, will the bolt heads draw nearer, move farther apart, or remain at the same distance? The magazine challenged its readers to answer "without experimentation." Can you, and give reasons for your answer?

Fig. 18. What will happen if you swing one bolt around the other without letting the bolts turn in your fingers?

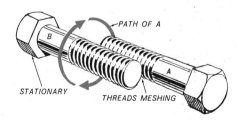

The answer is that the bolt heads will always stay the same distance apart, and it doesn't matter which bolt you orbit around the other. So long as the threads are kept in mesh, a clockwise movement of bolt A around B is exactly the same as a *counterclockwise* movement of B (seen from the bolt-head end) around A. Try it with your two index fingers! Therefore, while A is traveling up the threads of B toward the head of B, bolt B is at the same time moving *down* the threads of A, backing away from the head of A. Even if you reverse the rotary motion, the action of the two threads is simply interchanged and still cancels out.

VI

The Two Faces
of Friction

Because friction complicates the simple formulas applicable to the six basic machines, we have been ignoring it so far. In reality, of course, it can't be ignored. Much scientific research and engineering is devoted to minimizing friction. Without means of combating it, our machines—and that means our civilization—wouldn't last out the week.

But friction isn't altogether the static in the symphony of machines. It plays a dual role, one of them indispensable. Without it we couldn't walk or even crawl. One of the classic puzzles science students sometimes amuse themselves with is that of the frictionless ice. If it were possible to place a man (presumably by helicopter) in the middle of such an expanse, would he ever be able to get off it? Without friction, he'd find it difficult even to roll over. If he did manage it, he'd turn and turn in the same place without going anywhere, like a well-oiled axle. The problem isn't as far-fetched as it once was, for an astronaut who drifts away from his capsule without a safety line might, within arm's reach of safety, find himself unable to get back.

The movement of a hundred-car freight train, your own car, or a bicycle is altogether dependent on friction. Without it, none of them would move. And if by some miracle we could get ourselves or our vehicles under way, there would be no way of stopping except by crashing into some immovable object, for brakes too depend on friction.

Friction is simply the resistance opposing any effort to slide or roll one thing on another. That resistance doesn't vanish when you substitute a fluid or gas for solid matter. Friction between the fuel-air mix and the walls of the intake manifold limits the "breathing" of your auto engine, and therefore its r.p.m.'s and efficiency. (Hot-rodders sometimes install intake manifolds with polished interior surfaces to boost engine performance.)

Friction between the waters of a river and its banks makes the current flow more slowly along the shores than in midstream. Friction slows the falling of a steel ball in a bottle of oil, the movement of a ship, the flight of a plane. Internal friction absorbs the kinetic energy of a bullet as it hits and is deformed. The energy spent in overcoming friction is transformed into heat. Even in a bouncing ball, a little energy is converted into heat as the ball is momentarily deformed at each bounce. Because it loses that little energy, it bounces less high each time. Also, it is internal friction that makes vibrations finally die out of a bell after it is struck.

What causes friction between two bodies that are moved while in contact? Chiefly three things. One is the intermeshing of minute irregularities in the surfaces. Even on polished surfaces, there are myraid microscopic roughnesses that intermesh like tiny teeth. A second cause is adhesion between the surfaces, probably due to molecular attraction. This factor becomes greater, not less, with polished surfaces. The accurately flat-ground gauge blocks used in industry, for example, cling together if twisted against one another. Flat glass, if wrung together sufficiently to exclude air, will stick to itself. A third cause of friction is the indentation of one body by the harder one, which then has to climb out of the hole it has thus dug for itself. This is a factor in rolling as well as in sliding friction. There is some speculation about electrostatic attraction as a fourth cause of friction, but this is still in question.

Oil makes a big difference by providing a film between the two parts. In part this fills irregularities, so that the parts slide on a thin sea of oil instead of touching each other. (Oil molecules slide over each other much more easily than do those of the metal they lubricate.) There are other lubricants, of course. Wax, soap, graphite and certain chemicals have useful lubricating properties.

THREE KINDS OF FRICTION

Mechanical friction (aside from fluid and internal friction) shows three aspects. Static friction is the resistance to movement between two bodies in contact and at rest; it might be called starting friction. Sliding friction is the resistance to *continued* movement after a body has been set in motion. It is somewhat less than static friction. Rolling friction is least of all, as the builders of Stonehenge probably discovered by putting logs under their giant building blocks.

If you fasten a spring scale to a book or block, you'll find the pointer reads highest when you pull on the scale just hard enough to start the object sliding across a surface. Almost at once, if you keep it moving, the pointer drops back a little. Put a couple of round pencils under the book as rollers, and the scale will indicate a much smaller pull both to start and to keep the object moving.

One of Sir Isaac Newton's laws of motion, first enunciated in 1687, states that an object at rest will remain at rest, or if moving, will continue moving at the same rate in a straight line, *unless* subjected to some force that tends to change the situation. Theoretically, therefore, we should have to expend work only in starting, accelerating, or stopping an object—a car, one rolling on a level road, should do so indefinitely. But in practice, friction is the force that brings any mundane body to a halt sooner or later. The outstanding exceptions are our artificial satellites, which of course aren't mundane, but literally out of this world. Down here, we must exert continuous effort to keep anything in motion.

OVERCOMING FRICTION

How much work is required to overcome friction? Or, to put it more precisely, how much force in proportion to the weight of the object we want to move? That ratio varies for different materials. We would expect a brick to move more easily on ice, for example, than on concrete. But woods, metals, glass, ceramics and other things all vary somewhat in their coefficient of friction, as this ratio is called. It can be experimentally determined with the help of an inclined plane.

Imagine you place a 20-pound wooden box having a smooth bottom on the middle of an equally smooth horizontal wooden plank. Now raise one end of the plank every slowly. The greatest angle to which you can tilt it before the box begins to slide down is the limiting angle of friction, or the angle of repose, for the two materials in contact. This critical angle is of concern to engineers who don't want earth embankments or earth dams to slide and collapse. It's of interest to auto and highway engineers too. On how steep a hill can a car stand with locked wheels? Or how sharply may a road be banked without danger of making a stopped vehicle slide down sideways?

It is friction alone that prevents our imaginary box from sliding down the plank, and the inclined plane will let us measure it. In Figure 1, let the vertical line A–B represent the true weight of the box (20 pounds) to some handy scale. Drawing the line B–C at right angles to the plank and joining it with A–C, we can scale off A–C as the vector force tending to move the box down.

By completing the parallelogram with lines A–D and B–D, we can scale off A–D to find the force with which the block actually bears on the plank, which is something less than its full weight. If we have drawn the inclined plane at that angle at which the box just starts to slide, then force A–C divided by force A–D will give us the coefficient of static friction for wood on wood.

Since the triangle ABD and that formed by the inclined plane (XYZ) are similar—having identical angles even though they are of different size—we can determine the coefficient of friction even more easily, and without scaling off A–C and A–D. We need only divide the height of the incline (Y–Z) by its base (X–Z). For wood on wood, the answer will probably be about 0.35. (If the base line were 10 feet, for example, and the height of the plane 3½ feet.)

Knowing the coefficient of friction for wood on wood, we can closely estimate the force necessary to move a wooden object in other situations. To start a 100-pound box moving across a smooth wooden floor, for example, would take a 35-pound horizontal force (100 times 0.35).

There's still another way to find the coefficient of friction, and that is from the angle of repose alone. We've seen that this coefficient is the ratio between the forces A–C and A–D in our diagram (Figure 1). But A–C is the weight of the object times the sine of the angle, and A–D the weight times the cosine of the angle, as shown in Chapter 5. Mathematically this boils down to the ratio between the sine and cosine of the same angle, and this ratio has

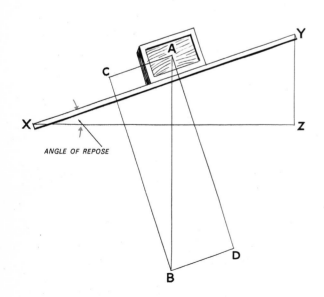

ANGLE OF REPOSE

Fig. 1. Calculating the coefficient of friction for moving a box on an inclined wooden plank.

already been worked out for all angles to 90 degrees. It's called the tangent of the angle, and may be found in trigonometric tables.

For an ideal case, let's suppose that the plane forms an angle of 19° 20′ to the horizontal. The tangent of that angle is .3508—the coefficient of wood on wood. (In practice any particular plank and block or box may have a slightly different coefficient of friction, depending on the kind of wood and its surface smoothness.) Nevertheless, typical coefficients for various materials have been worked out. They are found in physics and engineering handbooks, which give both static (starting) and sliding friction, often for both dry and lubricated surfaces. Here are some examples:

COEFFICIENTS OF FRICTION

Materials	Static	Sliding
Hard steel on hard steel	0.78 (dry)	0.42 (dry)
Steel on graphite	0.21 (dry)	
	0.09 (lubricated)	
Aluminum on mild steel	0.61 (dry)	0.47 (dry)
Brass on cast iron		0.30 (dry)
Glass on glass	0.94 (dry)	0.40 (dry)
	0.35 (lubricated)	0.09 (lubricated)
Cast iron on cast iron	1.1 (dry)	0.15 (dry)
	0.2 (lubricated)	0.07 (lubricated)
Bronze on cast iron		0.22 (dry)
		0.077 (lubricated)
Steel on babbitt	0.42 (dry)	0.35 (dry)
	0.17 (lubricated)	0.14 (lubricated)
Teflon on teflon or teflon on steel	0.04	0.04

Teflon, the material used to line frying pans, is one of the slipperiest materials known. As can be guessed from its low coefficient of friction (dry because it needs no other lubricant), it makes excellent bearings, gears and so forth, subject to certain limitations. Babbitt is a white antifriction alloy composed of tin, copper and antimony.

What determines friction, then, is only the force pressing the two surfaces together, and the coefficient of friction for those particular materials. But wouldn't adding weights to the 20-pound box in our inclined plane experiment start it sliding down sooner—that is, at a lesser angle? No. Provided you take care not to nudge the box when putting the weights in it, it will remain motionless at the same angle as before. Though the greater weight does in-crease the downward force A–C, it also increases the force bearing on the plane (A–D). As these increases are proportional and the coefficient of friction remains constant, the critical angle won't change. (Should you grease the plank, you'd be changing the coefficient of friction radically, and things would move.)

How about decreasing the contact area by turning the same box on its side or end? Since its weight remains the same, you'd only be increasing the load per square inch of area. Friction is independent of the area of superficial contact.

Mathematics is a two-way street, so if we know the coefficient of fric-tion, we need only look up that figure in a table of tangents to find the angle of repose. For example, iron on iron, when lubricated, has a coefficient of about 0.2. The nearest tangent is 0.2035, and that is for an angle of 11° 30′, at which an iron block on a lubricated iron surface should slide.

Suppose we place an iron block with a shallow hole in its top on a horizontal iron plate as in Figure 2. If we put a rod in the hole and apply a force straight down, it will simply press the block harder against the surface and we cannot expect the block to move. What's the minimum angle to the perpendicular at which applied force will make the block slide?

It's the angle of repose, or in the case of iron on lubricated iron, as we just found from a table of tangents, 11° 30′. At any smaller angle no force, however large, will move the block. So what? So the engineer who's designing a reversible worm gear must choose a helix angle greater than the angle of repose for the materials to be used, if he wants the worm to slide along the teeth of the gear when the latter turns.

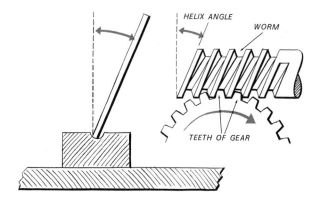

Fig. 2. Determining minimum angle from perpendicular at which iron bar will, under pressure, move iron block helps an engi-neer in designing a reversible worm gear.

ROLLING FRICTION

This is another type of friction, equal to the force it takes to make one body roll on another at constant speed. It is much less than sliding friction. Whereas cast iron on lubricated steel has a coefficient of friction of about 0.20, dry wheels on a dry steel rail may have a coefficient of as little as 0.002—a hundredth as much. Therefore each 20 pounds of locomotive drawbar pull can keep 10,000 pounds of freight rolling. (The calculation: 10,000 times 0.002 equals the force of friction, or the force needed to overcome it.)

Hard wheels on a hard surface are most efficient, for rolling friction results chiefly from deformation and indentation. A soft wheel that flattens where it rests on the ground will have increased rolling friction. (You burn more gasoline per mile if your tires are underinflated.) If the wheel is hard but the surface soft, things don't move well either; just recall the last time you had to drive in deep snow or mud.

Since rolling friction is so much less than sliding friction, it would seem a fine idea if we could substitute it for the other kind in bearings. One early attempt to do this was to support the shafts on the rims of wheels that turned under them. But the wheel shafts still turned on sliding surfaces. Solid-axle wagon wheels too, though they substituted rolling friction for sliding friction on the road, battled sliding friction between hub and axle.

The logs on which men once rolled great stones came closer to doing away with sliding friction than the early wheel, and were the primitive prototype of the roller bearing. In a true roller bearing, the inner shell or race is tightly fitted to the shaft. This race turns inside rollers that in turn run in an outer bearing shell or race (Figure 3). All parts are finished very smoothly and hardened to avoid indentation. The only sliding friction is a trifle between the rollers and the cage that spaces them evenly around the races.

Ball bearings are similar, their races being contoured to fit the balls so as to spread the load over a maximum area. Needle bearings (used in the con rods of outboard engines, among other applications) have rollers of comparatively small diameter lying alongside one another, with no cage intervening.

Figure 3 shows that some bearings are designed to carry radial loads (that of a car on its wheels for example), and others thrust loads (axial or endwise ones, such as occur when a car rounds a curve or a propeller pushes a boat). Some bearings are designed to carry both kinds of load. The tapered roller bearing (Figure 4) is the sturdiest for this purpose. First made for wagons years ago, tapered roller bearings now are indispensable in cars, trucks, tractors, railroad rolling stock and machine tools, often outlasting the equipment they're installed in. The drawing shows how a true rolling motion is

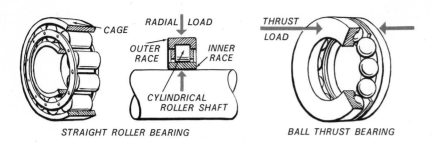

CAGE

RADIAL LOAD

OUTER RACE   INNER RACE

CYLINDRICAL ROLLER SHAFT

STRAIGHT ROLLER BEARING

THRUST LOAD

BALL THRUST BEARING

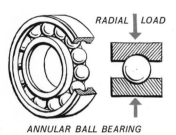

RADIAL LOAD

ANNULAR BALL BEARING

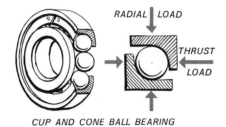

RADIAL LOAD

THRUST LOAD

CUP AND CONE BALL BEARING

Fig. 3. Four types of bearings.

A tapered roller bearing

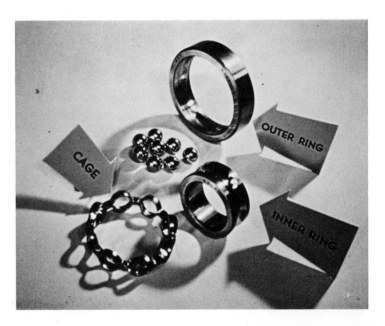

OUTER RING

CAGE

INNER RING

Parts of a ball bearing. *Courtesy Timken Roller Bearing Co.*

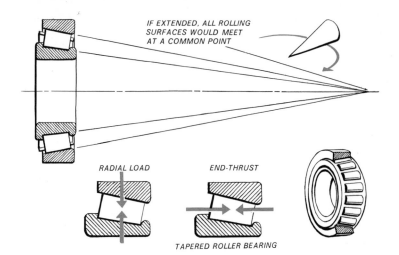

IF EXTENDED, ALL ROLLING
SURFACES WOULD MEET
AT A COMMON POINT

RADIAL LOAD   END-THRUST

TAPERED ROLLER BEARING

Fig. 4. How a tapered roller bearing achieves a true rolling motion.

achieved despite the taper; lines extended from the faces of the cone, cup and roller surfaces would all meet at the same point on the axis as shown, so that everything rolls like a cone laid on its side.

Ever wonder how they get the balls of a ball bearing inside a groove too narrow for them to fall out? The inner ring is placed eccentrically in the outer one, leaving a wide gap in which the balls are fed—all but one. In a special press, the outer ring is then squeezed slightly out of round, just enough to let the last ball be dropped in. The two parts of the cage are then fitted outside the balls and riveted together between them.

Noncontact bearings are a step forward even from high-quality ball bearings. Developed for gyro and missile guidance systems, these bearings have members that are never in contact except when at rest. When running, the moving member bears on a cushion of gas or fluid. There is no wear, so theoretically such bearings could run forever (the best ball bearings are good only for some thousands of hours).

Nor are these bearings limited to light loads such as those of guidance instruments. Honeywell, a leader in developing noncontact bearings, has built a spacecraft simulator supported entirely on a 17-inch diameter spherical gas bearing. The entire 9-ton weight of the machine floats virtually without friction on a cushion of pressurized nitrogen less than one-thousandth of an inch thick. (The average thickness of paper is two-thousandths of an inch.)

In Honeywell gas-bearing gyros, the gas supply is built in. Subject to no wear while running, the Gas-Bearing Spinmotor can make 10,000 start-stops with no detectable deterioration. The gyro cage is suspended on hydrostatic gimbals, swinging on a film of fluid maintained by a pump integral with the case.

Air cars and hovercraft, floating on a cushion of air, prove that even the wheel and the water-buoyant hull can be eliminated in the fight against friction. Proposals have been made to float wheel-less railroad cars on cushions of air maintained under flat shoes, which would skim just above the rails.

Already in use is an air bearing system to reduce the labor of freight handling. Special freight cars with hollow floors are equipped with hundreds of tiny valved openings. The weight of a crate or other heavy load opens the valves, releasing compressed air from the floor. Resting on an air cushion instead of on the floor, a ton of freight can be moved anywhere in the car more easily than you can shove around your favorite living-room chair.

FRICTION AT WORK

Friction not only moves your car along the road, but turns the wheels that do the moving. A gasoline engine has to be running before you can move your car, so it requires a make-and-break coupling that can pick up power from its revolving shaft "on the run." (Electric motors and steam engines need no such coupling or clutch; they can pick up their loads from a dead stop.)

A clutch has been defined as a mechanism that *must* slip while being engaged (to pick up its load smoothly) but must *not* slip when fully engaged. If it slipped then, it would waste power, fail to carry its rated load, and probably wind up damaging itself.

An early automobile clutch, remembered more for its faults than for any merits, was the cone clutch. A shallow cone on the driven shaft, faced with leather, was pressed by springs into a wheel on the driving shaft, this wheel having an internal taper that matched the cone (Figure 5). To "throw out the clutch" a fork lying in a grooved hub or collar on the cone pulled it out of its seat. But the wedging action of the cone-shaped elements caused rather abrupt engagement, and the unit was equally vulnerable to glazing and slipping under unfavorable conditions.

The cone clutch was therefore supplanted by the disk clutch, a type still in general use today. The smooth back of the flywheel is used as one of the driving plates (Figure 6). Bolted to the flywheel and going around with it is a cover, the clutch housing. Inside it and driven by it is a cast-iron disk called the pressure plate, so mounted that it is under strong forward spring tension but can be drawn back by the clutch pedal.

Between these two driving surfaces—the pressure plate and the flywheel—is the driven plate, faced with friction material on both sides, and

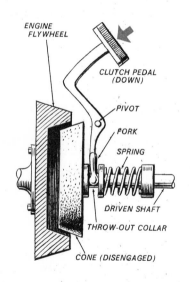

Fig. 5. Cone clutch was used on early automobiles.

fitted on the output shaft by means of splines, which lock it to the shaft rotationally but allow it to slide back and forth. As the springs normally press the pressure plate forward, the driven plate is sandwiched tightly between the two driving surfaces, so that it rotates with them. But stepping on the clutch pulls the pressure plate backwards, releasing its grip on the driven plate and so disengaging the clutch.

Obviously the friction facing on the driven plate must have a good coefficient of friction against cast iron (it's roughly about 0.40) and any oil on the driving surfaces will lower this coefficient to the point where the clutch slips and is unable to carry its torque load.

Multiple-disk clutches are similar but have, as the names suggests, a number of disks or plates. Automatic transmissions also use friction clutches, though these are not operated by the driver. Some synchromesh manual transmissions have metal-surfaced friction clutches which, engaging just before the gears mesh, bring them up to matching speeds.

FRICTION TO STOP WITH

When brakes are slammed on to stop a standard-sized car from a speed of 75 m.p.h., they have to absorb—and get rid of—about 800 hp of energy. Brakes do this by converting that energy into heat and dissipating the heat. When they can't move the heat off, their effectiveness fails and we have the sometimes frightening phenomenon called brake fade.

Old-style car brakes consisted of a flexible steel band lined with friction material, and so mounted that it could be clamped tight around the outside of a drum fixed to the wheel (Figure 7). Splashing through puddles often reduced the coefficient of friction so much that braking was only a memory until the linings dried out again.

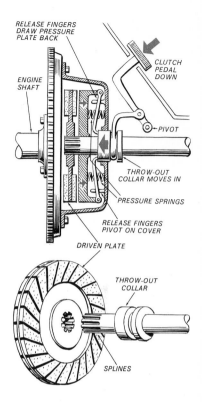

Fig. 6. Disk clutch supplanted cone clutch and is still used today.

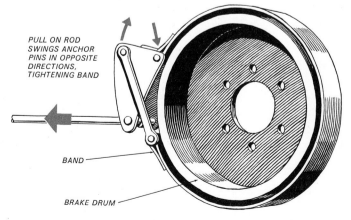

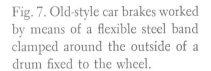

Fig. 7. Old-style car brakes worked by means of a flexible steel band clamped around the outside of a drum fixed to the wheel.

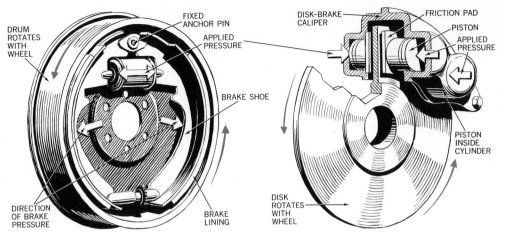

FIXED
ANCHOR PIN

DRUM
ROTATES
WITH
WHEEL

APPLIED
PRESSURE

DISK-BRAKE
CALIPER

FRICTION PAD

PISTON

APPLIED
PRESSURE

BRAKE SHOE

PISTON
INSIDE
CYLINDER

DIRECTION
OF BRAKE
PRESSURE

BRAKE
LINING

DISK
ROTATES
WITH
WHEEL

Fig. 8. Drum brakes (left) are used on most passenger cars. Disk brakes (right), once confined to racing cars, are now appearing on some passenger cars.

Today's internal brakes are less vulnerable to moisture. A typical wheel system has a pair of rigid, almost semicircular shoes hinged or pivoted at one end, with a hydraulic cylinder between their other ends. When hydraulic pressure forces the pistons out of the cylinder, they press the shoes against the inside of the brake drum (Figure 8).

Disk brakes, long popular on racing cars, are appearing on more passenger cars. Instead of drums, the wheels have sturdy disks fastened to them. Staddling the wheel disk is a housing (called a caliper) that incorporates two or four hydraulic pistons and as many friction pads. These embrace only a small part of the disk's circumference, whereas the shoes of drum brakes make contact with most of the drum's internal surface.

A combination of front disks and rear drums has recently appeared on a few passenger-car models. This system requires a line-pressure-proportioning valve for automatic adjustment of rear-wheel braking effort in relation to vehicle speed and weight transfer forward. With a low-cost emergency brake in the rear drums, the system offers the stability and fade resistance of disks.

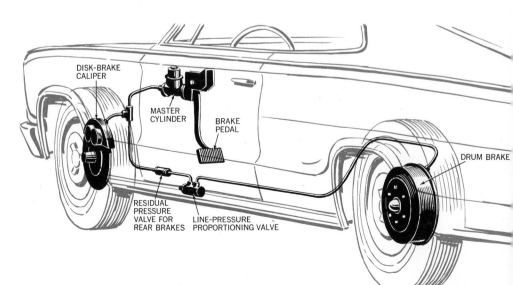

DISK-BRAKE
CALIPER

MASTER
CYLINDER

BRAKE
PEDAL

DRUM BRAKE

RESIDUAL
PRESSURE
VALVE FOR
REAR BRAKES

LINE-PRESSURE
PROPORTIONING VALVE

The smaller braking area of disk brakes demands higher operating pressure, but they have the advantages of better cooling and much greater fade resistance. The exposed disks are self cleaning and virtually unaffected by water. Friction pads can be replaced without removing the wheels.

Railroad brakes hark back to those of the covered wagon, so far as the braking elements are concerned. Iron shoes clamp directly against the wheel treads, the coefficient of friction of metal on metal being sufficient to do the job.

FRICTION DRIVES

Common in tape-recorder and phonograph mechanisms, friction drives are a form of nonpositive power transmission. One familiar turntable drive is shown in Figure 9. The rubber-rimmed idler wheel can be shifted to any of the

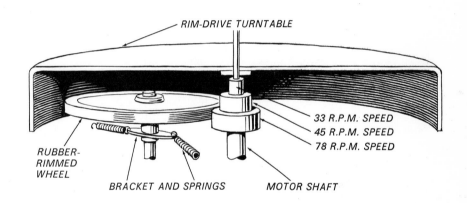

Fig. 9. Friction drive commonly used in phonograph turntables.

RIM-DRIVE TURNTABLE

33 R.P.M. SPEED
45 R.P.M. SPEED
78 R.P.M. SPEED

RUBBER-RIMMED WHEEL

BRACKET AND SPRINGS

MOTOR SHAFT

steps on the motor shaft for various record speeds, while it simultaneously bears against the inner surface of the turntable rim, spring tension insuring good contact.

Another turntable mechanism (Figure 10) is a good example of a

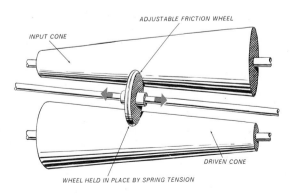

ADJUSTABLE FRICTION WHEEL

INPUT CONE

DRIVEN CONE

WHEEL HELD IN PLACE BY SPRING TENSION

Fig. 10. Turntable mechanism using a variable-speed cone drive.

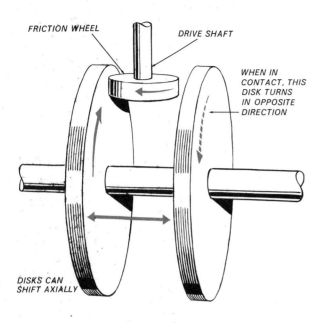

FRICTION WHEEL   DRIVE SHAFT

WHEN IN CONTACT, THIS DISK TURNS IN OPPOSITE DIRECTION

DISKS CAN SHIFT AXIALLY

Fig. 11. Friction drives with stepless ratio change, allowing output speed to be controlled within small limits.

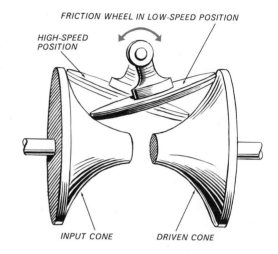

FRICTION WHEEL IN LOW-SPEED POSITION

HIGH-SPEED POSITION

INPUT CONE   DRIVEN CONE

variable-speed cone drive. An idler with a V-shaped rubber rim can be moved along the polished steel cone to vary the ratio and therefore turntable speed.

Some other friction-drive configurations are shown in Figure 11. One or both drive elements may be faced with rubber, leather, brake lining or other friction material. An advantage of the variable-ratio units is that the ratio change is stepless and therefore, in theory at least, output speed can be controlled within very small limits.

A drive that has been used successfully for fractional horsepower applications is shown in Figure 12. It acts as a clutch, a reverse, and a variable-speed transmission. A relatively narrow wheel, with friction material on its rim, can by means of a fork on a threaded shaft be moved to make contact with any radius of the driving disk. This disk has a recess at its center, where no traction will occur. Moving the wheel to one side of center can provide a progressively lower reduction ratio, while moving the wheel to the other side of center affords the same stepless ratio range in reverse.

Since 1955 a professional engineer, Charles E. Kraus, has done research and development work on drives having hard metal surfaces in contact, and running in low-viscosity oil. These work at contact pressures of 120,000 pounds per square inch and more. Properly designed, they do not slip, and their elements show no surface wear.

Such drives have sustained both severe shock overloads and long-period overloads without damage. Though the contact through which power transmission occurs would seem to be a thin line, the high pressure actually deforms or flattens the hard surfaces so that there is an area of contact instead. The coefficient of traction is not related to that of friction, but is the ratio of the tangential force TF in Figure 13 to the contact force CF.

Mr. Kraus has built traction drives in various configurations, with both fixed and variable ratios. One toroidal drive having eight traction rollers, each only .080 inch wide, served successfully as an automobile transmission until bearing trouble developed.

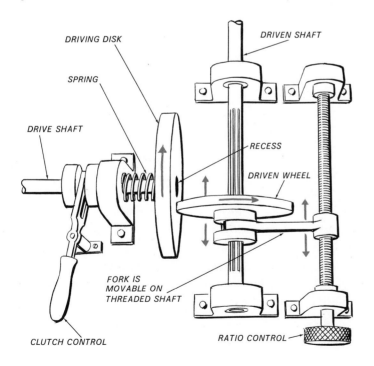

Fig. 12. Narrow wheel on this friction drive can be adjusted on threaded shaft to make contact with any radius of drive disk.

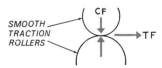

Fig. 13. Coefficient of traction of Kraus drives is determined by ratio of tangential force TF to contact force CF.

Fig. 14. New cone drive is capable of performing heavy-duty chores.

A radically new friction drive combines the functions of a clutch, a variable-ratio transmission, including reverse, and a differential. It runs dry instead of in oil, tolerates slip without damage, and promises long operating life. Called the V-Plex TAT (for triple action transaxle) by its inventor, Marion H. Davis, it has performed such feats as carrying golf-cart passengers up grades too steep to walk on, and with special fat tires hauling three men up a flight of stairs.

Turned by the engine, the input or driving shaft (Figure 14) has two thick cones of friction material back to back. Embracing these, one on each side, are two larger cones with smooth inside surfaces, which Mr. Davis calls "discups."

Each discup is mounted in a rectangular frame of its own, with a sprocket on the outer end of the discup shaft, from which a chain can drive one wheel either directly or through a countershaft. The drive wheels are thus independently coupled. At their lower outer corners, the discup frames are mounted on ball-and-socket joints. At the diagonally opposite top corner each is fastened to a torsion rod, the other end of the rod being pivoted on the main frame. A control rod fastened to the frame just below the torsion rod can swing the discup against the drive cones.

Normally the torsion rod centers the frame and its discup, which therefore does not contact either drive cone. Slight control effort will pull the discup against the small diameter of one drive cone—and, if the control is rigged to work simultaneously, will move the other discup against the smaller diameter of the second drive cone. The result is to start both output shafts turning in the same direction at a high reduction ratio (or low gear).

84

Greater control pressure swings the discup frames around the drive cones, shifting the drive contact to a larger diameter on the driving cones and a smaller diameter on the discups. In this action, the contact between the cones becomes a fulcrum on which the discup frame must swing, and in a direction opposite to its initial movement. At maximum travel, the drive is in low ratio or "high gear."

For reverse it is only necessary to move the control in the other direction. The same ratio range is available if anybody cares to travel backwards at top speed. The controls can be linked to actuate both discups simultaneously, or may be separate so that the operator can drive the two wheels independently at will. Mr. Davis has built a small garden tractor with castors instead of front wheels, and is able to make the machine maneuver very precisely by means of independent dual controls, which can make one wheel stand still while the other turns.

The differential action is something of a puzzle even to the inventor, and able independent engineers disagree in their explanations. The inner-wheel discup can be observed to shift down automatically on a turn, while the other shifts up. Only by holding the control forcibly in "high" can this action be overridden.

CENTRIFUGAL CLUTCHES

Friction clutches that engage when they're spun at certain speeds, disengage when their r.p.m.'s drop below that, are found on golf carts, scooters, midget racers and motorized garden equipment. One type, which may be used with belt, gear or chain drives, has blocks of friction material hinged or keyed to turn with the engine shaft, but free to slide outward or radially (Figure 15). As engine speed goes up, centrifugal force pushes these shoes out against the inside of a drum, which they then drive by friction. The pulley, gear or sprocket from which power is taken is fixed to the drum.

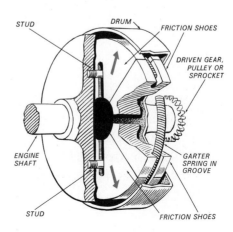

Fig. 15. Friction clutch works on principle of centrifugal force.

Another type, for V-belt drives only, uses the belt itself as a friction element. Two semicircular weights inside a housing are normally held together by a circular (garter) spring. Increased engine speed flings the weights out. They wedge between the housing and the sloping inner face of a floating cone that can slide along a hexagonal section of the hub. The other side of this cone is one flange of a V-pulley. As it is forced out, it grips the belt and starts it pulling. When engine speed again drops to idle, the floating cone lets the belt drop onto a free-rotating spring sleeve.

The versatile V-belt has, in thousands of applications, replaced flat and round belts. It grips well because the wedge-shaped section tends to bulge outward as the V-belt curves around a pulley (Figure 16). For this reason the pulley grooves must be deeper than the belts, for if a V-belt rides on the bottom of the groove its wedging action is sacrificed and it loses almost all traction. However, for some drives of 3 to 1 ratio or more, V-belts may run from a small V-pulley to a large flat-faced one.

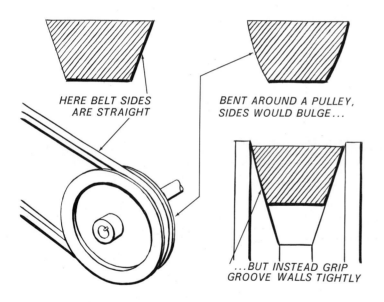

HERE BELT SIDES
ARE STRAIGHT

BENT AROUND A PULLEY,
SIDES WOULD BULGE...

...BUT INSTEAD GRIP
GROOVE WALLS TIGHTLY

Fig. 16. How a V-belt grips.

They also lend themselves to some ingenious transmission systems and torque converters. A simple V-belt clutch rig (Figure 17) is made by hinging the power plant (motor or engine) at the side farthest from the driven unit. Normally slack, the belt can be pulled taut and the drive thus engaged by tilting back the power unit.

Next simplest is a movable idler pulley that applies driving tension to the belt. Somewhat more ingenious is the two-belt, two-speed clutch and transmission in Figure 18. Four pulleys are paired to afford two desired drive ratios, and both belts are long enough to be slack, so that the drive is normally in neutral. A pair of idler pulleys on a control lever will tighten one belt when the lever is pushed one way, leaving the other still slack or tighten the other belt when moved in the opposite direction, so choosing between the two ratios.

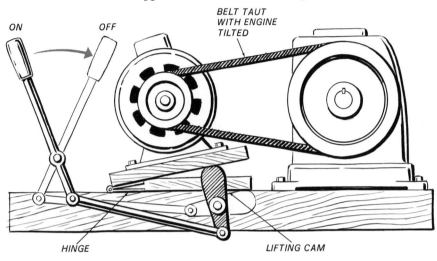

Fig. 17. Simple V-belt clutch rig.

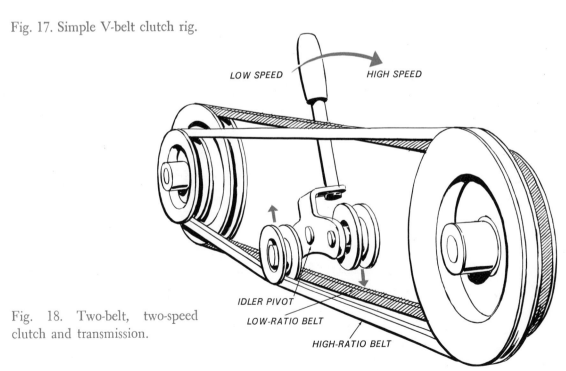

Fig. 18. Two-belt, two-speed clutch and transmission.

One of the automatic clutches described (made by V-Plex Clutch Corp., of Hagerstown, Indiana) has a belt groove sufficiently deep to allow a variable speed range. As engagement begins (Figure 19) the belt rides low in the groove and therefore drives from a small diameter. As shaft speed mounts, it is forced to a larger diameter, so altering the drive ratio.

It's necessary, of course, to keep the belt taut in all driving positions. One way to do this is to use a swinging countershaft (Figure 20). The spring maintains driving tension, and by adjusting its pull the ratio shift points can be changed to some degree.

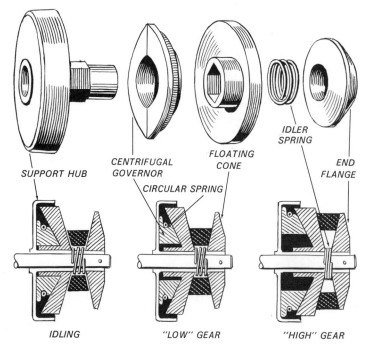

SUPPORT HUB

CENTRIFUGAL GOVERNOR

CIRCULAR SPRING

FLOATING CONE

IDLER SPRING

END FLANGE

IDLING

"LOW" GEAR

"HIGH" GEAR

Fig. 19. Automatic clutch with deep belt groove allows for a variable speed range.

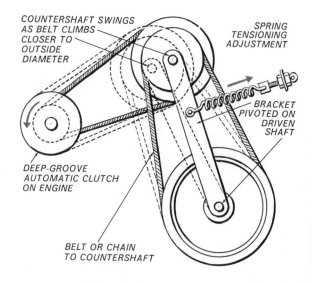

COUNTERSHAFT SWINGS AS BELT CLIMBS CLOSER TO OUTSIDE DIAMETER

SPRING TENSIONING ADJUSTMENT

BRACKET PIVOTED ON DRIVEN SHAFT

DEEP-GROOVE AUTOMATIC CLUTCH ON ENGINE

BELT OR CHAIN TO COUNTERSHAFT

Fig. 20. Swinging countershaft keeps belt taut in all driving positions. Spring maintains tension.

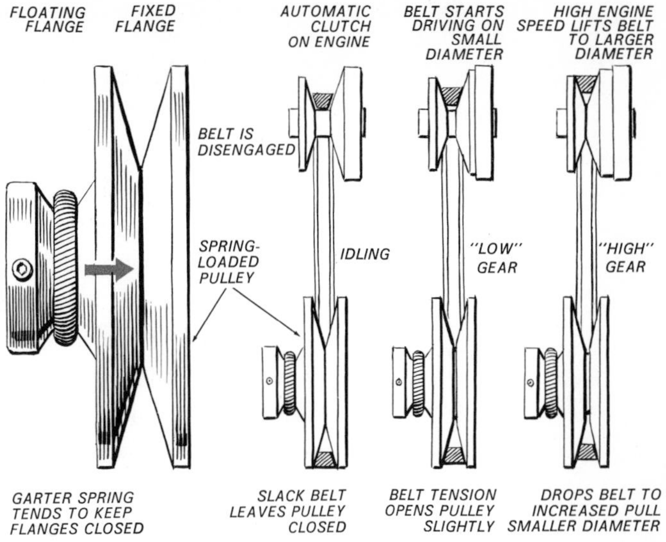

Fig. 21. Spring-loaded pulley, paired with an automatic clutch, achieves "high gear" by allowing belt to slip deeper into groove as speed increases.

BELT IS DISENGAGED

SPRING-LOADED PULLEY

IDLING

"LOW" GEAR

"HIGH" GEAR

GARTER SPRING TENDS TO KEEP FLANGES CLOSED

SLACK BELT LEAVES PULLEY CLOSED

BELT TENSION OPENS PULLEY SLIGHTLY

DROPS BELT TO INCREASED PULL SMALLER DIAMETER

Instead of a swinging countershaft, one could pair such an automatic clutch with a spring-loaded driven pulley. One flange of this slides axially, being held against the fixed flange by a strong garter spring (Figure 21). This forces the belt to ride on the outside or largest diameter of the deep groove. But as engine speed mounts, and the clutch flanges close up, forcing the belt to a higher diameter on that pulley, belt tension overcomes the garter spring on the driven pulley and wedges its flanges apart, letting the belt drop to a smaller diameter there. The net effect is to shift the drive ratio to "high gear."

Another kind of variable pulley, capable of transmitting more torque, has two internal cams. Driving torque makes these cams force the flanges together, maintaining belt grip even on overloads. Two variable pulleys of either the cam-follower or the spring-loaded type, when mounted on a jackshaft, can provide a widely variable ratio range (Figure 22). The jackshaft is either hinged or slide-mounted—with means for locking it in position—between the power unit and the driven one; both have only plain pulleys.

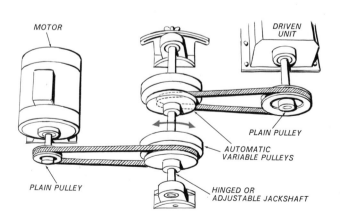

MOTOR

DRIVEN UNIT

PLAIN PULLEY

AUTOMATIC VARIABLE PULLEYS

PLAIN PULLEY

HINGED OR ADJUSTABLE JACKSHAFT

Fig. 22. Automatic variable pulleys on jackshaft.

There is no clutch effect, but moving the jackshaft nearer the power unit will allow its driven pulley to close up, shifting the belt to a larger diameter. This increases the drive ratio between the engine or motor and the jackshaft. Simultaneously the second variable pulley on the jackshaft, being pulled away from the driven unit, has been forced to open and let its belt drop to a smaller diameter, so the drive ratio between jackshaft and driven unit is also increased. The total is a very low "low gear."

But shift the jackshaft the other way and you reverse the ratio shift; the pulley driven by the motor opens its flanges and the one driving the driven unit closes up. This affords a lower ratio in both steps, and as the overall ratio is the multiple of the two steps, the total ratio change can be quite large.

GANGED V-BELTS

Two, three or more parallel belts running on as many pulleys can deliver very respectable amounts of power. Industrial V-belts, larger than those used on cars or home workshop machines, also have heavy-duty ratings. Some are cog belts; these have teeth (or if you like, notches) on the inside surface. The notches close up as the belt bends around a pulley, affording extra traction while not unduly stiffening the belt.

An ingenious little Dutch-made car, the DAF, which briefly made its appearance in the United States in 1959, exploits V-belt versatility to the full. Cogged V-belts and variable-ratio pulleys give it a fully automatic drive system that shifts for itself, does away with the differential, and provides positive traction on one wheel even if the other slips on ice (Figure 23).

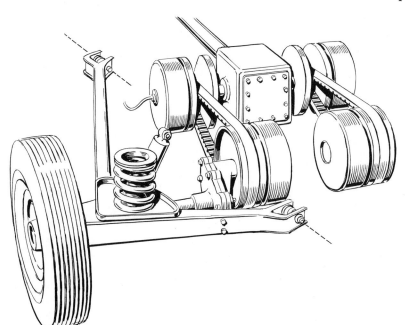

Fig. 23. Dutch car uses V-belts and variable pulleys to operate drive and shift.

The DAF engine has a centrifugal clutch that takes hold just above idling speed, driving a gear box under the rear seat. There bevel gears turn two output shafts, on which are mounted variable V-pulleys, each with a sliding flange. The pulley casings house automatic controls that move the sliding flanges, their position being governed partly by shaft speed, and partly by manifold vacuum. (When a gas engine is heavily loaded and breathing hard, manifold vacuum drops. This phenomenon is therefore used to call for a higher ratio.)

The control responds by pulling the flange out, dropping the belt to a smaller radius for "low gear". When the engine is running easily at good speed, manifold vacuum is high. The automatic controls then push the flange in, forcing the belt to ride on a greater diameter for "high gear."

Belt slack is taken up at all times, and driving tension maintained, by spring-loaded flanges on the driven pulleys. The overall ratio varies steplessly from 20 to 1 on starting to 4.4 to 1 in high. Part of the reduction is effected by sealed gear boxes on the inner ends of the swing axles.

On turns, the inner wheel is more heavily loaded by road friction and therefore shifts down, while the faster-moving outer wheel's drive belt correspondingly shifts up to higher speed. Thanks to the centrifugal clutch, even a beginner cannot stall the engine. On hills, the clutch stays engaged so long as engine revs are above idling speed, so that compression helps hold the car back. For really steep downgrades, the Dutch engineers thoughtfully provide a panic button. Yank it out, and the controls hold the belts in the maximum step-down ratio for ample engine braking.

When eventually the belts stretch, the turn indicator stays lit to tell the driver to tighten them. He puts a lug wrench on a shaft under the rear of the car and turns it until the indicator goes out. The DAF drive is not enclosed, but tests in flooded areas and deep snow have proved that it is self-cleaning and that the cog belts will keep pulling even after standing axle deep in snow or water. You can't ask much more of a V-belt drive than that.

A PUZZLE IN FRICTION

With the palms of your hands facing each other, lay a one-foot ruler with its 12-inch end on one hand and the 3-inch mark on the other. (A longer ruler, or even a yardstick, may be used if this hand is placed still farther from the end.) Challenge anyone to say which end of the ruler will drop if you move your hands together as evenly as possible. He will usually choose the end near the 3-inch mark.

But the hand that starts at the 12-inch end usually moves first. Soon after it passes the 9-inch mark, the other hand will start to move in. Then it will stop while the other catches up. If you keep the ruler level, both hands will meet at the center and the ruler will not fall at all.

Nor can you cheat by trying to move one hand more than the other. The laws of physics will keep you honest. The hand nearer the center of the ruler carries more of its weight; therefore the friction at that point is greater and the other hand moves until it is nearer the center. Then the frictional difference is reversed and the other hand moves in its turn. Hands and ruler must be clean and free from foreign substances for the experiment to work.

VII

Gears, Transmissions and Ratchets

Having learned how to make wheels go around, man soon began looking for ways to modify their action. The horizontal shaft of a waterwheel, for example, could not by itself turn a horizontal millstone, which necessarily had a vertical shaft. The angle at which an Archimedean screw pump had to be set to raise water made it awkward to crank by hand. This and other applications of power called for some means of making rotary movement turn a corner.

The obvious answer was to use gears. In their most primitive form, the peg-toothed wheel, gears are merely an elaboration of the four-spoked disk Hero used for his organ air pump. Round or square pegs driven tightly into holes in the rim of a wheel meshed with like pegs set the same distance apart in another wheel. If both sets of pegs were axially aligned, the two wheels could work at right angles to each other, transferring power from a horizontal to a vertical shaft or oppositely (Figure 1).

But gears could do much more than transmit power around a corner. If your waterwheel was undersized but ran at good speed, you could boost torque by using a smaller gear on the wheel shaft and a larger one on the millstone shaft. The smaller gear had to make more revolutions than the

Fig. 1. Peg-toothed wheels were the earliest gear forms.

stone, but who cared so long as the grain was ground? In this case and in countless others since (including your car, electric drill, and kitchen mixer) gears serve as torque converters.

GEARS AS SPINNING LEVERS

You can consider a gear as a cluster of evenly spaced levers mounted on a common fulcrum. The ends of these levers could impinge on those of a second cluster (Figure 2) so that one group could turn the other.

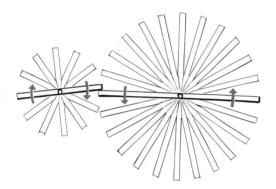

Fig. 2. A gear can be considered as a cluster of levers mounted on a common fulcrum.

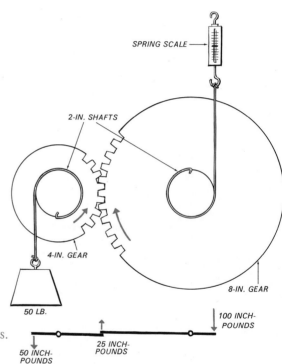

Fig. 3. How gears work like levers.

To carry the likeness of gears and levers further, imagine two 2-inch shafts (having a 1-inch radius), one of which carries a 4-inch gear on it, and the other an 8-inch gear. Suppose the shaft having the smaller gear has a rope wound on it, and a 50-pound weight hanging from the rope. This will create a torque of 50 inch-pounds on the shaft. A rope wound on the other shaft, but in the opposite direction, is fastened to a spring scale (Figure 3).

Taking a single pair of teeth in mesh between the gears as a pair of levers, we can momentarily ignore the far ends of these and instead diagram them as if their effective ends were the radius of the shafts, for this is where torque is developed on the small gear and where it must be read on the large. As the small diagram in Figure 3 shows, the 50-pound force on the 1-inch arm (shaft radius) is halved to 25 pounds on the 2-inch radius of the smaller gear. But it is applied to the 4-inch long arm of the larger gear, and multiplied on the 1-inch shaft radius to 100 pounds. The spring scale will therefore testify to 100 inch-pounds of torque, or twice that applied to the first shaft.

With gears instead of levers, this torque boost (and rotary motion) is of course continuous. If you were to fit a handle to the shaft having the smaller gear, you could crank up a load on the second shaft with only half the effort it would take if the load were fastened directly to the first shaft. As usual, you pay for the increase in torque by having to apply your own effort through a greater distance—twice in this case.

Conversely, you can use gears to increase shaft speed at the expense of torque. This is what the gears in an ordinary egg beater or a hand drill do for you.

Sometimes the need for increased torque is the whole reason for gearing. Very often it is also needed to reduce speed. Such power sources as gas engines and electric motors run much too fast to hitch directly to twist drills, boring bits, can openers and orange squeezers. (Though other things such as circular saws, router bits and malted-milk stirrers can be fastened directly to motor shafts.)

But where a lower speed at the business end is required, we can get it with appropriate gearing. This not only lowers the speed at the output shaft, but so multiplies torque that we can use a smaller motor.

OTHER EARLY GEARS

Getting back to man's first gears, when power was to be transmitted between two parallel shafts, such gears as those in Figure 1 performed poorly, the parallel pegs readily slipping out of mesh. A solution to this was the cage gear (Figure 4). It was made by boring matching holes in two disks mounted on a shaft, and driving pins between them. The resemblance to a cage is plain, but clockmakers who later used this type of gear profusely called it a lantern gear or lantern pinion. Anybody who has ever taken a wind-up alarm clock apart has seen small gears of this kind, made of steel pins driven into brass end-disks.

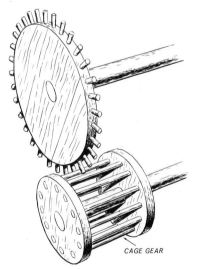

Fig. 4. The cage gear prevented teeth from slipping out of mesh.

The cage gear meshed dependably with radial pegs or even with pegs set at an angle between the axial and radial positions. Leonardo da Vinci suggested an angle drive of this kind for turning an Archimedean screw pump as shown in Figure 5.

Wooden-toothed gears survived down to American Colonial days. Some were several feet in diameter. Rectangular wooden teeth, wider and much stronger than pegs, were sometimes held in iron wheels with wedges and could be replaced when worn. Iron teeth were at times set into wooden wheels, while small gears were often cast in one piece, teeth and all. Pin gears were sometimes fitted with rollers to reduce working friction.

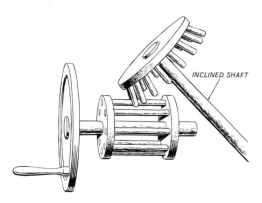

INCLINED SHAFT

Fig. 5. Cage gear meshed with radial gear set at an angle turned early Archimedean screw pump.

The shape of other gear teeth was largely a matter of opinion—often the mechanic's. Such primitive gears had a jerky action because the teeth did not transmit uniform velocity. Though wooden teeth were springy enough to bend instead of breaking under such varying stress, and often wore themselves to a more advantageous shape, the advent of metal gears made the science of tooth design indispensable.

Its foundations were laid in 1760 by a Swiss mathematician, Leonhard Euler (1707–1783). Well-designed gear teeth transmit uniform velocity and work in part with rolling instead of sliding friction. Two systems of generating the desired tooth form are in use, the *involute* and the *cycloidal*. These terms refer to the kinds of curves that give the teeth their shape.

An involute is a line traced by a fixed point on a nonstretchable string as it is unwound from the surface of a cylinder. Involute curves are used for the outer half or face of the gear teeth, the inner half or flank being radial. Cycloidal teeth are formed of two curves, an epicycloidal one for the face, and a hypocycloidal one for the flank. The first is a line traced by a point on a circle rolled around the outside of another circle (Figure 6). The second is a curve traced by a point on a circle rolling around the inside of the second circle.

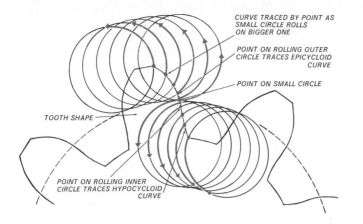

CURVE TRACED BY POINT AS
SMALL CIRCLE ROLLS
ON BIGGER ONE

POINT ON ROLLING OUTER
CIRCLE TRACES EPICYCLOID
CURVE

POINT ON SMALL CIRCLE

TOOTH SHAPE

POINT ON ROLLING INNER
CIRCLE TRACES HYPOCYCLOID
CURVE

Fig. 6. Cycloidal teeth on a gear are formed on two curves.

ANATOMY OF A GEAR

In theory, gears may be thought of as two smooth-surfaced cylinders in contact like a pair of wringer rolls, although in practice we need teeth to prevent slipping between them. The *pitch circle* is the imaginary boundary of such cylinder equivalent to the gear in question; it lies halfway between the top and the theoretical bottom of the gear teeth (Figure 7). That part of the tooth above the pitch circle is the *face*; the part below is the *flank*. The *addendum* circle is one that would pass through the top of every tooth; the *dedendum* circle would pass through the theoretical bottom of each tooth. We specify "theoretical" because in practice the space between the teeth must be cut a little deeper—to the *clearance* circle—to prevent the teeth from hitting bottom.

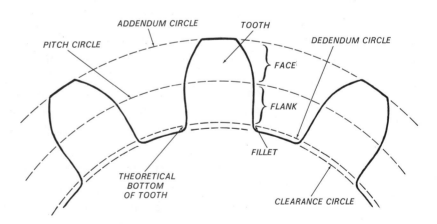

ADDENDUM CIRCLE   TOOTH

PITCH CIRCLE   DEDENDUM CIRCLE

FACE

FLANK

FILLET

THEORETICAL
BOTTOM
OF TOOTH

CLEARANCE CIRCLE

Fig. 7. Anatomy of a gear.

Circular pitch is the distance between tooth centers, measured on the pitch circle, or the width of one tooth plus one space. This measurement is an arc, equal to the circumference of the pitch circle divided by the number of teeth. *Diametral* pitch is the number of teeth in every inch of pitch-circle *diameter*. These terms are of course of interest chiefly to the machine and gear designer, and to the machinist who translates them into hardware.

Gears may be of almost any durable material, including iron, steel, brass, bronze, and various die-casting alloys. Precision die casting produces accurate, durable gears at low cost. Fiber and even rawhide gears have been made for quiet running. Nylon, teflon and other plastic gears outlast steel in some applications.

CALCULATING GEAR RATIOS

For rough estimates, one can use the gear diameters in figuring their ratios. But precision demands counting the number of teeth on each gear. Once that is done, the mathematics required for finding other information is very simple. In the following formulas, let D represent the number of teeth on the driver (or driving gear), and let R represent the speed of this gear in revolutions per minute. Similarly, d stands for the number of teeth on the driven gear, and r for its speed in r.p.m. By substituting the actual known figures for their symbols, you can find the needed (unknown) values. For example:

A driven gear having 40 teeth is to turn at 900 r.p.m. The driving shaft turns at 1,800 r.p.m. How many teeth must the driver have?

D = d × r ÷ R, or

D = 40 × 900 (36,000) ÷ 1,800

36,000 divided by 1,800 equals 20

The driving gear should have 20 teeth. It will in one complete revolution turn the 40-tooth driven gear through one half revolution, so reducing the 1,800 r.p.m. speed of the driving shaft to 900 at the driven.

In this simple example you could of course take a mental shortcut. Since the desired speed is one half that of the driving the shaft, the driving gear should have just one half as many teeth as the driven. But in less obvious cases the formula is useful, especially when the number of teeth on one or both gears is a prime number that cannot be evenly divided.

If you know the number of teeth on the driver, its speed, and the number of teeth on the driven gear, and wish to know at what speed this one will turn:

$r = D \times R \div d$

Supposing the driver has 48 teeth and turns at 650 r.p.m., while the driven gear has 14 teeth. Then:

$r = 48 \times 650 \ (31,200) \div 14$

31,200 divided by 14 equals 2,228.5 +

as the speed of the driven gear

To find what size driven gear will give you a desired speed, knowing the size of the driver and its r.p.m., the formula is:

$d = D \times R \div r$

To find the required speed of the driver, when you know its size (number of teeth), the size of the driven gear, and the speed at which you want it to run:

$R = d \times r \div D$

Where ratio is of more concern than actual speeds (in automobile gearing, for instance) you can often get it by reducing the ratio expressed by the number of teeth to its lowest denominator. A pair of gears with 20 and 50 teeth for example have a ratio of 1 to 2½. Often the numbers won't divide so neatly, however. The pinion and ring gear of an automotive rear end may, for example, have 13 and 47 teeth respectively. The ratio is just that, 13 to 47, but for quick comparison with other ratios you can mentally reduce it to approximately 1 to 3½, or as more commonly expressed, 3½ to 1, meaning the smaller gear will make 3½ revolutions to 1 of the larger.

FIGURING GEAR TRAINS

A pair of common spur gears will turn in opposite directions. If you want them to turn in the same direction, it is necessary to interpose a third gear, often called an idler. This will turn oppositely to the other two, while the first and third gears will turn in the same direction. In figuring the ratio, you use only the number of teeth on the driver and driven gear, ignoring the idler entirely because it simply provides a 1-to-1 transfer between the other two.

Nor does it matter how many idlers there are. In a simple sequential gear train (Figure 8) you can still calculate ratio and speed by using the num-

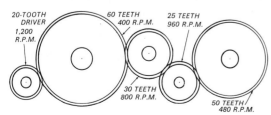

20-TOOTH DRIVER 1,200 R.P.M. 60 TEETH 400 R.P.M. 25 TEETH 960 R.P.M. 30 TEETH 800 R.P.M. 50 TEETH 480 R.P.M.

IGNORING IDLERS, 20 DRIVER TEETH × 1,200 = 24,000
24,000 ÷ 50 (TEETH ON FINAL GEAR) = 480 R.P.M.
SHORT CUT: DRIVER IS ⅖ SIZE OF FINAL GEAR
⅖ OF 1,200 = 480 R.P.M.

Fig. 8. How to calculate ratio and speed of a simple sequential gear train.

ber of teeth on the driver and the final or driven gear, all the intermediate ones being left out of your calculation. If power is to be taken off one of these, however, its speed can be figured by taking the ratio between it and the driver, again ignoring any idlers between them.

This kind of simple gear train must not be confused, however, with a more common and compact type having two gears keyed together or fixed on a common shaft as an intermediate step (Figure 9). Here it is necessary to figure each step from the driver to the final driven gear, as shown in the drawing, by using the appropriate formula.

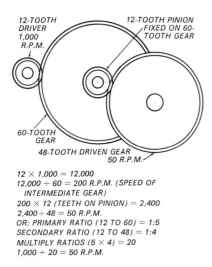

12 × 1,000 = 12,000
12,000 ÷ 60 = 200 R.P.M. (SPEED OF
    INTERMEDIATE GEAR)
200 × 12 (TEETH ON PINION) = 2,400
2,400 ÷ 48 = 50 R.P.M.
OR: PRIMARY RATIO (12 TO 60) = 1:5
SECONDARY RATIO (12 TO 48) = 1:4
MULTIPLY RATIOS (5 × 4) = 20
1,000 ÷ 20 = 50 R.P.M.

Fig. 9. How to calculate ratio and speed of a complex gear train.

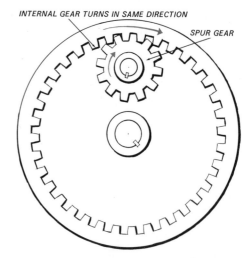

Fig. 10. Internal spur gear.

INTERNAL SPUR GEARING

The basis for some amazing mechanisms, including the famous Model T Ford transmission and present-day automatic drives, internal spur gearing in its simplest form (Figure 10) consists of a small spur gear or pinion running on a fixed shaft inside a larger internal gear—one that has its teeth on the inside. This arrangement is more compact than external gearing and, because the larger gear encircles the smaller, affords more tooth contact, strength and quietness. Furthermore, both gears revolve in the same direction instead of oppositely.

STAGGERING THE TEETH

External spur gearing has two faults: it is noisy because only one tooth on each gear can mesh at a time, making a series of abrupt contacts, and its strength for that same reason is that of a single tooth, which momentarily must carry the full working load. An early effort to improve this situation was the step gear (Figure 11). By staggering two, three or even four sets of teeth across the width of the gears—spaced one half, one third or one quarter of the tooth pitch apart—the engagement of one set was aided by the turning effort of other teeth already in mesh.

But to make the best of a good thing, why not carry the idea to its ultimate? Imagine slicing a wide spur gear into infinitely thin sections and staggering them in infinitely small steps. The result is a helical gear (Figure 11). These run more quietly than equivalent spur gears and will withstand shock loads better.

As you may guess from looking at them, helical gears tend to push apart —to exert an axial sliding action or side thrust. This can be counteracted by suitable thrust bearings. But the elegant answer is to double up two sets of helical teeth on one gear, with the teeth at equal but opposite angles. With such *herringbone* gears, as they are aptly called, all axial thrust neatly cancels out. These gears are highly efficient and can be almost noiseless. (Figure 12).

MODERN RIGHT-ANGLE DRIVES

To transmit power between shafts that are not parallel, we can hark back to the medieval miller and use a crown gear and pinion (Figure 13) though with an updated tooth form. You can see this kind of gear drive on

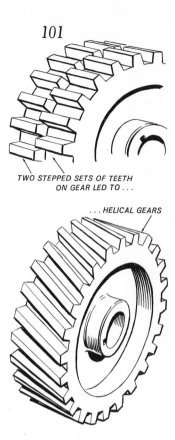

TWO STEPPED SETS OF TEETH
ON GEAR LED TO ...

...HELICAL GEARS

Fig. 11. Step gear and helical gear improved efficiency of external spur gearing.

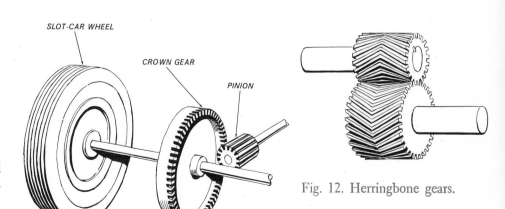

SLOT-CAR WHEEL

CROWN GEAR

PINION

Fig. 13. Crown gear and pinion transmit power between nonparallel shafts.

Fig. 12. Herringbone gears.

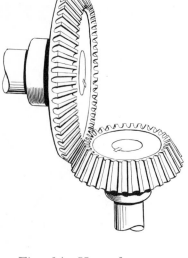

some of the popular little slot racers. For heavy duty, we can use spur bevel gears (Figure 14). The angle of the teeth must be chosen to match the ratio of the gears. For a 1 to 1 ratio between right-angled shafts (the purpose being merely to transmit power without altering speed or torque) the teeth must be at a 45-degree angle. But a miter gear like this must run with another just like it, and will not mesh properly with a smaller or larger one.

In the years that spur bevel gears were used for the final or rear-end drive of automobiles, broken teeth were routine, for again a single tooth might at times bear the full brunt of heavy shock loads. Nowadays we are hardly ever troubled with broken pinion or ring-gear teeth. The first great improvement responsible for this was the spiral bevel gear (Figure 15), the bevel-gear equivalent of helical gears. In this, the teeth are not only angled, but curved, and there are always more than one pair in contact.

Fig. 14. Heavy-duty spur bevel gears.

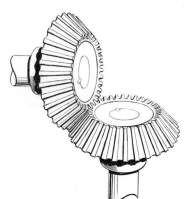

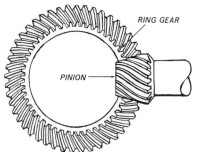

Fig. 15. Spiral bevel gear.

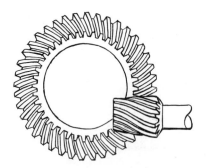

Fig. 16. Hypoid bevel gear.

Even before the trend to lower car bodies, and dissatisfaction with the high floor hump needed to clear the drive shaft, a maker of gear-cutting equipment (the Gleason Works, in Rochester, New York) developed what was to make today's low-slung cars a reality. This was the hypoid bevel gear, in which the pinion may be inches below the center line of the ring gear (Figure 16). While retaining all the advantages of spiral bevel gearing, this allows the drive shaft to be set lower and the car hump greatly reduced.

Worm and gear drives, as shown in Chapter 5, may be reversible or nonreversible depending on their helix angle. A "fast" or reversible helix angle may require a two-, three- or four-thread worm, with a corresponding reduction in ratio. The worm and gear (or worm and segment) drive is the basis of many automotive steering systems.

An improvement in the basic worm is what is sometimes known as the Hindley worm—an hour-glass shape instead of a straight screw. This embraces a good-sized segment of the gear, putting more teeth into contact to share the load (Figure 17).

Figure 18 shows a curious variation of the worm-drive principle. The driving member consists of a spiral tooth (or a spiral groove) which meshes with a transverse spur gear. The ratio is the same as that of a single-thread worm-gear drive, or 1 to the number of teeth on the gear.

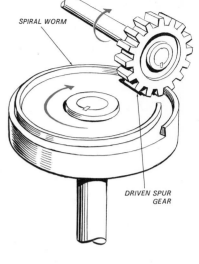

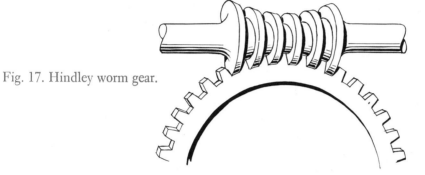

Fig. 17. Hindley worm gear.

Fig. 18. Variation of the worm-drive principle.

Rack and pinion gearing consists of a pinion (a small spur gear) meshing with teeth cut on a straight line (Figure 19). This straight-toothed member is called a rack. Rack and pinion gearing is also used in automobile steering mechanisms, though chiefly in foreign rather than American-made cars.

Fig. 19. Simple rack and pinion gear mechanism.

Spiral gears will transmit power between two shafts in different planes (that is, at different levels) and at a considerable angle to each other. These gears have what at first appear to be helical teeth, but they are designed to mesh smoothly at the requisite shaft angle and involve more sliding than rolling action. Though standard spiral gears are made for shafts at 90 degrees to each other, they can be designed for other angles (Figure 20).

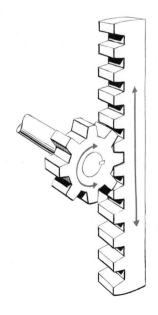

Fig. 20. Standard spiral gears with shafts 90 degrees to each other.

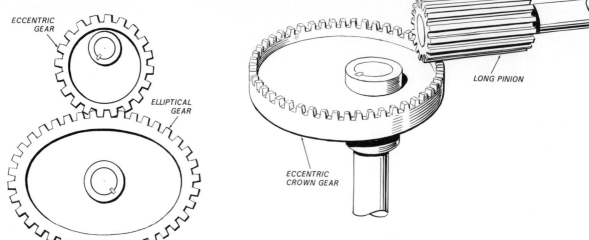

Fig. 21. Eccentric and elliptical gears.

It is possible to make square, elliptical, scroll and swash-plate gears that will run together. Aside from their novelty, their chief purpose is to obtain varying shaft velocities during each revolution. A similar effect results by meshing an eccentric pinion (a round gear mounted off center) with an elliptical one (Figure 21). The scroll gears in Figure 22 also provide a gradual change of ratio, and therefore of speed, during each revolution.

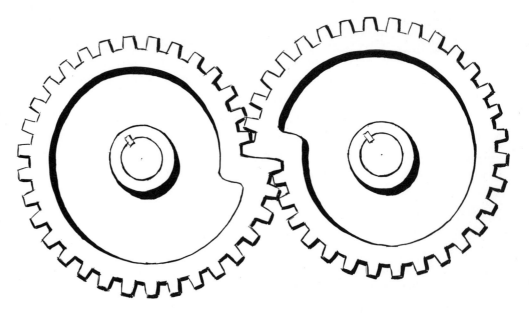

Fig. 22. Scroll gears.

SOME SIMPLE GEAR MOVEMENTS

If you mount three miter gears as in Figure 23, after grinding half the teeth off the bottom one, and then turn this mutilated gear at a steady rate, it will turn one of the others half a revolution, then let it stand still while it revolves the opposite gear in the opposite direction for half a turn. (You could use only one driven gear, instead of two, if you want to drive only a single shaft.)

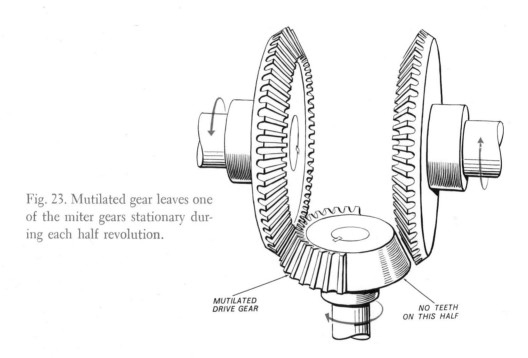

Fig. 23. Mutilated gear leaves one of the miter gears stationary during each half revolution.

MUTILATED
DRIVE GEAR

NO TEETH
ON THIS HALF

A variation of this was long used in hand-powered valve grinders. The vertical shaft had a complete gear on it, but two opposing crown or head gears each had teeth on only half their circumference. These were both fixed on a single shaft, which had a hand crank on it. Turning the crank forward meshed the teeth of the right-hand gear with the pinion, turning it and the vertical shaft (along with the valve being ground) clockwise. Half a revolution of the hand crank later, the teeth on the other half-gear engaged the pinion, turning it and the valve counterclockwise for an equal time (Figure 24).

Figure 25 shows an odd combination of a crankpin, a slotted lever, a gear segment and a rack. Steady rotation of the shaft with the crankpin on it is converted into a back-and-forth quick-return movement of the rack.

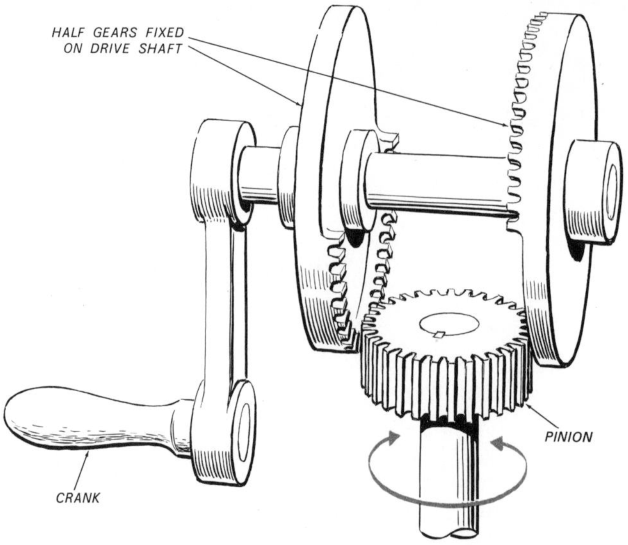

Fig. 24. Gear system once used in hand-powered valve grinders reversed rotation of pinion and shaft every half revolution.

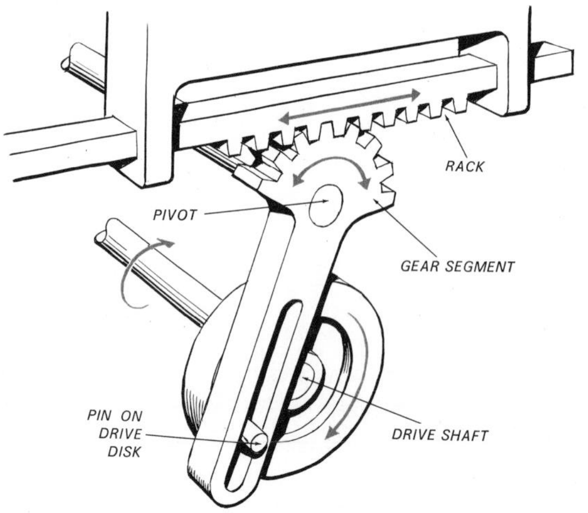

HALF GEARS FIXED ON DRIVE SHAFT

PINION

CRANK

Fig. 25. Rotary motion of drive shaft is converted into reciprocating motion of the rack by a clever gear and crankpin arrangement.

RACK

PIVOT

GEAR SEGMENT

PIN ON DRIVE DISK

DRIVE SHAFT

The hand-powered air pump that delivered air to hard-hat divers (often the subject of sabotage in undersea movie epics) had a double rack mechanism inside it (Figure 26). The pinion is fixed around the fulcrum of the hand lever or rocking bar. As the bar is worked, the pinion turns part of a revolution one way, and then an equal distance the other, alternately moving one rack up and the other down, with the pump rods and pistons fastened to them.

Another rack mechanism has two rows of teeth on a single member (Figure 27). The pinion has teeth on only half its circumference. As in turning clockwise the pinion meshes with the lower teeth, it moves the rack to the left. After half a turn, the pinion teeth mesh with the upper row, moving the rack to the right.

More gear movements, and their modern applications, will be found in the next chapter.

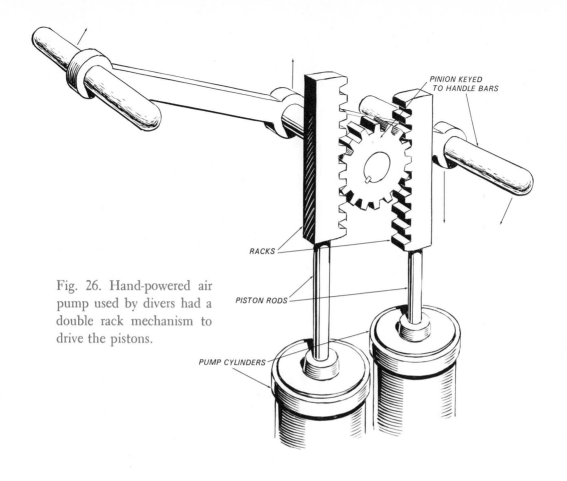

PINION KEYED
TO HANDLE BARS

RACKS

Fig. 26. Hand-powered air pump used by divers had a double rack mechanism to drive the pistons.

PISTON RODS

PUMP CYLINDERS

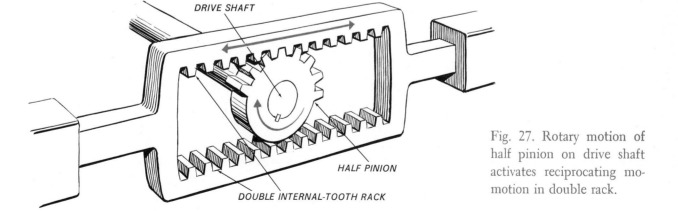

DRIVE SHAFT

HALF PINION

DOUBLE INTERNAL-TOOTH RACK

Fig. 27. Rotary motion of half pinion on drive shaft activates reciprocating mo-motion in double rack.

VIII

Gears in the Modern World

It seems almost incredible today that the crank, an essential element of almost all piston engines, was not always free for all to use. In the days of James Watt it became the subject of a British patent. Unable to use it for that reason, Watt invented an outrageously ingenious substitute.

Watt's first engines, like others of their day, were originally built for pumping water out of mines. This required only a reciprocating motion, readily obtained by coupling the pump more or less directly to the piston rod. But Watt soon saw the desirability of rotary motion for powering textile and other machinery. A modest man, Watt once said of himself, "I am not so quick as some." But when balked by the crank patent, he showed himself a versatile engineer by developing the famous "sun and planet" motion. This converted the back-and-forth push of the piston into the steady rotation of a shaft.

At first glance this weird mechanism (Figure 1) seems to resemble a crank. Actually it is quite different. What appears to be a crank arm is not keyed to the shaft (as a crank has to be) but instead swings freely on the shaft. This was probably one factor in establishing noninfringement of the patent. Watt's mechanism requires two gears of the same size to be in constant mesh,

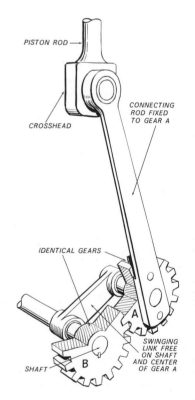

PISTON ROD

CONNECTING ROD FIXED TO GEAR A

CROSSHEAD

IDENTICAL GEARS

A

B

SWINGING LINK FREE ON SHAFT AND CENTER OF GEAR A

SHAFT

108

Fig. 1. James Watt's ingenious "sun and planet motion."

but one of them doesn't turn! Furthermore, the shaft makes *two* complete revolutions to *one* up and down stroke of the piston rod.

In Figure 1, the piston rod moves a crosshead up and down much as for a crank, but the connecting rod is rigidly fixed to the planet gear A (so called because it swings around the sun gear B like a planet). Gear A is held in its orbit, and so in constant mesh with B, by a short link, which pivots freely on the shaft and on a stud at the center of A. Because A cannot turn, it will instead in swinging around B cause this one (and the shaft) to rotate—and that twice as A swings around only once. Why?

If you have on hand two little spur gears of the same size, you can demonstrate this odd action. Mount one on a peg, nail or screw so that it can turn. You can hold the other in mesh while swinging it around the first, but be sure to keep the planet gear in the same position at all times. A dot of paint or a bit of tape on one tooth of both gears will help you do so and show what happens.

You'll find, as Figure 2 shows, that when gear A has moved only a quarter of the way around B, this gear will have made half a revolution. Have

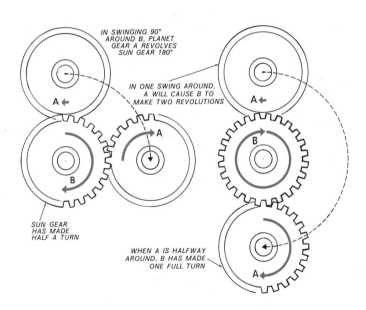

Fig. 2. How Watt's "sun and planet motion" works.

one fourth of the teeth on A meshed with half of those on B? Certainly not; they can mesh only in a one-to-one relation. But gear A has two distinct motions. While swinging a quarter of the way around, it also makes a quarter turn *with relation to B*. The two motions are cumulative, adding up to half a turn of the sun gear.

As Figure 2 further shows, when A is halfway around B, the latter will have made a full turn. When A has returned to its original position (the piston having made a full return stroke) B will have made a second complete revolution.

Another way to look at it: The center of planet gear A describes a circle of twice the radius of the sun gear B. Since the gears are in mesh and of equal size, B must move the same distance in the same time. This it can only do by making two revolutions to A's one.

EPICYCLIC GEAR TRAINS

Watt's sun-and-planet motion is an example of this strange breed. More recently, planetary gear trains whirled around for millions of car miles in the famed Model T Ford. Today they are rolling up many more millions in automatic transmissions.

Let us take another look at the two gears in Watt's mechanism, but this time unfasten the planet gear so that it may simply be rolled around the sun gear, as you can do readily with a couple of loose gears. If you hold the sun gear fast, you will probably not be surprised that the planet gear makes two revolutions in rolling around the other once, one by reason of its change in position, the other because of its own rotation.

This holds true of any ratio; the planet gear always makes one extra turn. A 7-tooth planet gear rolling around a 49-tooth sun gear will make not 7, but 8 turns! To prove it to the hilt, we might try a small sun gear and a much bigger planet gear. If the sun gear has 50 teeth and the planet gear 150, the latter, in rolling around the sun gear, will make not $\frac{1}{3}$ of a turn, but $1\frac{1}{3}$.

Most planetary gear trains have, in addition to sun and planet gears, a third one. This is an internal or ring gear concentric with the sun gear, the planet gear meshing with both (Figure 3).

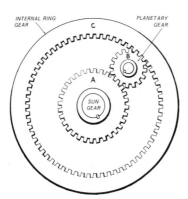

Fig. 3. A typical planetary gear train.

Let us assume that, in the system shown, the sun gear A is 1 inch in diameter, the planet gear B ½ inch, and the ring gear C 2 inches. We will also assume that the number of teeth on each gear is exactly proportionate to its diameter.

Some surprising things now appear.

If we hold C motionless and pull B around inside it (which makes the sun gear turn too) we should with a gear ratio of ½ to 2 inches expect B to make four turns while rolling around inside C once.

Not so. It makes only three.

If we hold the sun gear and turn C one revolution, the planet gear will make two, while itself swings around only ⅔ of a turn.

Again hold the ring gear, and swing the planet gear around one revolution. It will make three turns on its own center, while the twice-as-big sun gear will keep direct step, also making three turns.

Without going further into mathematics, you can see that a handful of such gears offers a bucketful of possibilities—far more than there is space to explore. Henry Ford made good use of them. His Model T had a remarkably sophisticated transmission, despite its Tin Lizzy look—far more ingenious, in fact, than the manual sliding-gear transmissions in more costly cars of that day.

To work mechanical magic with the simple planetary gear train of Figure 3, we need only add two simple elements. One is an arm fastened to a shaft (or more commonly a spider with several arms, since two, three or four planetary gears are usually used to share the load). This arm or spider enables us to take off the swinging action of the planetary gears by a shaft, or to impart such action to them from a rotating shaft.

The second new element is—of all things—a brake band around the outer or ring gear. In Figure 4, both these elements have been added. Sup-

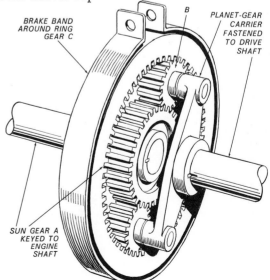

Fig. 4. Planetary gear train adapted to early auto transmission.

BRAKE BAND
AROUND RING
GEAR C

B

PLANET-GEAR
CARRIER
FASTENED
TO DRIVE
SHAFT

SUN GEAR A
KEYED TO
ENGINE
SHAFT

pose the sun gear is mounted on the engine shaft of a car (it thus becomes the driving gear), and that we plan to take power from the planet carrier or spider. This will therefore be keyed to the drive shaft which carries power back to the car wheels. Remember that this shaft will be turned only as the planetary gears swing around; it will *not* be powered if these gears simply turn on their own axes. Remember too that the drive shaft is loaded, being connected by the rear-end gears to the car wheels, which normally resist movement.

With the engine turning the sun gear, the planet gears must also revolve. If the brake is off, the ring gear is free to turn, so the load-inertia of the planet carrier (which you remember is connected to the car wheels) will hold it motionless. The spinning planet gears will simply turn the ring gear around and around. No torque is being applied to the wheels, so the car stands still.

But now apply the brake to the ring gear. As you slow it down, more and more force is applied to the planet carrier. When the ring gear is locked, the revolving planet gears must start to roll around inside it. (As a simple analogy, consider a man walking on a treadmill. He will stay in one place, but if you suddenly jam the treadmill, he will move forward.)

In rolling around inside the ring gear, the planet gears and their carrier will revolve in the same direction as the sun gear, and turn the drive shaft that way. The wheels turn and the car moves forward. The brake on the ring gear in effect does the job of a clutch!

But this system does more than transmit and control power. It also multiplies torque, for in the situation described the sun gear will make three revolutions to one of the planet carrier. This means a 1:3 speed reduction and a tripling of torque.

If now we add some kind of clutch that can directly couple the planet carrier (and so the drive shaft) to either the sun gear or the ring gear, we have a simple two-speed transmission. We would need interlocking controls to let the clutch engage only when the ring gear brake is off. Now, when the brake is on, the engine would drive the drive shaft at a 1:3 reduction for starting the car from a dead stop or for climbing steep hills. When the brake is released and the clutch engages, none of the gears could turn in relation to the others. The entire system would revolve as a unit, turning the drive shaft at a 1:1 ratio (direct drive) for easy highway cruising.

There is still more to the planetary bag of tricks. If we can lock the planet carrier and (with another clutch) couple the drive shaft to the ring gear instead, the latter will turn *backwards*, again multiplying torque but this time in a 1:2 ratio, and move the car in reverse.

But drive the planet carrier, lock the ring gear, and take power from the sun gear—and you have an overdrive. With our example of ½-, 1- and 2-inch gears, the sun gear and drive shaft would make three revolutions to the engine's and planet carrier's one.

Or drive the ring gear, lock the planet carrier, and the sun gear will turn backwards but in overdrive—that is, with less torque but more speed. (With the gears specified, it would make two turns to one of the engine.)

Still other combinations are possible, and of course the ratios obtainable can be varied by selecting different sizes of sun, ring and planet gears.

AUTOMATIC AUTOMOBILE TRANSMISSIONS

By adding automatic controls to planetary gear trains, we can build transmissions that seem to think for themselves, automatically selecting the ratios best suited to the speed and load of a car at any moment.

A forerunner of today's automatic transmissions was the overdrive first added to manual transmissions in the thirties. This mechanism provided a fourth or "higher" gear beyond third gear. A typical overdrive has a single planetary unit behind the manual gearbox. At low car speeds it is locked up, providing direct drive-through that has no effect whatever.

When the car reaches a certain speed, however, electrical and centrifugal controls automatically lock the sun gear. The planet carrier, driven from the manual transmission, then turns the ring gear with an increase in speed and a diminution of torque. The engine makes fewer revolutions per car mile, and a smooth, gliding ride results. On an upgrade, the automatic controls release the planetary system to re-establish direct drive, with a resulting increase in torque.

Further controls allow the driver to "kick down" out of overdrive simply by tramping on the throttle, even at speeds above that at which overdrive would normally engage, when he wants to accelerate rapidly or climb hills more speedily. The overdrive incorporates a free-wheeling device that uncouples the engine when the car is coasting below overdrive-engagement speed.

By ganging two planetary gear sets, one behind the other, with appropriate controls we can dispense with manual shifting entirely. Each planetary system is rigged to afford two speeds—one in direct drive and the other in a reduction ratio. By choosing the gears so that the two systems have different reduction ratios, we could get four overall ratios.

For starting, both gear trains are used to provide a double speed reduction, so delivering great torque. For "second" gear, the automatic controls put the forward unit in direct drive while leaving the rear one in speed reduction.

For "third" we switch this around, using the rear train in direct drive but the forward one in speed reduction. But as this ratio is a bit lower than that of the other system, we get somewhat more speed (and less torque) than in the second combination.

Finally, for fourth or "high" gear, we flip both planetary systems into direct drive. The drive shaft then rotates at engine speed, the only reduction being that afforded by the pinion and ring gear in the rear axle.

This rear-axle reduction is of course in the power train at all times, and its ratio is fixed. (An exception was the Ruckstell accessory rear axle made for the Model T Ford, which could be shifted to either of two ratios, thus giving the Tin Lizzie four forward speeds and two in reverse.)

Engineers try to match rear-axle ratio to those of the transmission so as to provide the range of overall ratios best suited to the car and what is expected of it. The astute car buyer can choose a low rear-axle ratio, such as 3 to 1, for high-speed cruising in flat terrain, whereas a San Francisco motorist might select a 4 to 1 rear-axle ratio to cope better with the many steep hills in his area. The driver who likes to make leapfrog starts might choose a similar high ratio for quick pickup.

HYDRAULIC CLUTCHES AND TORQUE CONVERTERS

Though a brake band on one element of a planetary gear train can be used as a clutch, engineers have generally preferred to use it to change ratio, and instead have added to the modern automatic transmission either a fluid clutch or a fluid torque converter. This unit is directly behind the engine, though power is sometimes routed to it in an indirect fashion through the first planetary unit.

A fluid coupling eliminates the friction clutch with its disks and linings. It takes up the load smoothly as the throttle is opened, without jerk, yet virtually ends the possibility of stalling an engine. A crude analogy of a fluid clutch would be a child's windmill held in front of a fan; the air stream would "couple" the fan to the windmill and make it revolve. Liquid being almost incompressible, hydraulic action is more positive.

The simplest fluid coupling (Figure 5) has one set of internal vanes (resembling the skin segments of a grapefruit after the pulp has been removed) mounted in a ring that is driven by the engine. Oil in the casing is driven outward by centrifugal force but constrained by the casing to flow against a second set of vanes fastened to the output shaft. It is also moving fast in the direction the driving member turns, and imparts this motion to the driven member. The oil circulates continuously back to the driving vanes to do

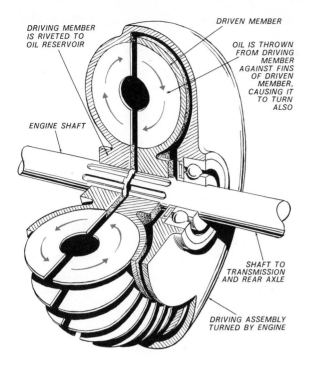

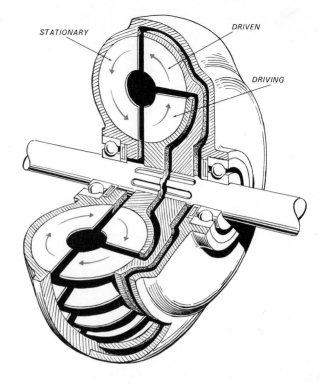

Fig. 5. Simple fluid clutch.

Fig. 6. Hydraulic torque converter.

its work over and over again. Because of centrifugal force, it follows such a path as a bug might pursue in crawling from the front to the back of a doughnut. The oil is also being swirled around in the direction of rotation, causing the driven member to rotate. There is of course 100 percent slip when the car is standing still and the engine is idling. But there is very little slip at high speed.

Hydraulic torque converters are fluid couplings with an added set of stationary reaction blades (Figure 6). Located between the two others, these give the driven blades something to push against (or, to put it otherwise, the oil hurled off the driven blades meets resistance at the stationary ones, and in reacting gives the driven blades an extra push). The result is a multiplication of torque, greatest at low speed, shifting in a smooth curve to a direct or 1:1 ratio at higher speeds.

Losses in a torque converter are higher than in a plain fluid coupling, and go up with speed. Some converters are therefore built with automatic clutches that lock them up at moderate to high speeds, so providing a direct drive-through. Another solution is to mount the reaction blading on roller bearings. These vanes stand still at low speeds, multiplying torque. But at high speeds the blading automatically starts to revolve or free-wheel on the rollers, dispensing with torque multiplication when it is no longer needed, while transmitting power at the higher efficiency of a plain fluid coupling.

To further improve efficiency, modern torque converters may have not merely a single stage, but two or three, with as many sets of driving, driven, and reaction blading (Figure 7).

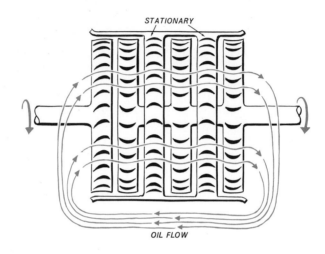

Fig. 7. Two-stage hydraulic torque converter.

HIGH-RATIO EPICYCLIC GEARING

Fantastic ratios are possible with only a few gears arranged in an epicyclic train. One such involving only six bevel gears has a ratio of 250,000 to 1. A more modest example, however, will be easier to understand.

The short parallel lines in Figure 8 represent the teeth of two gears mounted side by side, but for purposes of illustration unrolled or stretched out in a straight line. (In practice the gears have more teeth than the few shown.) One gear, at the left, is fixed so that it cannot turn. The other, next to it, is keyed to the output shaft, and this gear has one tooth less than its mate. Meshing with both gears is a small planet gear, so mounted on a stud, spider or carrier that it swings around them, and the carrier is the power input.

In the diagram, a dotted line represents the single tooth of the planet gear that is in mesh with the two sun gears at any one time. At A in Figure 8 this tooth aligns teeth 1 and 2 of the two larger gears. In moving around, it aligns succeeding teeth step by step or in a 1 to 1 sequence, so when at B it is between teeth 4 and 5 of the output gear, this gear has turned slightly, as shown by the fact that its tooth No. 1 has shifted out of alignment with tooth

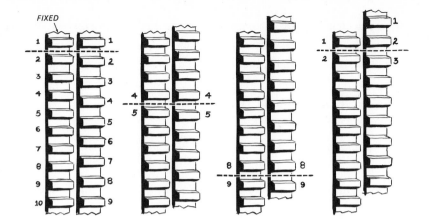

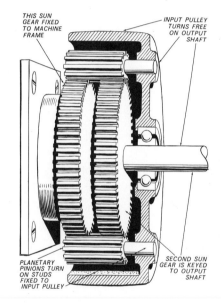

Fig. 8. Diagram of high-ratio epicycle gear system.

Fig. 9. Actual view of high-ratio epicycle gear system.

THIS SUN GEAR FIXED TO MACHINE FRAME

INPUT PULLEY TURNS FREE ON OUTPUT SHAFT

PLANETARY PINIONS TURN ON STUDS FIXED TO INPUT PULLEY

SECOND SUN GEAR IS KEYED TO OUTPUT SHAFT

No. 1 of the stationary gear. At C, the planet gear has moved farther around, aligning the seventh teeth, while at D, after a complete revolution of the planet gear, teeth 1 and 2 of the fixed gear are aligned with teeth 2 and 3 of the movable one.

One full revolution of the input shaft and the planet gear has turned the output gear and its shaft only one tooth space, a ratio of 10 to 1. As more teeth are used, the ratio becomes higher. If the sun gears have 100 teeth and 99 teeth, the ratio will be 100 to 1.

Figure 9 shows a practical gear train of this kind. Mounted on the output shaft, but free to turn on it, is a pulley that may be belt driven from a motor or other power source. On one face of the pulley is a stud (or more than

117

one) on which a small but wide planet gear may revolve freely. The output shaft carries the rotating sun gear, while the stationary one is fixed to the machine frame in some manner not shown. The planet gear (or gears) meshes with both.

The formula for this kind of gearing is:

$$\text{Reduction ratio} = 1 - \frac{\text{fixed teeth}}{\text{planet teeth}} \times \frac{\text{planet teeth}}{\text{output teeth}}$$

Supposing the planet gear has 12 teeth, the fixed sun gear 59, and the driven sun gear 60 teeth. Then:

$$\text{Ratio} = 1 - \frac{59}{12} \times \frac{12}{60}$$

Cancelling out the 12's, we get $1 - \frac{59}{60}$, or 1/60

The driven gear will make $\frac{1}{60}$ revolution to one of the planet gear or input pulley.

Not enough? Then why not mount another 12-tooth planet gear on the output shaft and let it run around another pair of 59- and 60-tooth sun gears? This second stage will have the same 60 to 1 reduction ratio as the first. And the total reduction will be 3,600 to 1!

Still not enough? Well, the planet gears need not be smaller than the sun gears, and instead of one planet gear we can use two coupled together (or machined from a single piece) so that they act as one. If we use a 101-tooth stationary sun gear meshing with a 100-tooth planet gear, and let the second section of this have 99 teeth, meshing with 100 on the output gear, our equation becomes:

$$\text{Ratio} = 1 - \frac{101}{100} \times \frac{99}{100}$$

This works out to 1 minus $\frac{9,999}{10,000}$, or 1/10,000

AN AUTO'S BOX OF GEARS

What we call the transmission the British motorist dubs the gearbox, an apt name. It is there to compensate for the gas engine's lack of torque at low speeds. We know we cannot rev the engine up fast and then let in the clutch—the car will jerk into motion most unpleasantly. For smooth starts, as well as to provide the torque to set a ton or more of metal into motion, we need some way of letting the engine run fast and so develop the needed torque, while starting the wheels very gradually from a dead stop. This requires a speed reduction drive or a high gear ratio (which automotive custom has perversely named "low" gear, or more properly, "first").

Once the car is moving, we cannot be content to have the engine buzz while the car crawls. Merely to get up to a decent speed, we need a less high drive ratio, though one still high enough to afford good acceleration. In a three-speed transmission, this is "second" or intermediate gear. It still multiplies torque for acceleration, passing and hill climbing.

On a flat road, we can use a still lower ratio, to let the engine turn at a comfortable rate while the car cruises at a good speed. This is "high" or third gear. In most transmissions, this is not really a gear ratio at all, but a straight drive-through from the clutch to the rear end. The actual engine-to-wheels ratio is only that of the rear-axle gears.

The obvious way to change gear ratios is to slide gears back and forth so that they mesh or disengage from other gears. This—with much gnashing of teeth at times—is what happened in early auto transmissions. To let the gears slide and yet key them positively to their shafts, the latter were sometimes made square to work in matching square holes in the gears. Later the shafts were splined—machined with a number of equally spaced grooves and lands all around. The gears were similarly machined with holes having lands to fit the shaft grooves, and grooves to clear the shaft lands. Thus a gear was firmly keyed to the shaft yet free to slide along it. For moving the gear, a groove was machined in its hub and a fork fitted to lie in the groove. By shifting the fork, the gear could be slid into or out of mesh.

Sliding gear transmissions were used for decades. Disengaging the clutch gave the driver a sporting chance—provided he gauged engine and road speeds properly—to shift gears without tooth-gnashing violence. The true adept could even shift gears without declutching—a tour de force that might require costly gear dentistry if one's timing was off.

Then came the constant-mesh transmission, in which certain gears remain in mesh at all times. They are engaged in the drive train, as required, by sliding positive clutches (sometimes called dog clutches). These have a movable member that slides on a splined shaft and has teeth that enter matching notches in the gear hub or another shaft (Figure 10).

A second great improvement was the synchronized transmission. To facilitate engagement, the dog clutches are first brought up to the same speed

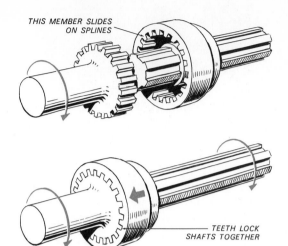

Fig. 10. Constant-mesh
transmission.

TEETH LOCK
SHAFTS TOGETHER

as the gears. The shifting action first moves a small friction clutch into contact, which instantly synchronizes the movement of dog clutch and gear. Completing of the shift slides the dog clutch into full engagement (Figure 13).

An added advantage of the constant-mesh box is that helical gears can be used, spur gears being needed only for sliding ones. The greater strength and quietness of helical gears make this alone an improvement.

Figure 11 shows a representative three-speed manual transmission. A gear on the engine (or more properly clutch) shaft is in constant mesh with a somewhat larger one on the countershaft. So is the second countershaft gear A and a slightly bigger one B that is free to revolve on the output shaft. Between the input shaft and gear B is a sliding positive clutch.

A still larger sliding gear C can engage with the third countershaft gear D or with the reverse gear E. This is on a second countershaft that is constantly turning, for its forward gear F is in mesh with D. These are spur gears and not synchronized, but as they are shifted only for first and reverse this is tolerable.

Now we can follow through a complete upshift. For first gear, the shift lever moves sliding gear C into mesh with D on the countershaft, the dog clutch remaining in its neutral position. The power path is from the input shaft to the countershaft, then from gear D to C. As each pair of the four gears involves a speed reduction, the overall ratio is high, though this position is often called "low gear."

For second gear, the shift lever first slides C out of mesh. Up to now gear B, though constantly revolving because in mesh with A, has done no work but merely run free. Now the shift moves the dog clutch back, locking gear B up to the output shaft. Power flows from A to B, at a slightly lower ratio— that is, with less speed reduction—than in first.

120

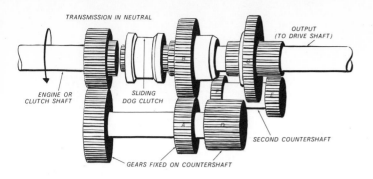

TRANSMISSION IN NEUTRAL

OUTPUT
(TO DRIVE SHAFT)

ENGINE OR
CLUTCH SHAFT

SLIDING
DOG CLUTCH

SECOND COUNTERSHAFT

GEARS FIXED ON COUNTERSHAFT

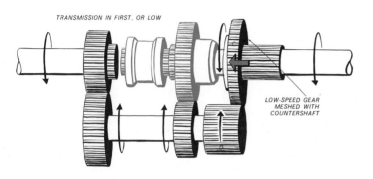

TRANSMISSION IN FIRST, OR LOW

LOW-SPEED GEAR
MESHED WITH
COUNTERSHAFT

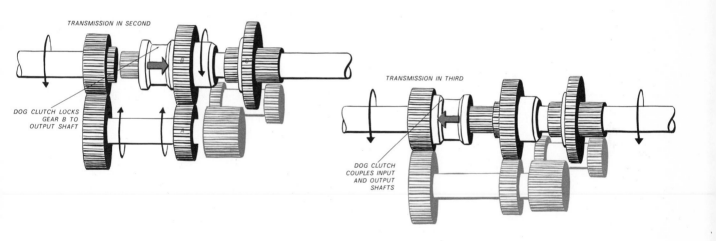

TRANSMISSION IN SECOND

DOG CLUTCH LOCKS
GEAR B TO
OUTPUT SHAFT

TRANSMISSION IN THIRD

DOG CLUTCH
COUPLES INPUT
AND OUTPUT
SHAFTS

Fig. 11. Typical automotive three-
speed manual transmission.

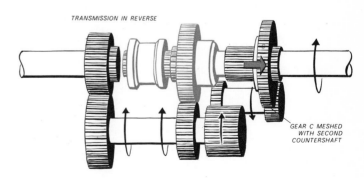

TRANSMISSION IN REVERSE

GEAR C MESHED
WITH SECOND
COUNTERSHAFT

121

For third gear, the dog clutch releases the output shaft gear B and slides forward, so coupling the output shaft directly to the engine shaft. Though the countershaft keeps on spinning, no gears are transmitting power.

For reverse, the big sliding gear C is drawn back to engage the rear one E on the reverse shaft. As this puts extra countershaft in the train, the output shaft now rotates backward, opposite to engine rotation. The ratio is high to afford a torque increase, for we may have to climb a steep slope in reverse at times, and it is in any case undesirable to back at high speed.

In today's hectic traffic, many a driver itches to shift back into low even before the car rolls to a stop, in order to be ready for a swift getaway. But shifting into low with the car moving even slightly can result in noisy engagement. Skilled drivers can do it by double clutching—briefly letting the clutch up, revving the engine to synchronize the gears with the dying speed of the car, and quickly declutching again to shift them into mesh. This takes split-second timing and a "feel" for the gearbox.

To make it easier—and it is often desirable in traffic to be able to get underway without hesitation—there is a growing move toward synchronization even of first gear. Though this calls for a somewhat different transmission than the one shown, the same principles apply.

THE AUTOMOBILE DIFFERENTIAL

Those who made ancient war chariots and the Conestoga wagon could cheerfully ignore something that has haunted builders of powered vehicles from the first. It is the awkward fact that the wheel on the outside of a curve (that is, whatever wheel happens to take the longer path on a curve) must turn faster than the inside one (Figure 12). Chariot and wagon wheels turned independently of each other on fixed axles, so each could set its own pace and there was no problem. But on powered vehicles two wheels are usually coupled to the engine, and if you so connect them that both are driven, how will you arrange for independent—that is, different—speeds when a curve comes up?

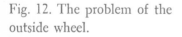

Fig. 12. The problem of the outside wheel.

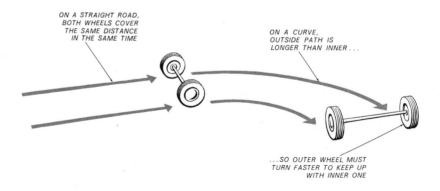

ON A STRAIGHT ROAD, BOTH WHEELS COVER THE SAME DISTANCE IN THE SAME TIME

ON A CURVE, OUTSIDE PATH IS LONGER THAN INNER . . .

. . . SO OUTER WHEEL MUST TURN FASTER TO KEEP UP WITH INNER ONE

Some builders of early automobiles, tractors and more recently go-karts tried to solve the problem by pretending it didn't exist. They simply keyed both wheels to a rigid axle and let them battle it out. The vehicle would slide, skid and slither around turns somehow, but the skidding tires suffered extra wear and control of the vehicle was impaired.

Locomotive makers were more successful in this brash course. Metal wheels slip enough on rails to get by, and besides, railroad curves are of far greater radius than those a road vehicle must negotiate. Locomotive wheels were also, in theory at least, helped somewhat by a slight taper on the wheel treads. This is too slight to see readily, but the wheel diameter is a trifle larger at the flange than it is at the outside of the wheel. On a curve, centrifugal force shoves the whole engine toward the outside. The flange of the outer wheel then rides hard against the rail and the slightly larger tread diameter is in contact, while the flange of the inner wheel moves away from its rail, letting that wheel drop down on its smaller diameter.

A simple solution for road vehicles was to drive only one wheel, leaving the other loose on the axle to find its own rate of rotation on turns. This works at some sacrifice of traction, for only one wheel has to supply all driving effort. It will also make the vehicle swing into some turns (those with the driving wheel inside) more rapidly than others. However, one-wheel drive is fairly successful on go-karts and similar small vehicles, and amazingly so on the King Midget, a small one-cylinder automobile.

Rather more ingenious is the solution applied to some garden and snow-removal machinery. It is to drive both wheels from a common axle, but through over-running ratchets. These will drive the wheels positively in a forward direction, and at equal speeds. But on going into a turn the outside wheel (which wants to move faster, like the outside marcher in a columns-abreast formation) is free to over-run the axle. While it does so, the inside wheel shoulders the driving load. But this too halves the tractive effort at such times.

The truly elegant solution was fittingly provided in 1827 by a Frenchman, Onesiphore Pecquer, who devised a gearbox that drove two separate axles —one for each wheel—with equal speed and torque. Until—and this is the miracle of mechanics he created—the vehicle entered a curve. This tended to slow down one wheel while speeding up the other. Pecquer's differential gearbox instantly shifted torque effort to match, and in precisely the desired ratio to suit either a gentle curve or a sharp one!

It may help to understand an automobile differential if we first consider a rack and pinion mechanism, the pinion being free to turn on its own axis, or to move along the rack, while the rack itself is fixed (A in Figure 13). If we

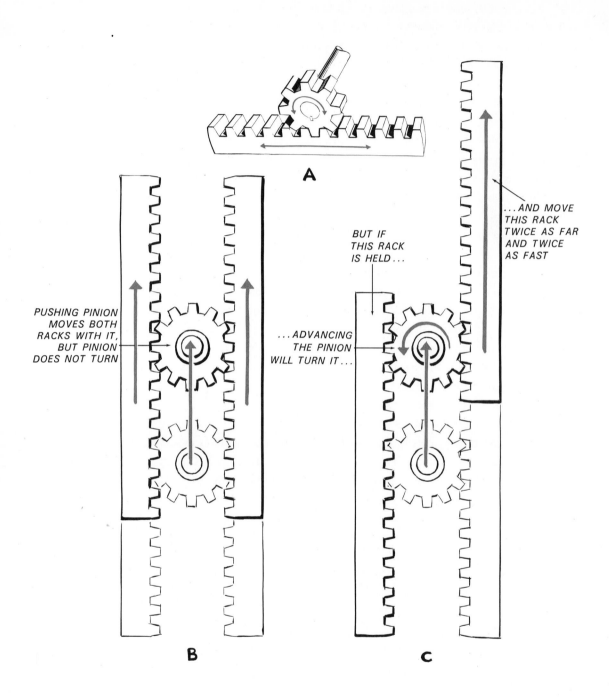

PUSHING PINION
MOVES BOTH
RACKS WITH IT,
BUT PINION
DOES NOT TURN

BUT IF
THIS RACK
IS HELD...

...AND MOVE
THIS RACK
TWICE AS FAR
AND TWICE
AS FAST

...ADVANCING
THE PINION
WILL TURN IT...

A

B

C

Fig. 13. Rack and pinion mechanism.

push the pinion as shown by the arrow (perhaps through a pin or stud in the center hole, on which the pinion can also turn) the gear will roll along the rack, both advancing and revolving.

Now let us add a second rack as at B, and provide guides for both racks so that they are no longer fixed, but free to move lengthwise. If now we push the pinion by its stud, it will not turn, but simply act like a bar connecting the two racks, which will move at the same rate as the pinion.

While this is going on, suppose we suddenly block one rack as at C in Figure 16. A curious thing happens. The pinion instantly has to roll against the locked rack, just as it did at A. Therefore it has to revolve as it advances. Its straight-line movement *plus* its enforced rotation will now advance the movable rack at *twice* the speed of the pinion itself.

Or we can block the other rack, releasing the first, and reverse the situation. The pinion's motion will instantly transfer itself to the free rack.

As an incidental effect, if we leave both racks free to move but hold the pinion, moving one rack forward will move the other backward at equal speed.

Automobile rear-axle gears work exactly like this, though they are all true circular gears and not racks. Each wheel has its own axle, and each axle has at its inner end a small bevel gear called a *differential* gear or side gear (Figure 14). These gears replace the racks in our previous example.

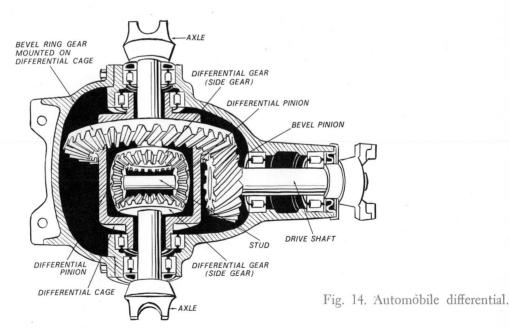

Fig. 14. Automobile differential.

Mounted on one axle but free to swing around it is the differential cage, which in the drawing is shown as a simple right-angled bracket. (In practice it is round.) Mounted on the bracket-like extension is a differential pinion, free to turn on its stud but meshing with both differential gears, as the pinion does with the two racks in Figure 13.

To move the pinion (which we simply pushed in our former example), we have to mount a bevel gear on the differential case. This is called the ring gear, and it meshes with a bevel pinion on the drive shaft of the automobile. Once it is understood that all these two gears do is push around the differential pinion, we can forget they are there.

The differential behaves just like the two racks and pinion observed before. On a straight road the differential pinion acts like a solid connection joining the two differential gears. Both axles turn at the same speed and with equal torque, the pinion swinging around at the same rate but not turning on its own axis at all. The whole assembly might as well be welded together.

But suppose the car enters a sharp turn. Road friction tends to slow down one wheel and make the other revolve faster. It is the same as when we put a frictional drag on one of the racks at C in Figure 13. The differential pinion starts to roll around the slower differential gear. Its rotational movement is immediately added to its movement around the differential gears, so driving the one on the outside axle proportionately faster.

If we had the car on a lift, with both wheels off the ground, and could suddenly apply the brake to stop one wheel, the other would turn just twice as fast. This gives us an easy way, incidentally, to find the rear-axle ratio of a car (that of the ring gear to its pinion). Holding one wheel, we turn the other and count the number of times the drive shaft turns to one revolution of the wheel. Dividing by two (because, remember, the differential doubles the speed of the free wheel) gives us the numerical ratio.

If the drive shaft is held and one wheel turned, the other will turn backwards at the same speed. In practice, the differential cage may carry two, three or four differential pinions instead of one, thus spreading the load between them.

Pecquer's differential had one great drawback, which you have probably encountered on slippery roads. If one wheel is free to slip on ice or snow, the gears cheerfully transfer all effort to that one, letting the wheel that has traction stand still. Today's limited-slip differential counteracts this. Two cross shafts carrying four differential pinions are free to move to a limited degree in V-notches in the cage. As wheel resistance pushes the cross shafts up the V-slopes or ramps, the pinions are forced outwards in a direction parallel to the axles (Figure 15).

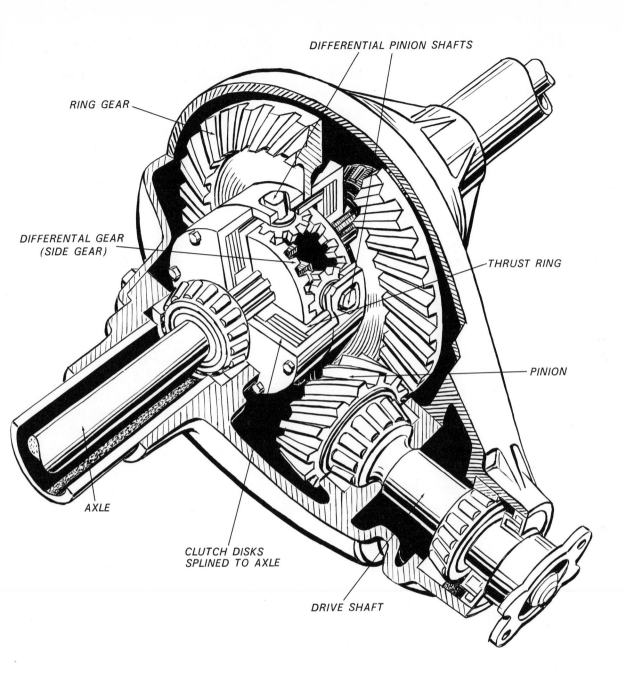

DIFFERENTIAL PINION SHAFTS

RING GEAR

DIFFERENTAL GEAR
(SIDE GEAR)

THRUST RING

PINION

AXLE

CLUTCH DISKS
SPLINED TO AXLE

DRIVE SHAFT

Fig. 15. Limited-slip differential.

127

As this occurs, the pinion shoulders bear on thrust rings that engage small clutch disks on both sides. The clutches tend to couple the cage directly to the wheels, which *on a straightaway* is the way the differential acts anyway.

On a curve, however, the over-running outer wheel tries to make the pinions overspeed the cage. This lessening of torque load lets the cross shafts ease down the V-ramp, releasing the clutches and letting normal differential action occur.

But a wheel spinning on ice is a different matter. It is not over-running, but being driven, and this requires some torque. Though modest, the load resistance of the slipping wheel makes the cross shafts climb their ramps, engaging the clutches. This makes the whole differential try to turn as one unit, and therefore it drives the other wheel—which puts still more of a torque load on the system, further tightening up the clutches. In this way the nonslip differential transfers ample torque to the wheel that would normally be standing still.

FLEXIBLE GEARS

Flexible gears would seem to be as useless as rubber knives. But in 1961 the United Shoe Machinery Corporation of Boston announced a remarkable speed-reduction system called the harmonic drive, which has one rigid internal gear meshing with another flexible enough to change its shape moderately. The harmonic drive is claimed to be capable of delivering as much torque as much bigger and heavier conventional gear reductions, and at ratios up to 1,000 to 1.

Figure 16 shows one such system. The outer rigid gear has internal teeth, while the inner flexible gear has external teeth, but two less than the other gear. This flexible gear, which may be of plastic or metal, is held against rotation. The outer gear is fixed to the output shaft.

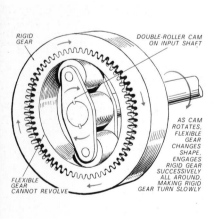

RIGID GEAR

DOUBLE-ROLLER CAM ON INPUT SHAFT

AS CAM ROTATES, FLEXIBLE GEAR CHANGES SHAPE, ENGAGES RIGID GEAR SUCCESSIVELY ALL AROUND, MAKING RIGID GEAR TURN SLOWLY

FLEXIBLE GEAR CANNOT REVOLVE

Fig. 16. Harmonic drive.

On the input shaft is an arm having a ball-bearing roller at each end, which in effect makes it a double-lobed cam. As the arm turns inside the flexible gear, the rollers squeeze its teeth into mesh with those of the rigid outside gear at two diametrically opposite places, such contact passing successively around the gears.

The four duct rotating devices in the new Bell X-22A V/STOLL aircraft are powered by harmonic drives. Weighing only 40 pounds, each harmonic drive unit provides a torque capability in excess of 220,000 inch-pounds.

A pair of harmonic drives in the front hood of the new Dodge Charger actuates the headlight closures. Exploded view of harmonic drive is shown above. At right, three stages in the closure operation that conceals the headlights.

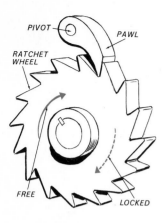

Fig. 17. Ratchet and pawl mechanism.

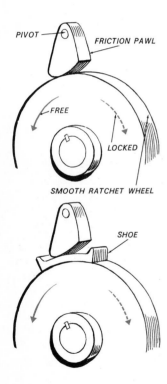

Fig. 18. Quiet ratchet works by friction. Pawl may be fitted with a shoe as in bottom drawing.

But in matching up tooth for tooth, the two gears cannot keep in step, for one has two more teeth than the other. Every time the cam makes one full revolution, the outer ring turns by this two-tooth difference. You may recognize the action as akin to that of the epicyclic train in Figure 10. An outer gear having 200 teeth, working with a flexible gear of 198 teeth, will thus turn $\frac{1}{100}$th of a revolution to one turn of the roller cam, or at a ratio of 100 to 1.

The system can also be built with the outside gear fixed and the flexible gear as the output member. Wear is low because the relative movement of the gears is small and the load is divided between two meshing areas at all times. The harmonic drive can even transmit power through a sealed container without stuffing boxes or glands. This would be done by placing the rigid gear inside the flexible one (with appropriate external and internal teeth) and making the container flexible enough to allow external rollers to transmit action inside.

Already tested for some military uses such as turning tank turrets and radar antennae, the harmonic drive could actuate aircraft and helicopter controls, drive machine-tool feeds, and multiply torque while reducing the high speeds of gas-turbine rotors. One of its first commercial applications, developed by the Bendix Corporation under license, was a servo system for Boeing 707 jet planes.

RATCHETS AND OVER-RUNNING CLUTCHES

As every boy who has dissected an old alarm clock knows, the familiar ratchet on wind-up mechanisms is a sort of biased gear, the teeth having a sharp slope on one side and a more gradual one on the other. Held against the teeth is a pawl or detent (Figure 17) that catches positively against the nearly radial slope so that ratchet and pawl are locked against each other in one direction. But if the ratchet is turned the other way (or the pawl in the opposite direction) it is allowed to more as the pawl climbs the longer slope.

On a railroad brake or a winch, the pawl may be pivoted on a solid member so as to engage of its own weight, and can be flipped out of the way when not wanted. In a spring-wind mechanism it is usually mounted on another rotating member and requires a light spring to keep it engaged at all times.

Such a ratchet clicks or chatters when running free. It can be fitted with a friction collar and lever that lift the pawl away from the teeth in the free-running direction. A quiet ratchet that will not only lock anywhere the wheel stops (instead of only in tooth increments) is shown in Figure 18. The friction pawl may be weight or spring loaded, and it is sometimes fitted with a loose shoe or pad to increase the contact area and lessen wear.

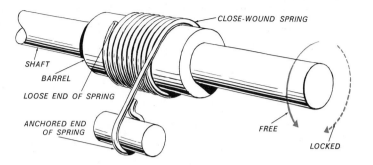

CLOSE-WOUND SPRING

SHAFT

BARREL

LOOSE END OF SPRING

ANCHORED END
OF SPRING

FREE

LOCKED

Fig. 19. Stepless ratchet makes use of torsional friction.

Another stepless ratchet makes use of torsional friction. In Figure 19, the shaft is to turn freely counterclockwise when seen from the right-hand end, but lock when turned in the other direction. Fixed to the shaft is a small barrel, and wound around this is a very close-fitting coil spring. One end of the spring simply lies against the barrel, but is not fastened to it. The other end is hooked around a fixed pin or otherwise firmly anchored.

The shaft being turned counterclockwise, friction between the close-hugging coils of the spring and the barrel will tend to open or unwind the coils. This allows the shaft to turn freely. But if the shaft is turned clockwise, friction at once tightens the coils around the barrel, wrapping them so firmly that the shaft cannot be turned.

An over-running clutch in an automobile overdrive resembles a roller bearing, but with one important difference. The outer race, which has a smooth concentric bore, is the driven member (Figure 20). The inner race is the driving member, but its outer surface is not circular. Instead, it has a number of evenly spaced sloping flats or cam ramps machined on it. Between the inside of the outer race and each of these ramps is a roller.

When driving torque is applied to the inner or cam race, it moves inside the rollers, wedging them between the ramps and the outer race so firmly that the whole clutch revolves as a unit. Thus torque is transmitted from the inner to the outer race.

If you lift your foot from the throttle, letting the engine idle while the car coasts, the outer race will overspeed the inner one. This rolls the rollers down to the lower part of the cam ramps, where they may revolve without wedging. The outer race therefore free-wheels independently of the inner one. But if the engine is revved up again, the inner race overtakes the outer one, the rollers are forced up the ramps, and once more wedge the outer race tightly.

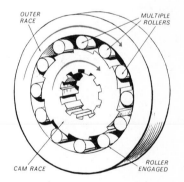

OUTER RACE

MULTIPLE ROLLERS

CAM RACE

ROLLER ENGAGED

Fig. 20. Over-running clutch.

IX

Steam and Hot Air Engines

Muscle, wind and water were for centuries the only known sources of power. The stupendous discovery that heat could be converted into physical energy vastly enlarged the world of the machine and ushered in modern technology.

That heat is a form of energy was by no means obvious. As late as the early 19th century, when heat engines were already hard at work, some thinkers attempted to explain heat in terms of something they called the caloric fluid. This was assumed to be able to penetrate any material, expand it, and even vaporize some substances. When heat appeared as a result of friction, the theorists explained, it was because caloric was being ground or squeezed out of the material. But all attempts to find, isolate or weigh the mysterious fluid failed—because of the imperfections of their instruments, the champions of caloric maintained.

A Massachusetts adventurer, Benjamin Thompson, who fled the country in revolutionary times because of Tory leanings, was the first to deal the caloric theory a severe blow. Winning a high post under the Elector of Bavaria, along with the title of Count Rumford, he was supervising the boring of cannon one day in 1798 when he noticed the intense heat generated. He found that this was independent of the amount of metal removed, that he could in fact generate more heat with a dull tool than with a sharp one even though almost no metal was cut. He rightly concluded that heat could not be caloric fluid or any other material, but must be generated by motion, or work. Surrounding the cannon with water, he measured its rise in temperature and the foot-pounds of work required to bring it about. Though the figure he arrived at was far too large, he had equated heat with energy.

Sir Humphrey Davy, James Joule and other physicists carried on from that idea, eventually showing that heat and work were indeed interchangeable forms of energy. Their findings established the basic theory of heat engines. But in this case science lagged far behind its application.

In fact, there was a lag of centuries if we accept Hero's aeolipile as the first simple heat engine (Figure 1). It was a hollow metal ball, mounted on two bearings so that it could turn. Fixed in it were two jets pointing in oppo-

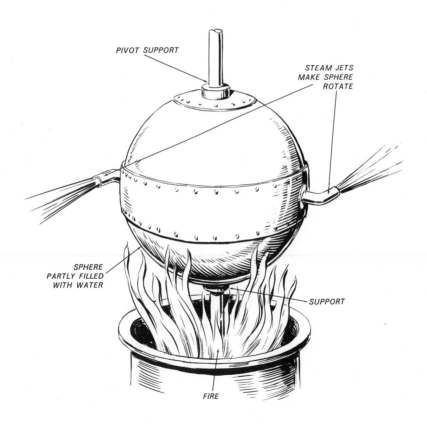

Fig. 1. Hero's reaction turbine.

site directions like half a swastika. The sphere was partly filled with water and placed over a fire. As the water boiled, steam issued from the jets, and the reaction pushed the jets backward, making the ball spin. But the device was no more than a temple toy and did no useful work. Hero is also credited with a device that opened temple doors by the expansion of heated air when a fire was kindled on the altar. Centuries later—in 1629—one Giovanni Branca left us a record of an impulse turbine—a vaned wheel made to spin by the velocity of a steam jet issuing from a stationary nozzle. This is an altogether different principle from that of Hero's aeolipile. Branca showed a stationary boiler, fancifully wrought in the shape of a man's bust, with the steam coming from his lips. He proposed that the turbine wheel could, through gearing, drive a pounding machine or stamp mill, but there is no proof that he ever built the contraption.

By the 17th century certain facts had been established about water and steam—that water when boiled forms about 1,700 times its volume of steam, that this enormous expansion can burst a gun barrel or a boiler if confined, and that if the steam in a closed vessel is condensed, it reverts to water, leaving a vacuum in the vessel.

You may find it amusing to demonstrate this last point. Get a clean screw-top can, put a little water in it, and let it boil on a stove with the cap off. When it is steaming well, *shut off the fire* and instantly put the cap on tightly. The can should now be filled only with steam. Move it under a cold water tap, and the can will be crumpled as if a giant hand had crushed it.

Condensation of the steam has left a partial vacuum inside the can. But atmospheric pressure outside the can remains normal—15 pounds per square inch. This is the giant hand that enfolds the can, and that began the Industrial Revolution.

In England at the end of the 17th century there was a severe problem of flooding in mines. Many were kept working only by constant pumping. Done by horses, this work was slow, laborious and expensive. About 1698 Captain Thomas Savery, a military engineer, devised a steam pump he called a fire engine, and for marketing dubbed the Miner's Friend. Like steam engines for decades to come, it did not use steam pressure directly, but the vacuum created by the steam when condensed. Steam was admitted to a closed, barrel-like container (Figure 2). Then, the steam valve being shut by hand, water was poured over the outside of the container. The resulting vacuum caused atmospheric pressure to push up water from the mine through a flap valve in the container. Now steam was again admitted (the flap valve was a one-way contraption that would not let the water out again). The steam pressure drove

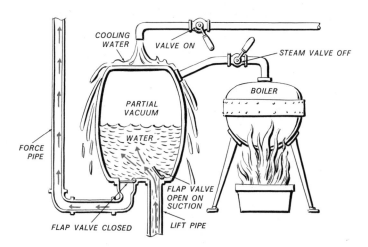

Fig. 2. Savery's steam pump.

the water out of the chamber, usually to a greater height, through another valve. This left the container filled with steam, ready for the next cooling cycle. There were about six per minute.

Because it was atmospheric pressure that pushed the water into the chamber, and this pressure could raise water no higher than 34 feet, the engine had to be located closer than that to the water level. But the height to which water could be lifted out of the chamber was dependent on the steam pressure used in that stage. Savery pushed boiler pressure up to 150 pounds per square inch (p.s.i.)—a fantastic figure for those days—and eventually used twin chambers working alternately to speed up the flow of water. The Miner's Friend worked successfully in a number of mines, though at such high pressure and with no safety valve it proved disastrously unfriendly on occasion.

CYLINDER AND PISTON

Apparently the cylinder and piston were known as far back as 250 B.C., the time of Archimedes. A contemporary of his, Otesibius, invented a force pump using a cylinder and piston. This ingeniously simple device (Figure 3) makes it possible to alter the volume inside a closed vessel, to create a vacuum by mechanical means, and to convert the expansion of a gas or the pressure of a fluid into mechanical force. It is the principle of the hypodermic needle, of the shock absorber, of the reciprocating pump—and the muscle of your automobile engine.

It kindled the fires of primitive people in southeast Asia and possibly some of the Pacific islands. Their "fire pump" was a few inches of bamboo, horn or wood with a hole in it, but closed at one end (Figure 4). In this cylin-

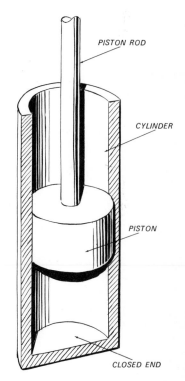

Fig. 3. Ancient force pump.

135

Fig. 4. Primitive pump used for starting a fire.

der was fitted a piston of similar material, having at its end a hollow that would hold a bit of kindling. With this in position, the piston was inserted and driven down hard with a blow of the hand. Suddenly compressed, the air inside became hot enough to set the kindling alight. Thus these people used *compression ignition*—the principle of the Diesel engine—to make fire. The fire pump was introduced in Europe early in the 19th century, where it was used only until the invention of the friction match in 1827.

The ball in a cannon is a free piston, and the cannon might be considered the first practical—if destructive—heat engine. From it the Dutch physicist Christopher Huyghens conceived the idea of a gunpowder engine. With commendable courage, he actually built an experimental one in 1680. Though a far cry from a working engine, it did successfully lift a piston. But the violent explosions soon damaged its parts. It is worth noting chiefly as the first effort to use a cylinder and piston to *generate* power rather than to pump air or water—tasks which require power.

Ten years later Denis Papin, a French Huguenot refugee working in England, repeated Huyghen's experiment with steam instead of gunpowder. He put a little water into the cylinder and a fire under it. The resulting steam raised the piston to the top of the cylinder. When the fire was removed and the steam condensed, on cooling, atmospheric pressure pushed the piston down again with more force than the steam had raised it. Small wonder that it was this part of the cycle that was considered capable of real work.

With great daring, Papin looked forward to pumping water, powering paddle steamers, and even driving horseless carriages with steam. In 1707 Papin, then living in Germany, actually built a paddle-wheel boat powered by a condensing steam engine. Big enough to carry two tons of cargo, the boat successfully negotiated a river. But local boatmen attacked him and destroyed his ship.

Though he went no further with a steam engine, Papin invented the safety valve—a device many of his successors ignored at their peril—and the pressure cooker, which we still use today.

Working on his idea, an English ironmonger and part-time preacher named Thomas Newcomen designed an atmospheric pumping engine for drawing water out of deep mines. Built in 1712 with the help of his partner John Calley, a plumber and glazier, the first Newcomen engine had a boiler made from an old brewer's kettle and a hefty cylinder 21 inches in diameter and 7 feet high (Figure 5).

The piston rod was attached to a walking beam by a chain that ran over an arch head, so the piston could pull but not push. A heavy pump rod and

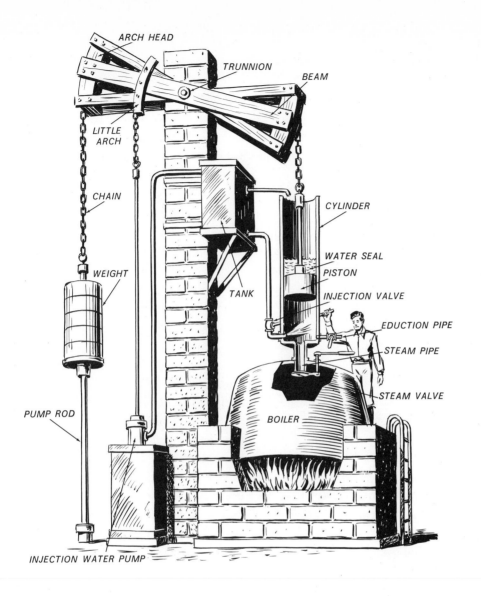

ARCH HEAD

TRUNNION

BEAM

LITTLE
ARCH

CHAIN

CYLINDER

WATER SEAL

PISTON

WEIGHT

INJECTION VALVE

TANK

EDUCTION PIPE

STEAM PIPE

STEAM VALVE

PUMP ROD

BOILER

INJECTION WATER PUMP

Fig. 5. Newcomen engine.

weight chained to the arch head at the other end of the beam pulled the piston up on the return stroke. It was during this that steam was admitted under the piston. As it reached the top, the steam valve was closed and another opened that sprayed cold water directly into the cylinder—a much more efficient means of condensing the steam than pouring water over the outside as Savery had done.

As the steam condensed, it left a partial vacuum under the piston.

Atmospheric pressure (15 pounds per square inch of piston surface) then drove the piston down, hauling up the pump rod at the other end of the walking beam with its burden of water. When the piston reached bottom, the injection valve was closed and the steam valve reopened. The valves were at first worked by hand, the engine making only 12 strokes per minute. In that time it raised 50 gallons of water a distance of 156 feet. One contemporary writer declared that the engine was made self-acting "by the ingenuity of Humphrey Potter, a boy employed to mind the engine, who contrived a series of catches and strings worked from the beam, by which the several valves were opened and closed in due order." There is no proof of this Tom Sawyerish story, but somebody watching the regular sequence of engine events was bound to hit on the idea of automating the valves sooner or later.

The company Newcomen formed was successful, and it controlled the making of steam engines until 1733. The following from a 1716 issue of the *London Gazette* gives a fascinating insight into the business and promotion practices of that pre-Madison Avenue day.

> Whereas the invention for raising water by the impellant force of fire, authorized by parliament, is lately brought to the greatest perfection, and all sorts of mines, etc., may be thereby drained and water raised to any height with more ease and less charge than by any other methods hitherto used, as is sufficiently demonstrated by diverse engines of this invention now at work in the several counties of Stafford, Worwich, Cornwall and Flint. These are, therefore to give notice that if any person shall be desirous to treat with the proprietors for such engines, attendance will be given for that purpose every Wednesday at the Sword Blade Coffee House in Birchin Lane, London.

Machining problems abounded, the most important centering around the cylinder and piston. It should be noted that the round form of these was the only practical one, for it could be generated by even a primitive lathe or boring machine. Any other shape would have been far more difficult, and any involving corners would have offered insoluble problems of sealing (which we are only now solving for the Wankel and other rotary engines).

It was hard enough to make a round cylinder fit a round piston with some measure of steam tightness. Cylinders were likely to vary in bore (internal diameter) at various places along their length, so that if the piston fitted well at one point, it might be deplorably loose or so tight as to bind at some other. A piston was considered a good fit if it came within one eighth of an inch of fitting the cylinder bore everywhere. A groove around the piston was packed with rope, oakum, tallow or similar material to keep steam from blowing past it. Newcomen provided a pipe to keep the top of the piston flooded with water as an added seal against leakage.

Despite all difficulties, the Newcomen engine worked wonders in reclaiming drowned mines. One built in 1739 to pump water out of a French coal mine from a depth of 90 feet had a 30-inch cylinder and a 9-foot stroke. In 48 hours it did work that had previously taken 50 men and 20 horses, working in shifts around the clock, a full week.

When the Newcomen patents expired, others refined his design. John Smeaton brought it to its peak. Though the cylinder boring machine he invented in 1769 was grossly inaccurate (John Wilkinson made a much better one in 1776), Smeaton's engines were the best built up to that time. In 1775 Catherine II of Russia commissioned him to construct a huge engine for pumping the water out of the Kronstadt dry docks. Previously this had been done by windmills 100 feet high, and the task took a full year. Smeaton's engine pumped the docks dry in two weeks!

THE MAGIC CONDENSER

But at the height of its power, the Newcomen engine was already doomed by a young Glasgow instrument maker, James Watt. In 1765 he was asked to repair a model Newcomen engine used at the University of Glasgow for instruction. The caloric theory was then very much in vogue; much research on it was being done at this seat of learning. Watt, who came from a family of mathematicians and teachers, frequently discussed the current theories with knowledgeable men of the day.

His work on the model engine—which he found needed a bigger boiler—set him thinking about the way heat was used in Newcomen engines. These were gluttons for fuel; the bigger they were, the more heat (in the form of steam) was necessary to bring the cylinder, the piston, and the sealing water on top of the piston to steam temperature at each upstroke. In cooling all these parts on the next part of the cycle, as was necessary to produce the vacuum, all this heat had to be thrown away. This wasteful alternate heating and cooling continued so long as the engine was running.

By experiment and calculation, Watt determined that only one third of the steam used was doing useful work. Then came his inspiration—why not use a *separate* vessel for condensing the steam, with a valve between it and the steam cylinder? This valve would be opened when the piston was on its downward power stroke, the steam rushing out of the working cylinder into the vacuum formed in the separate vessel, which Watt called the condenser. This way the cylinder would remain hot, while the condenser could be kept cool at all times by injected cold water to produce the necessary vacuum. To get rid of the condensation water, injection water and stray air that would otherwise accumulate in the condenser, Watt used a vacuum pump developed some years before.

It worked admirably, and these new engines, built by the firm of Boulton and Watt, were generally sold on a guarantee of substantial fuel savings. Eventually Watt tried applying steam to the top of the piston as well as to the bottom. Though at first he meant this top-admitted steam only to keep the cylinder hot, he later exhausted it to the condenser as well. This made the engine double-acting—that is, power was produced on both the upstroke and the downstroke of the piston.

With the piston alternately pushing and pulling, the chain linking the piston rod to the walking beam became useless and had to be superseded by rigid members. In this way Watt's straight-line motion came into being. These and other engines of the day, with their many links and pivots, may seem quaintly grotesque to us. But there were practical reasons for such construction, not the least of which was the difficulty of machining long straight surfaces true for the crosshead guides that later became almost universal. Also, the walking beam was a simple means of transferring power from the upper end of a vertical cylinder to a pump rod some distance down in a mine.

The passage from an "atmospheric" engine to a true steam engine was therefore completed in easy stages. Newcomen engines worked on a pressure of something less than 15 p.s.i. on top of the piston (less because the vacuum was never perfect). If more power was wanted, the only way to get it was to use a bigger cylinder and piston. But with steam pressure (instead of atmospheric pressure) working on both sides of the piston, maximum working pressure was limited only by what the boiler could safely generate—and often the adverb was ignored. Even Watt's modest 6 p.s.i. boilers would, when the other side of the piston was valved to the vacuum of the condenser, exert a working force of something close to 21 p.s.i. on the piston. Yet this was only the beginning of efficient power production.

In 1782 Watt proposed closing the inlet valve early, and letting the steam already in the cylinder continue working for the rest of the stroke by its own expansion. This was thermodynamically a sound proposition, though Watt himself never made the most of it. To get the full benefit of early cutoff, he would have had to go to higher boiler pressures. This he refused to do. It remained for others to exploit the dramatic possibilities of high-pressure steam that made possible the steamboat, the steam bus, and the steam locomotive.

ENGINES THAT TURNED SHAFTS

Some naive folk, eager to have rotary power for running mills and other machinery, suggested using the steam engine to pump water to a height, from which it could fall to turn a water wheel. Some such installations were probably built. (Strangely enough, something like this is now being done to "store" alternating current.) But Watt realized that the engine itself could and should provide rotary motion, and set about building one that would.

To convert the back-and-forth movement of the piston rod into that of a turning shaft, he proposed to use the crank, a venerable device even then. A multiple crankshaft for a four-cylinder pump had been proposed as far back as 1589, so he anticipated no trouble. But James Pickard, one of his workmen, went to a competitor with the idea and obtained a patent on it.

Enraged by this, Watt devised and patented not one, but several methods of converting reciprocating into rotary motion. The one he finally used was the sun-and-planet motion described in Chapter 8. As the gears of that time were crude, being cast instead of machined, they were not only noisy but consumed an excessive amount of power. Eventually Watt and other engineers went back to the simple and effective crank mechanism.

Watt's contributions to steam engineering did not end with engines. To find out what was happening inside the cylinder at every instant, he devised the indicator. This was a small cylinder connected to one end of the engine cylinder. Inside it was a small spring-loaded piston, which rose and fell against the spring tension as steam pressure inside the engine cylinder varied. The indicator piston was linked to a stylus that drew a continuous line on a revolving paper drum, so plotting a curve that showed cylinder pressure at all points of the piston's travel.

Watt also adapted the fly-ball governor (which had long been used to control millstone spacing automatically) to keep his engines running at a uniform speed despite variations in the boiler supply. As engine revs went up, the balls flew farther apart. Through linkage they actuated a valve that cut down the steam going to the engine. As the engine slowed, the balls dropped and opened the valve again. You have probably seen the cousin of this device on hand-wound spring phonographs.

A mercury steam pressure gauge, and the poppet valve (used in every four-cycle car engine today) were also Watt's inventions. He even had the courage to establish a standard method of rating engine power, which had commonly been expressed in terms of the number of horses a given engine would replace. But as a horse might be large or small, sick or well, there was a wide margin for misjudgment.

Finding that a husky draft horse could exert 22,000 foot-pounds of energy per minute, Watt added 50 percent for good measure and set 33,000 foot-pounds per minute as the equivalent of one horsepower for his engines. It has become the standard of the world.

The slide valve is credited to William Murdock, one of Watt's assistants. It was also called the D valve, because in cross section it resembles the letter D. For a long time it was almost universally used for both stationary and locomotive engines. You can recognize it by the presence of a boxy structure on the cylinder. This is the steam chest, which is connected to the boiler through the throttle and steam pipe.

Inside the steam chest, the cylinder has a flat valve face with three holes (ports) in it, as shown in Figure 6. Through passages drilled in the metal, the two end holes communicate with the two ends of the cylinder. The middle hole leads to the outer air or to the condenser, if the engine has one.

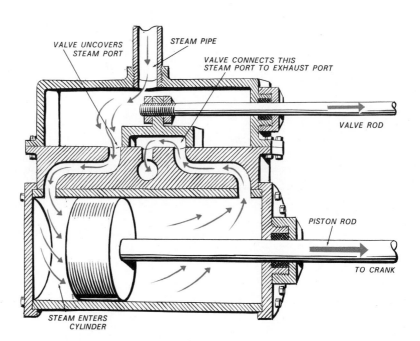

Fig. 6. Murdock's D-valve engine.

The valve itself is a rectangular piece with a recess in its underside, and a fork or other means on the other side by which it can be linked to the valve rod. This rod passes through a hole and gland in the steam chest.

When the valve is in the position shown, it covers (and therefore connects) the exhaust port and that steam port leading to the bottom end of the cylinder. But it uncovers the steam port to the top end. As the steam chest and valve face are exposed to boiler pressure, steam enters the top of the cylinder and drives the piston down, while exhaust steam escapes from the other end.

As the connecting rod and crank turn the engine shaft, an eccentric moves the valve rod back. When the piston has reached the bottom of the cylinder, the valve recess is covering the top steam port and uncovering the bottom one. Steam now enters below the piston, pushing it up, while exhaust steam from the top escapes.

Correct proportioning of the valve parts can provide early cutoff, making the steam do extra work by expanding in the cylinder. It is also possible to admit steam a little before the piston ends each stroke, so cushioning its reversal and getting a quick start on the next power stroke.

Why water explodes. Several engineers realized that higher steam pressure was the way to more efficient engines. Yet Watt's fear of high pressure was well founded. Little was known of the strength of materials in his day. Boiler plates were often of questionable quality, boiler construction more experimental than scientific.

In an open pot, at sea level where barometric pressure is about 15 p.s.i., water boils at 212 degrees F. and can get no hotter. Supply more heat, and it simply boils away faster. Where atmospheric pressure is even lower—on a mountaintop for instance—water boils at a lower temperature. At some altitudes boiling water isn't hot enough to cook eggs or vegetables properly—unless you use a pressure cooker.

This changes the situation by maintaining a pressure higher than the atmosphere's. When you put a tight lid on a pot, the steam pressure inside climbs. As it does, you have to supply more heat—the water must be made hotter—to keep it boiling. The water in a pressure cooker can therefore be made hot enough for cooking foods at high altitudes.

Your car takes advantage of this fact for another reason. Today's pressurized cooling systems have a tight cap that lets vapor pressure build up. Under that pressure, the cooling water will not boil at 212 degrees, but go to 240 degrees or more before boiling. The engine runs warmer and, because the water needn't be cooled as much, the radiator can be smaller.

When an engine overheats, some drivers stop and take off the radiator cap. This is a good way to invite scalding, for if there's any water left, it usually spouts like a Yellowstone geyser. Why? Because it is already superheated beyond 212 degrees. When you remove the cap, pressure in the system at once falls to atmospheric, and that superhot water boils up all of a sudden. (If it is so hot that it is already boiling under pressure, it boils that much faster). At best, you're likely to lose considerable water, so it is advisable to wait for a time, and first release the cap only to the first detent.

In a steam boiler with 150 p.s.i. pressure, the water must be heated to 356 degrees to keep boiling and making steam. Water that hot represents a lot of potential energy. What happens if a boiler seam gives way with such super-heated water inside?

As the pressure above it suddenly drops to that of the atmosphere, all that water is suddenly far beyond its normal boiling point. Immediately it flashes into steam—an enormous amount of steam. It is this instant, explosive boiling that is the catastrophic power behind a boiler explosion.

The flue boiler. Nevertheless, higher steam pressure had to come. One of the men who knew this was Oliver Evans. An American farm boy, at fourteen he apprenticed himself to a wagonmaker, studying mathematics and mechanics in his spare time. Seeing some other boys explode a plugged gun barrel by boiling water inside it set him thinking about the possibilities of steam power. He made some experiments and outlined various improvements on steam engines.

In 1786 he petitioned two state governments for the exclusive right to apply these improvements not only to engines, but to steam carriages. The legislators laughed his petitions out of the house.

Blocked in that direction, Evans turned to stationary engines. In 1802 he spent his life savings to build a small high-pressure engine in Philadelphia. As important as the engine itself was the boiler he built for it. Its barrel was horizontal, and through it ran a horizontal flue or pipe. The combustion gases (and heat) had to travel first around and under the boiler to the back end of this flue, then through it for the whole length of the boiler again, before going up the chimney. It was an efficient design, similar to the famous Scotch marine boiler of later years.

The engine cylinder had a bore of 6 inches, and the stroke (length of piston travel) was 18 inches. Instead of Watt's straight-line motion, Evans used a walking beam pivoted on a swinging link at one end (Figure 7). The other end, to which the piston and connecting rod were attached, could thus move vertically to accommodate the straight-line motion of the piston rod. The beam's odd loping motion caused this to be known as the grasshopper action. It was later used on some locomotives.

Being able to demonstrate a successful engine, Evans secured backing and eventually saw his engines working from Connecticut to Ohio. Unfortunately he dropped the condenser, exhausting steam directly into the air.

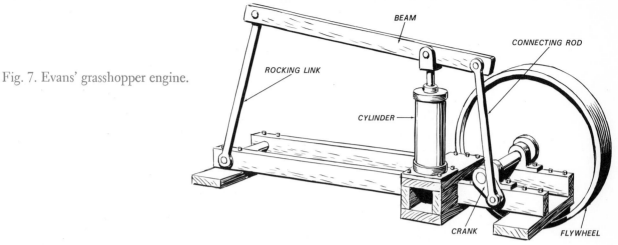

Fig. 7. Evans' grasshopper engine.

Labels on figure: ROCKING LINK, BEAM, CONNECTING ROD, CYLINDER, CRANK, FLYWHEEL

Though this lowered the cost of his engines, it lost much of the advantage they gained from high pressure. His last big engine, made for a waterworks, used steam at 200 p.s.i. pressure.

Another engineer to use high pressure was Richard Trevithick, a young Englishman who had grown up with the Newcomen engine and saw ways to improve even Watt's. In 1800 he built an ingenious double-acting engine, but like Evans he omitted the condenser and so secured only part of his gains. In fact, the engine exhausted at such high pressure that it became known as the "puffer" type.

The compound engine. Jonathan Hornblower in 1781 suggested an important improvement in the true steam engine. As steam expands in driving the piston, it loses heat and cools the cylinder. On the next stroke, incoming steam is chilled by the cooler cylinder walls and thus loses some of its energy. Why not, suggested Hornblower, let the steam expand only part way in one cylinder, then on exhausting lead it to a second, larger cylinder where its lower pressure will do more work as it expands the rest of the way? Expanding in two steps, it would lose less heat in each step and therefore cool the cylinder less.

Though he built a compound engine that worked, Hornblower lacked the data to size the cylinders to best advantage. An associate later worked out a more successful design. But Watt claimed infringement of his own patents, and in 1799 won a long lawsuit over Hornblower, who was ruined in the process. Since then compounding has been important both in reciprocating engines and in steam turbines. It had, however, to await the use of high-pressure steam to demonstrate its full value.

145

STEAM FOR TRANSPORTATION

Joseph Hulls, an Englishman, in 1736 proposed a paddle-wheel boat with a Newcomen engine, but if it was ever built it must have been badly underpowered. In 1786 William Symington installed a Watt engine in a boat that reached a speed of 5 m.p.h. A year later an American, John Fitch, operated a ship with steam-powered oars on the Delaware River. The signers of the Constitution came to see it, but the boat could not carry enough cargo to be a commercial success.

Symington's second steamboat did 7 m.p.h. His third, the Charlotte Dundas, in 1802 towed two 70-ton barges against heavy winds. It had a double-acting engine and a condenser, driving a paddle wheel in a well between double sterns. But the shareholders of the canal in which the boat was to work feared it would damage the banks, and the Charlotte Dundas was taken out of service.

Robert Fulton, in launching his famous Clermont in 1807, added nothing new to the steam engine. He used a standard Boulton and Watt model. But from then on steam shipping developed rapidly. By 1819 the Savannah, aided by sail, had made the first Atlantic crossing from America to England.

Shallow-draft steamboats—little more at first than barges with boilers and engines on them—opened trade lanes between north and south in the burgeoning United States. Timid passengers took reassurance from the words LOW PRESSURE displayed in huge letters on some of these vessels, but boiler disasters were all too common. Races between rival boats often invited such, especially when in the heat of the contest a captain threw pitch, turpentine, tallow or other highly combustible cargo into the fires.

By 1840 the Cunard liner Brittania, with a one-cylinder engine developing 740 horsepower at a boiler pressure of only 9 p.s.i., began service between the new world and the old. The maritime age of steam was under way.

In 1769 a French artillery officer, Nicholas Cugnot, was first to apply engine power to a wheel. It was literally a single wheel, the boiler and engine being built above it. There were two rear wheels, but the vehicle was so cumbersome and overbalanced by its machinery that it tipped over almost at once, after attaining a speed of only 3 m.p.h. Oliver Evans in 1804 built a curious steam-powered amphibian, a barge on wheels, that ran on Philadelphia streets and on the Delaware River.

Some early engineers worked on both road vehicles and rail engines. William Murdock built a model locomotive in 1784, and a model steam carriage two years later. Trevithick in 1803 operated a full-size steam car, and in

1804 had a little steam locomotive running on a Welsh railroad. It had a return-flue boiler like Evans', but it was Trevithick's idea to lead the exhaust steam up the stack. This induced a sharp draft that made the fire burn fiercely; it was an important development in the steam locomotive. Trevithick was also the first to couple all the wheels, so that the full weight of the vehicle helped obtain traction on the rails.

For his steam car, which operated at a boiler pressure of 60 p.s.i., Trevithick suggested a gearbox by which ratios could be changed. (It was later proved, by the success of the Stanley, the Doble, and other steam cars, that the characteristics of the steam engine made such a gearbox unnecessary.)

Coaching was the way to travel in those days; a good horse-drawn stage could over long trips average 12 to 15 miles per hour. What more could you ask? It was in fact almost two decades before Trevithick's car had any successors. In 1822 Julius Griffith built a steam carriage (with a gear shift) but it worked only a short time before the boiler failed.

Others wrought to better effect. Sir Goldsworthy Gurney in 1827 built a steam carriage in which two cylinders were directly coupled to the rear axle. A water-tube boiler—one consisting of a number of interconnected tubes round which the fire played—supplied steam at 100 p.s.i. A fan created a forced draft for the fire. Instead of being exhausted to the atmosphere after its work in the engine, steam was channeled into the boiler-water tank, so transferring its heat even as it was being condensed for re-use. Though it produced no vacuum in this way, this was probably the first use of a feed-water heater, a standard fuel saver on later engines.

Gurney's first coach achieved a speed of 15 m.p.h. carrying eighteen passengers, and operated around London for two years. By 1831 other Gurney steam carriages were making three trips daily over a 9-mile suburban route.

Walter Hancock, also of England, designed and operated efficient steam carriages. He used a vertical engine coupled to the rear axle by a chain. One of his vehicles reached 20 m.p.h. and traveled a total of 4,000 miles between London and its suburbs.

Charcoal was the favored fuel, as it burns hot with little smoke, though cinders were often troublesome. The carriages were 15 to 20 feet long and weighed up to 2 tons. There are tales of their reaching speeds of 30 m.p.h. on occasions.

Stagecoach proprietors were bitter enemies of steam transport. They succeeded in getting road tolls for powered vehicles raised to ten times that for horsedrawn ones, and sometimes blocked the highways, an act which caused at least one boiler explosion and five deaths. In 1865 the British Parliament was induced to pass the Red Flag Act, which required a man to walk ahead of any steam road vehicle with a red flag in hand, so delaying the advent of the automobile.

The Ackermann arrangement. Those early steam hot-rods used the pivoted forecarriage standard on horse-drawn vehicles. The two front wheels were mounted on a rigid axle with a vertical pivot at its center, and connected by a chain to the steering shaft. When the driver turned the wheel or tiller bar, the entire forecarriage swung about, just as on a child's coaster wagon. If one front wheel hit a rock at road speed, the shock could be severe enough to twist the forecarriage out of the driver's control.

Today's automobile has each front wheel on its own stub axle, which pivots on a vertical kingpin. That kingpin and stub axle idea was first proposed by a Frenchman in 1714, developed further by a German in 1818, and patented for him in England by a coach builder named Ackermann. The system bears his name today. One of its advantages is that the two wheels, linked by a tie rod, can follow slightly different radiuses to let the outer wheel trace a larger curve than the inner one on turns.

Those early steam coaches had no differential; on turns the two powered wheels battled it out between them, each doing its share of skidding. The differential invented by Pecquer in 1828 was first applied in England in 1833. The first four-wheel drive, however, with bevel gears powering both front and rear axles, dates back to 1825.

The Rocket and the Novelty. George Stephenson, son of a colliery fireman, early showed such aptitude for repairing Watt engines that in 1814 he was able to get funds for building a "traveling engine." He overcame the problem of stalling on dead center, which had plagued earlier locomotive builders, by setting the cranks of his two cylinders 90 degrees apart. Thus one was always at midstroke when the other was helpless at one end of its stroke. His engine pulled a 30-ton train at 4 m.p.h. and established Stephenson as a leading engineer of his day despite the fact that he had little formal education.

The directors of the Liverpool and Manchester Railway, which they had meant to operate by horse power, were reluctantly persuaded to offer a prize for the best locomotive meeting their own conditions. Stephenson readied his entry, an odd machine weighing four tons, brave in yellow and black. It had a horizontal boiler with a high stack to induce good draft. Two cylinders placed high near the back of the boiler drove the two larger front wheels through diagonal piston and connecting rods. The resulting vertical

The Enterprise omnibus was one of the first road vehicles powered by steam. It was built by Walter Hancock for a London firm and began regular passenger runs in 1833.

component of the drive forces is said to have given the engine an undesirable rocking action, but this is not what gave the locomotive its name.

One of the many bitter opponents of steam locomotives, indignant at the idea of being hurled across the countryside at 15 m.p.h. or more, declared he would as soon be fired off on a rocket. Tongue in cheek, Stephenson named his engine the Rocket. He might have been amused to learn that today's traveler, finding more and more long-distance trains stricken from the time table, must often do what Stephenson's heckler would not—ride a jet plane that is first cousin to a rocket.

One of Stephenson's competitors in the famous Rainhill Trials deserves special mention. He was a young Swede, John Ericsson, who had already made two memorable contributions to steam engineering. One was his steam-powered fire engine, capable of playing streams of water on the highest towers in London. Only hand pumps had been available before, and often sadly inadequate. Conservative to the death, the London Fire Brigade and the city's insurance companies rejected Ericsson's engine. It was, however, eventually adopted in many large cities.

149

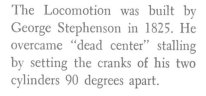

The Locomotion was built by George Stephenson in 1825. He overcame "dead center" stalling by setting the cranks of his two cylinders 90 degrees apart.

Stephenson's Rocket, built in 1829, had two high cylinders driving the front wheels through diagonal pistons and connecting rods. It did 24 m.p.h., with light load, pulled 17 tons at 10 m.p.h.

The Novelty was built by John Ericsson to compete with the Rocket. With water tube boiler and forced draft, its cylinders were at axle height so the rods moved horizontally.

One of the first locomotives to use a horizontal boiler was the Experiment, built in 1832 by John B. Jervis for the Mohawk and Hudson Railroad line.

The express passenger locomotive Lightening had two large and two small drive wheels and four pilot wheels. It hauled in 1849 a train of eight cars 16 miles and 88 feet in 13 minutes and 21 seconds.

The President hauled passengers and freight in the 1850s. This ten-wheeler was a forerunner of modern steam locomotives and an example of the work of designer and builder Walter McQueen.

The William H. Vanderbilt plied the rails in 1880, was the first locomotive on the New York Central and Hudson River Railroad to be equipped with air brakes.

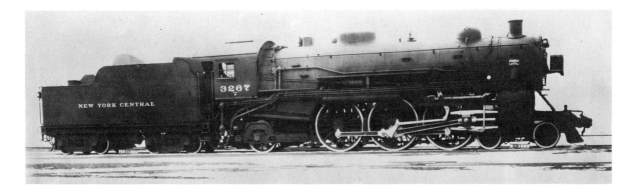

From 1904 well into the 1920s, the Pacific locomotive with its high driver wheels chuffed up 2,000 horsepower to pull the average 10 passenger trains of its day. Later Pacifics were beefed up to carry much greater loads.

The great Hudson was the workhorse of the New York Central Railroad during the 1930s and set new records in safety, efficiency and power in the passenger service for which it was built.

The Mohawk 3000, with its set of eight 72-inch driving wheels, one of the giant powerhouses that carried heavy loads in both freight and passenger service in the United States during the Second World War.

Commissioned to install an engine and boiler of his own design in a paddle-wheel steamer, Ericsson invented the surface condenser. Without this, marine steam power could scarcely have sailed out of sight of land, for a ship could carry only a limited amount of fresh water for its boiler. It was vital to condense exhaust steam and so use boiler water over and over.

But the old method of spraying cold water into the condenser was impossible at sea, for the only cooling water available was salt, and its contamination would have ruined the boilers in short order. Ericsson sent the exhaust steam into a grid of copper pipes, and circulated cold sea water around these, so condensing the steam without admixture of salt.

This was the man who, when twenty-six years old, heard belatedly of the locomotive competition and decided to enter one of his own. With incredible energy, he and his partner John Braithwaite designed and built it in seven weeks.

Named the Novelty, and weighing only half as much as the Rocket, it had a water-tube boiler and forced draft. Its cylinders were at axle height, so that the rods moved horizontally. Running light the first day of the trials, it reached a speed of 30 m.p.h.

The Rocket did 24 m.p.h., pulled 17 tons at 10 m.p.h., and in a later test with lighter loading covered 12 miles in 53 minutes.

But the Novelty countered by pulling 6 tons at over 20 m.p.h., and as a final fillip proceeded to set the world's speed record. Running light, Ericsson and his partner covered a mile in 53 seconds—a speed of over 67 m.p.h. The directors gave the prize to the Rocket.

LOCOMOTIVES IN AMERICA

In 1811, Colonel John Stevens petitioned the New Jersey legislature for a railroad charter. As the war of 1812 intervened, it was not until 1825 that he was able to build a demonstration locomotive, which he ran on a circular track on his own Hoboken, New Jersey, estate. It had a vertical boiler and a one-cylinder horizontal engine. Another American, Horatio Allen, at the age of twenty-five was sent to England to study railways and buy four English locomotives. Only one was actually run here—the Stourbridge Lion. Its weight of seven tons was deemed unsafe for the trestle on the railroad it was intended for, though Allen defied the danger by driving it across on its demonstration run.

Its wheels were hardwood, with iron tires. Two vertical cylinders at the back of the boiler drove the four wheels (which were coupled with rods) through grasshopper beams. Parts of this engine are now in the National Museum at Washington.

Peter Cooper built an interesting experimental locomotive that became legendary for its race with a horse. Justifiably dubbed the Tom Thumb, the little engine had a single cylinder of 3½ inch bore and 14 inches stroke. Its vertical boiler had gun barrels for tubes, with a belt-driven blower to provide good draft. On August 28, 1830, pulling a car with directors of the Baltimore and Ohio Railroad on board, it became the first locomotive to haul passengers on this side of the Atlantic.

During the demonstration, Cooper challenged a horse-drawn car on a parallel track to race. The Tom Thumb stayed well ahead until its blower belt began to slip. The fire diminishing, steam fell off and the horse came in first.

Matthias Baldwin, a watchmaker, in 1831 had a miniature locomotive running indoors in the Philadelphia Museum. Also in that year, the Baltimore and Ohio Railroad offered a $4,000 prize for the best American locomotive. This was won by the York, built by Phineas Davis, of York, Pennsylvania. It had an upright boiler with a vertical cylinder on each side. The con rods drove to the center of the coupling rods joining the wheels on each side, an unusual arrangement. The engine hauled the York express between Baltimore and Ellicott Mills, Maryland, a distance of 13 miles, in one hour.

The first locomotive to pull a train in America was the Best Friend of Charleston, built at the West Point Foundry, which began running in December 1830. On the following June 17, it earned the dubious distinction of being the first American locomotive to have a boiler explosion. The fireman, annoyed by the sound of escaping steam, had held down the safety valve. This engine had a vertical boiler and slightly inclined 6-by-16-inch cylinder set inboard of the frame. Rebuilt after the explosion, it went back into service under the apt name Phoenix.

The success of his museum locomotive enabled Baldwin to win an order for a full-sized one from the Philadelphia, Germantown and Norristown Railroad, which had up to then used horses. He tested the engine on November 23, 1832, covering 6 miles at 28 m.p.h.

This locomotive, Old Ironsides, was of the English "Planet" style, with an oak frame outside the wheels and the cylinders within, driving to cranks on the rear axle, which had 54-inch wheels. Both axles were sprung, the axle boxes sliding in hornplates fastened outside the frame. The boiler was horizontal.

Receiving only $3,500 of the $4,000 agreed upon, Baldwin vowed to quit locomotive building. But he was not to remain a watchmaker. A year later he began his second locomotive, and by 1835 had built his eleventh, this with the outside cylinders that were to become common in America, though English engines kept inside connected cylinders right down to present times.

The piston valve. As steam pressure went up, it was found that it held the slide valve so tightly on its working face as to cause undue friction as well as wear. This led eventually to the development of the piston valve, which is essentially a D valve in the round. The steam chest is a small cylinder alongside the working cylinder. The valve proper is in the shape of a spool—or a rod with two fixed pistons spaced somewhat apart on it. Usually fitted with rings or packing, these pistons act like the surfaces outside the recess of a slide valve, covering and uncovering the steam ports. Instead of being small slots, the ports could be annular, so offering a larger passage area through which more steam could pass in a given time.

Usually steam was admitted between the valve pistons, this "inside admission" being the opposite of the usual D valve arrangement (Figure 8). Outside admission, with the exhaust between the pistons, was also possible. In either case, steam pressure was equal all around the piston valve and so exerted no pressure against the sliding surfaces.

Valve gears. Such factors as lap, exhaust clearance, lead and cutoff made valve timing and the gear that controls it the subject of much invention. Stephenson devised a valve gear with two eccentrics set 180 degrees apart, and connected to the two ends of a slotted, curved line. One eccentric was oriented to drive the locomotive forward, the other to run it backward. The valve rod ended in a block that could slide in the link slot, the link being raised

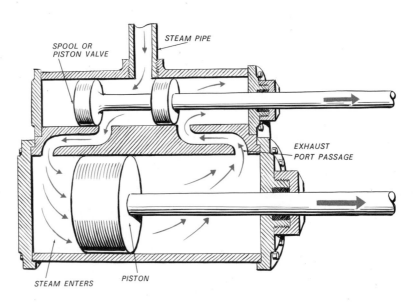

Fig. 8. Piston valve.

or lowered through a bell crank by the engine driver. With the link down, the forward eccentric actuated the valve. When the link was raised, the reverse eccentric governed its action.

If the link was raised only enough to bring the block to its center, the valve rod would not move at all, even though both ends of the link did. By moving the link only part way to this neutral position, the engineer could reduce the travel of the valve and so control steam admission and cutoff, saving fuel when the load was light or the track level. On starting, and on inclines, the valve gear could be set to feed steam for most of the stroke and so develop maximum torque. You may remember the deep-throated exhaust blasts of a steam locomotive picking up its load or hauling a heavy train up-grade, compared to the light, staccato puffs of one rolling easily at high speed.

Stephenson's link motion was one of a number, among these being Joy's, Baker's and Walschaert's. In the latter, the eccentrics were replaced by a return crank outside the crankpin and drive rod. Valve action was controlled not only by the return crank, but in part by a link to the crosshead.

Among other advances in locomotives was the superheater—a loop of steam pipes passing through the fire, which heated the steam as it passed from the boiler to the engine. This increase in temperature was also an increase in energy, and greatly bettered efficiency. Boiler pressure went up to 300 p.s.i. in later engines, and for greater drawbar pull the number of drive wheels was increased (although an eight-wheeler had been built as early as 1834). The decapod (an engine with ten drive wheels plus two on a pony truck) was not uncommon. Though the condenser proved impractical, some experiments were made with compound locomotives. Eventually roller bearings were applied.

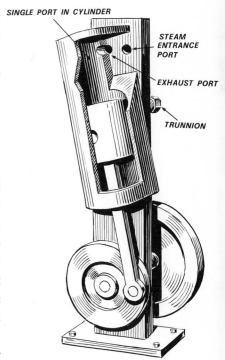

SINGLE PORT IN CYLINDER

STEAM ENTRANCE PORT

EXHAUST PORT

TRUNNION

STEAM ENGINE CURIOSITIES

The oscillating-cylinder engine (Figure 9) is charmingly simple and outrageously inefficient. The cylinder has attached to it a block with a flat face and a pivot pin or trunnion on which it can swing or oscillate. The face has a single steam port connecting with the closed end of the cylinder. In the simplest single-acting engines of this kind, the piston is very long so that through the piston rod it can impart an oscillating movement to the cylinder without undue wear or leakage. The piston rod is fitted directly to the crank. As the shaft turns, the piston moves in and out while oscillating the cylinder from side to side.

The port block also has a flat face, against which that of the cylinder

Fig. 9. Oscillating-cylinder engine.

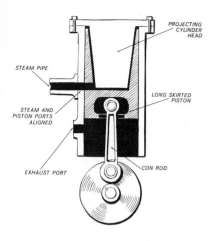

Fig. 10. Valveless automatic engine.

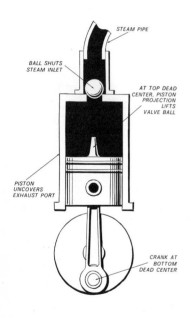

Fig. 11. Ball-valve automatic engine.

makes a steamtight fit. In the port block are a steam and an exhaust port, at the same radius from the cylinder pivot as the cylinder port, and far enough apart so that the latter cannot bridge them.

As the crank moves past top dead center (t.d.c.) the cylinder port starts moving over the steam port, and is fully aligned with it when the crank is 90 degrees past t.d.c. Just past bottom dead center, the cylinder port starts to register with the exhaust port, being wide open to it at 270 degrees.

By closing the other end of the cylinder and providing a gland for the piston rod to pass through, as well as a second set of ports, the engine can be made double acting. Many ingenious schemes were tried to improve the oscillating engine, including eccentrics to actuate auxiliary valves, and ported plates between the cylinder and port block to effect better steam cutoff as well as reversing. Nowadays you see an oscillating cylinder chiefly on toy engines, aquarium aerators, and small oil pumps. (Most steam engines, if themselves driven, will pump air, water and other gases and fluids.) Yet there was a day when huge multicylindered oscillating engines propelled steamers.

Automatic steam engines were designed to run without attention for such work as pumping and generating electricity. Though many were of conventional design, the odd one in Figure 10 is intriguing because it has no valves. As the curious trunk piston reached top dead center, a slot in its side was fully open to a steam port in the cylinder wall. Steam entered above the piston, pushing it down, whereupon the long piston skirt closed the steam port. At bottom dead center the piston port uncovered an exhaust port.

Another type of automatic engine had a valve seat in the head, closed by a loose ball. Steam pressure above the ball (and sometimes a loose plug in addition) held the ball firmly on its seat (Figure 11). But as the piston came up to t.d.c., a projection on its top nudged the ball off its seat, instantly admitting steam. Near the bottom of its stroke, the piston uncovered an exhaust slot in the cylinder side.

A moment's thought may engender a doubt as to how these engines could run at all, for plainly steam began to enter just as many degrees *before* t.d.c. as it was cut off after t.d.c. Why didn't they try to run backwards until, coming up on the other side, they again admitted steam trying to turn them back the other way?

But run they did, and at high speed. In fact, such an engine would run with equal facility in whatever direction it was started. High revs were essential to their operation, for it was the kinetic energy stored in their flywheels that carried them past that back impulse of early steam transmission. They could not "lug," or labor at low speeds, as slide-valve engines could, but had rather the

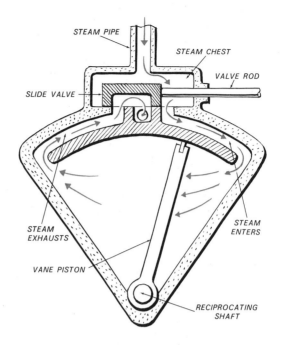

Fig. 12. Oscillating-piston engine.

STEAM PIPE

STEAM CHEST

VALVE ROD

SLIDE VALVE

STEAM EXHAUSTS

STEAM ENTERS

VANE PISTON

RECIPROCATING SHAFT

characteristics of a split-phase electric motor which maintains a good torque so long as it runs at its rated speeds. Before the model gas engine became cheaply available, model airplane engines of the same ball type, but amazingly small, were powered by compressed carbon dioxide. Some were as small as ⅛-inch bore and stroke.

A curious oscillating piston engine is shown in Figure 12. The piston is a flat leaf, sweeping back and forth in an arc-shaped space. A D valve gives it double action. This engine may be recognized as the prototype of the vacuum windshield wiper. (The main difference, that in the wiper a partial vacuum induced on one side of the piston causes atmospheric pressure to push on the other side, is a minor one.)

There were also steam engines with rotary valves and with poppet valves. The famous Corliss engine had rotary valves tripped by an ingenious arrangement that resulted in excellent steam economy.

The flash boiler, invented in 1740 and much improved in following centuries, is a coil of heated tubing, into one end of which water is pumped to emerge as very hot steam at the other. Used in steam cars, the best of these flash boilers could raise steam in less than a minute.

In a mistaken attempt to get higher working pressures from less heat, some attempts were made to use other fluids than water in boilers. Even alcohol and naphtha were tried. Aside from the great hazards involved when these flammable fluids were boiled, these engines gained nothing in efficiency. It is the drop in heat between the input and exhaust temperatures of an engine that produces useful work. Since less heat went into vaporizing these working mediums, less input energy was available.

But using a fluid with a *higher* boiling point would increase efficiency, if a suitable one can be found. Such a medium is mercury, which is used in some big power installations in the binary-vapor cycle. Boiling into mercury vapor at about 1,000 degrees F., it runs a mercury turbine. It is then condensed at 500 degrees F., the heat removed in the condenser being used to boil water, which powers a steam turbine.

THE STIRLING HOT-AIR ENGINE

About 1816 a Scottish minister, Robert Stirling, suggested an engine with no boiler, no water, no explosion hazard and no valves. He built the first successful one of this kind in 1827. It was to be multiplied by thousands, then forgotten for decades, and finally revived with amazing results.

The simple Stirling hot-air engine consists of two cylinders, with a furnace at one end of the larger. This is the displacer cylinder (Figure 13). Inside, mounted on a rod by which it can be moved back and forth, is the displacer—a closed body that is a loose fit in the cylinder. Its function is to *displace* the air in the cylinder from the heated end to the cool end, or vice versa, the displaced air flowing back and forth in the space between the displacer and cylinder wall.

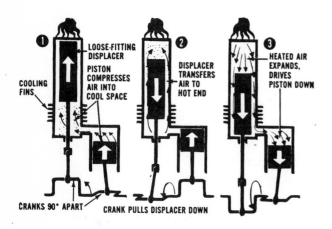

Fig. 13. Operation of the simplest Stirling hot-air engine. As the piston is pushed in (on starting or by flywheel momentum), it compresses air into the finned cold space of the displacer cylinder (1). When the power piston is at the top of its stroke, the displacer has moved halfway down and transferred some of the air to the hot end (2). The compressed air expands as it is heated (3) and drives the power piston out, while still more air is transferred as the displacer moves farther down.

Connected to this cylinder is a second, smaller one with a close-fitting piston coupled to a crank on the shaft. The displacer rod is linked to a second crank at 90 degrees to the first. Both cylinders are closed to the atmosphere; theoretically the same air inside them is used over and over again.

As the displacer moves to the cool end, the air displaced to the hot end of the large cylinder is heated and expands, its pressure increasing. This drives the power piston out, turning the shaft. But the second crank has by now moved the displacer to the hot end, displacing air to the cool. In cooling, the air loses volume and pressure. The power piston is now returned by the momentum of the flywheel, compressing the air above it. As this compression takes place at lower temperature, the flywheel energy it absorbs is less than that developed in expanding the air at a higher temperature, and an excess of power is developed in the cycle.

In practice the simple Stirling engine works somewhat differently. It is almost impossible to make the power piston and displacer gland airtight enough to maintain the same amount of air in the system with which it starts. Soon after the engine is fired, expansion forces some air out, so the total amount left is somewhat less than when the engine is cold. Thereafter, when the displacer moves the air to the hot end of the cylinder, pressure increases to slightly above atmospheric and moves the piston out. But when cooled, the same volume of air drops to a pressure slightly *below* atmospheric. The piston, instead of compressing the air in the system, is instead pushed in by atmospheric pressure and the engine becomes double acting.

Thermodynamically it is far better to compress a constant amount of air while cold, even though flywheel energy is absorbed in the process. The engine gets it all back, with a profit, on the expansion side of the cycle. This is exactly what happens with every gas and diesel engine.

Engineers therefore tried adding a small pump to the Stirling engine, not only to replenish the lost air, but to pump up the engine to work on mean pressure much higher than atmospheric. Such pressurization resulted in a considerable increase in power, for the more air there is in the system, the greater the expansion. Others, including John Ericsson (the builder of the Novelty locomotive) designed open-cycle engines that took in outside air, compressed it, heated and expanded, and then enhausted it. (Exactly that happens in your car engine, except that the fire is *inside* the cylinder, as discussed in the next chapter.)

Ericsson made his fortune on hot-air engines, building thousands that pumped water, ran printing presses, blew fog signals in ships and lighthouses, and did myriad other chores. There were engines that ran sewing machines all day once a gas burner was lit under them. In hot climates it was once common to light a burner under a vertical hot-air engine driving a 24-inch fan, although one imagines that the resulting breeze was rather prewarmed. Nowadays one finds such engines only as antiques.

Ericsson at one time experimented with a solar-heated hot-air engine, and the topic is again under research as a possible power source for fuel-poor areas. (He also built a 260-foot ship driven by a hot-air engine with 14-foot cylinders [the construction of which was itself a feat].) Though successful to a degree, the ship was sunk by a sudden storm and eclipsed by Ericsson's famous Monitor of Civil War fame.

Shortly before World War II, the old Stirling engine captured the attention of the Dutch electrical giant, N. V. Philips Gloeilampenfabrieken. Searching for a simple generating unit, scientists found this long-ignored engine was theoretically capable of an efficiency higher than that of the diesel. With modern materials and heat-transfer data, they proceeded to build engines approaching this promise. Though World War II intervened, research was resumed and went on in the United States as well. Today, under license from Philips, General Motors has plans for Stirling power plants "from five to 5,000 horsepower for applications ranging from below the sea to outer space," to quote a G.M. research scientist writing in an S.A.E. journal.

Philips developed a surprising design that results for the first time in a perfectly balanced one-cylinder engine. This is the rhombic drive (Figure 14), in which the displacer and power piston both drive crossheads, from which twin connecting rods drive two shafts in opposite directions, gears maintaining precise orientation between them. Instead of separate cylinders, the displacer and power cylinders are in tandem, and the air is channeled through a regenerator—a device originated by Stirling which in its present form, saves a tremendous amount of fuel. The regenerator may consist of very fine metal wire, thin plates, or some other form with a large surface. As hot gas passes through it to the cold space, the gas gives up most of its heat to the regenerator; on returning, it picks it up again. The amount of heat required is greatly reduced and engine efficiency quadrupled.

The smoothness of the Stirling engine is phenomenal. As the medium is heated progressively instead of in one explosive instant, the power impulses are vigorous pushes rather than hammer blows. Because of a buffer zone under the piston of the rhombic engine, the piston is pushed in as well as out, as already explained for the simple Stirling engine. Thus there are two power impulses per revolution, and a four-cylinder Stirling engine would have eight power impulses per turn—twice as many as a V-8 car engine!

Fig. 14. In the rhombic drive, twin shafts are offset on both sides of the piston rod. This piston is at top and bottom dead centers when the crosshead pin, crankpin, and shaft centers are in line as shown in the diagram. But the dead centers are not 180 degrees apart as in other engines. In moving clockwise from top dead center, the crankpin makes less than half a turn to bottom dead center. If it moves counterclockwise, it must make more than half a turn to reach the same point of bottom dead center.

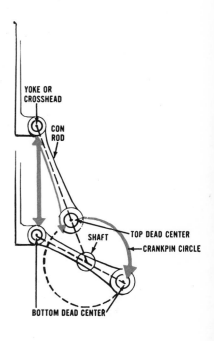

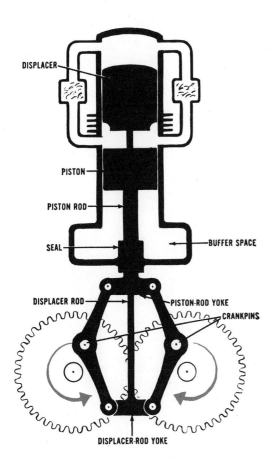

In today's Stirling engine, a crosshead or yoke on the piston rod, and another on the displacer rod, are joined by links or con rods to a common crankpin on each of the two shafts. These are geared together so that the crankpins follow identical though opposite paths. Link and shaft spacing gives the displacer a 110-degree lead over the piston. A pressurized buffer space is added.

163

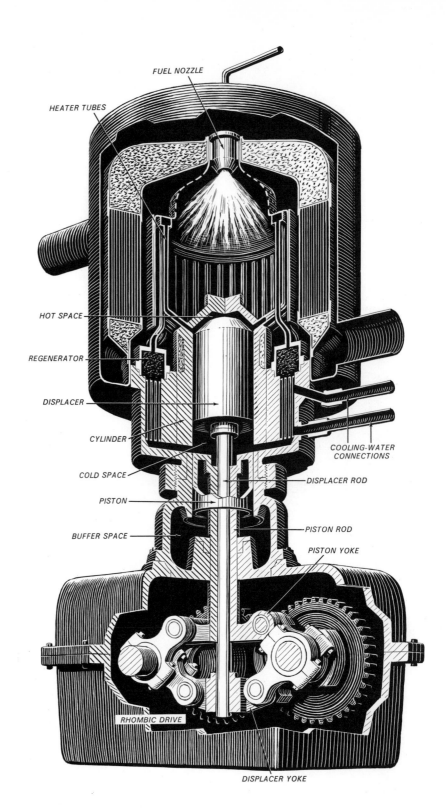

FUEL NOZZLE

HEATER TUBES

HOT SPACE

REGENERATOR

DISPLACER

CYLINDER

COLD SPACE

PISTON

BUFFER SPACE

COOLING-WATER CONNECTIONS

DISPLACER ROD

PISTON ROD

PISTON YOKE

RHOMBIC DRIVE

DISPLACER YOKE

Cutaway view of the modern Stirling engine. Strange crank geometry makes a perfectly balanced one-cylinder engine possible for the first time. The working medium—air, helium or hydrogen—is completely sealed off in the cylinder and in a buffer space below. It is moved from a hot space to a cold one by a transfer piston or displacer. Because of the buffer space under the piston, the engine has two power pulses per turn.

One rhombic engine has been developed for powering electric generators by solar heat to supply the needs of satellites and other space vehicles. For this it is proposed to use helium rather than air as the working medium. (The most efficient gas is hydrogen, and various test engines have been run successfully on this gas.)

These engines are pressurized, working at a mean pressure of about 1,500 p.s.i. Because of a buffer space under the piston, they are double acting, with two power impulses each revolution. Yet a 40-hp one-lunger of this kind vibrates so little you hardly know it is running.

General Motors has also built Stirling powered generating plants for military use (the engine is almost silent, having neither explosion nor exhaust) and pilot plants for submarine propulsion. With a thermal storage tank, such an engine could run under water. The insulated tank is filled with aluminum oxide pellets that are heated while the sub is on the surface. For subsea run-

Quiet mowers you might start with a match are a possible application of the hot-air engine.

Pumps and generators run by solar heat would be feasible for countries having little fuel.

Inboard or outboard boat engines would be highly efficient, almost silent, very reliable.

Satellite engine would drive generators on sun heat collected by an immense reflector.

ning, circulating air would carry heat from the tank to the engine. Pilot plants have shown such a system to have eight times the running capacity of a comparable storage-battery system.

Another aspect of the Stirling engine now vigorously being researched is its use for refrigeration. If the engine is driven from an outside source, one end of the displacer cylinder becomes hot (like an air pump when you're filling a tire) and the other end cold. This application is highly successful in the comparatively new science of cryogeny, or achieving very low temperatures.

Competitors of the piston are few. The earliest is undoubtedly the bellows, which blew up the hearthside and blacksmith's fire and supplied the draft to make fuel burn fiercely enough for smelting ores. Its direct if more sophisticated descendant is the diaphragm in your fuel pump, which compensates for its shorter stroke by moving more rapidly.

More amazing is the rolling diaphragm invented only a few years ago by two Dutch scientists for use in Stirling refrigeration machines. It is a stepped piston, with a thin diaphragm fastened in a sort of annular loop between it and the cylinder wall. As the piston moves up and down, the diaphragm rolls with it, forming a positive seal.

So thin that it would rupture instantly in itself, the diaphragm endures only because it is backed by oil. This oil remains at constant volume at all times because of the step in piston and cylinder. As the diaphragm rolls down, taking up more space, the larger piston diameter sinks below the step, opening out more space for the oil. A little oil is moved in and out to prevent creasing of the diaphragm. So reinforced, it sustains pressures of hundreds of atmospheres (one atmosphere being 15 p.s.i.) and in tests where it operated at 1,500 strokes per minute has lasted more than 10,000 hours.

Even while the steam engine was turning the great wheels of the Industrial Revolution and conquering the wide open spaces of America, men were working to create another kind of prime mover—the internal-combustion engine. Its birth was unpromising, its growth painful. But it emerged as a young giant that forged the automobile industry and gave man wings. How it came into being is the subject of the next chapter.

Putting the Fire Inside the Engine

Both the steam and the hot-air engine are external-combustion engines, their heat sources being outside the cylinder. As already mentioned, Muyghens was the first to hit upon the idea of an *internal*-combustion engine, but his gunpowder engine of 1680 was not robust enough to withstand the power of its explosive fuel, and Papin, though he made some experiments along the same line, eventually turned to steam.

A FLEA-POWDER ENGINE

Two French brothers named Niepce in 1807 invented an internal-combustion engine using lycopodium as fuel. This is a fine powder, the active agent in many insecticides. As it exploded, it drove the piston up in the cylinder. When the hot gases cooled (which they did more rapidly than steam, and without the injection of water) our old friend atmospheric pressure drove the piston down again.

The Niepce brothers (one of whom was to invent photography not long after) soon gave up this solid fuel in favor of fluid fuels. It is said that their engine met with some success in powering boats.

About 1819 a young French artilleryman, Sadi Carnot, became interested in steam engines and in the woeful lack of useful theory on the subject. After doing some experimental work on gases, he wrote a paper which, though not published until 1824, was to become the Book of Genesis to thermodynamics. In this, after acknowledging the vital role of the steam engine, he went on to state:

> We have long sought to ascertain whether there are in existence agents preferable to the vapor of water for developing the motive power of heat; whether atmospheric air, for example, would not be preferable.

Carnot also discussed the use of alcohol instead of steam, which some theorists felt would produce more work because it would develop higher pressure than would water at the same temperature. He pointed out that this was a blind alley, recognizing that it was temperature, not pressure, that was critical to engine efficiency. The greater the difference between the temperature at which heat was supplied the engine and that at which it was rejected (or exhausted), the more of the heat furnished would be turned into useful work. Having suggested that air might be a better working medium than steam, Carnot also pointed out that:

1. Air would cool more quickly than steam and so lend itself to a greater temperature difference during the work cycle.

2. While steam had to be generated in a boiler, air might be heated directly "by combustion carried on within its own mass."

3. For maxmium increase in temperature and volume the air "must first be taken in under sufficient pressure, by a pump or other means, before heating it."

This brilliant young man (he was twenty-three years old at the time) clearly foresaw not only the internal-combustion engine that would carry fire inside itself, but also the importance of compression before ignition. Not understanding this, inventors were to flounder around for decades in their attempts to produce practical engines. Though Carnot's proofs were faulty because based in part on the caloric theory of heat, his facts were nonetheless true. Had he lived longer, he might well have advanced the science of thermodynamics by years. (He died during a cholera epidemic at the age of thirty-six.)

Some experiments were actually made with engines in which air was heated in a "boiler" and then valved to a cylinder. Some were moderately successful, though clumsy and heavy for the amount of power generated. A great difficulty was, as Stirling had discovered with his hot-air engine, that air boilers tended to burn out. In steam boilers, the presence of water kept temperatures down to reasonable limits. The air boiler had no such limiting factor, and today's heat-resistant metals were of course not yet available.

DETOURS AND BLIND ALLEYS

An Englishman, Sam Brown, is said to have powered a car with an atmospheric internal-combustion engine in 1826, and a boat in the following year, but if he did, little came of it. W. L. Wright in 1833 built an engine in which the pressure developed by the burning fuel charge did the work. This was a step nearer a true engine than Niepce's and Brown's, which depended on atmospheric pressure for their work strokes. In 1838 William Barnett made an experimental engine that compressed the fuel-air charge before firing it, as Carnot had advised. But both these engines were crude and little more is known of them.

Other inventors remained intrigued by the idea of letting atmospheric pressure provide the muscle, though obviously this limited working pressure to less than 15 p.s.i.

One curious engine, hard to define as either an internal- or an external-combustion machine, had as its heat source a flame burning outside a port in the upper end of the cylinder (Figure 1). A sliding valve worked by a cam closed this port when the piston reached bottom dead center (or a bit before then) and kept it shut during the return stroke, opening it only on the next intake stroke.

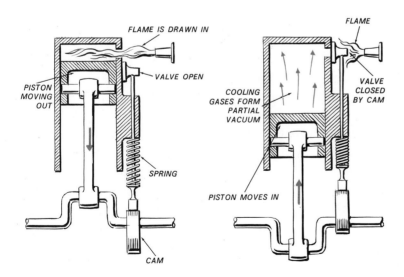

Fig. 1. Externally fired atmospheric engine.

As the piston moved out, it sucked flame and hot air in through the open port. When the valve closed, these gases almost at once began to lose heat to the cylinder (usually a massive chunk of iron). By the time flywheel momentum had carried the crank and piston past bottom dead center, the gases had cooled enough to contract, so leaving a partial vacuum in the cylinder. The valve being closed, atmospheric pressure pushed the piston in.

About 1860 a Frenchman named Etienne Lenoir put on the market an engine built similarly to a double-acting steam engine, even to the slide valve. It drew in illuminating gas for part of the piston's outstroke, then ignited it, the explosion providing a working push for the rest of the stroke. Though abominably inefficient, having no compression whatever and working on only half its stroke, the engine sold in quantities to a power-hungry world. It is probable that atmospheric pressure provided some power on the return stroke as the hot gases in the cylinder cooled.

Two years later another Frenchman, Beau de Rochas, set forth the four-cycle principle as developed from Carnot's paper. But de Rochas' work was on paper only and had no immediate effect. Inventors continued to work on the compressionless Lenoir principle or the atmospheric engine (or combinations of both) even though de Rochas' work had clearly outlined the sequence of events that must underlie a practical engine.

WHY COMPRESSION IS VITAL

All gases, including air, expand $\frac{1}{273}$ of their volume (as measured at 0 degrees Centigrade) for every 1 degree C. rise in temperature. If a gas is enclosed so that it cannot expand, its pressure will increase $\frac{1}{273}$ for every 1 degree C. rise in temperature.

Obviously, the more air you can crowd into a given space, the more expansive force it will exert when it is heated.

Imagine a cylinder closed at one end, with a theoretically leakproof, free-sliding piston in it. Suppose also that a valve opens to let the piston draw in air while it moves out 1 inch from the end of the cylinder (A in Figure 2). The valve is then closed.

If now the air is heated (either from outside the cylinder or by burning fuel inside it), enough to double its pressure, it will push the piston out another 1 inch as it doubles in volume, as at B.

Now imagine the piston returned to top dead center (all the way in) and the valve open while it draws in air its full stroke (C). Then, with the valve closed, let the piston be pushed back within 1 inch of the end of the

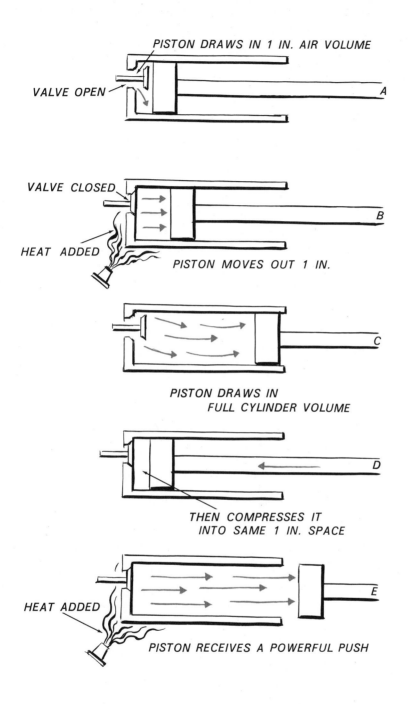

Fig. 2. The importance of compression in the internal-combustion engine.

cylinder, as at D in Figure 2. But now we have compressed a whole cylinderful of air to a fraction of its original volume—for example an eighth. (This would be a compression ratio of eight to one.) We'll have to imagine that whatever pushed the piston in holds it until the air can be heated to the same degree as before.

Again the air doubles in pressure, and tries to expand to twice its volume. But that original volume was so much greater than before that it now expands to twice the *total* volume of the cylinder instead of a mere 2 inches, probably blowing the piston out as at E.

This is the difference compression makes, as foretold by Carnot. It is the big difference between the auto engine of the thirties and that of the sixties. As compression ratios have risen, engine power has quadrupled.

THE OTTO ENGINE

In 1861 Nikolaus August Otto, a German, began experimenting with an engine similar to Lenoir's, which fired a charge when the piston had already moved part way out. Otto noticed that if the charge was drawn in for only one-quarter of the outstroke and then fired, the piston rarely reached bottom dead center. It would instead draw back before moving out that far. He concluded that the hot gases were cooling so quickly that they produced a partial vacuum too soon, so pulling the piston in.

Otto altered the engine to ignite the charge at half stroke. The machine now continued to run. Again he altered it to fire at three-quarters of the outstroke. Performance once more fell off, probably because the expansion was both too great and too late, holding the piston at bottom dead center and producing insufficient vacuum to pull it back effectively. To continue in Otto's own words:

> I then found the right idea; ignition and combustion must take place at the beginning of the piston stroke, and this idea was at once successful. I sucked in explosive mixture to one-half and eventually three-quarters, tried to press the piston back as far as possible by turning the flywheel backwards, then I ignited and behold, the flywheel vigorously rotated several times. That was the starting point of a four-stroke gas engine. In that very year the drawing of such an engine was completed.

Such exciting action, after the indifferent performance of the Lenoir engine, must have been thrilling to the experimenter. If this account is to be believed, Otto discovered the importance of compression without knowledge of the de Rochas paper. However, the existence of this paper did later deny Otto patents in France and Germany.

The thrill of discovery was stifled for some years. The explosions of the compressed charge proved too much for Otto's experimental engine and ruined it. Without funds himself, he formed a partnership with Eugene Langen, an engineer, and the two men worked to develop a better two-stroke atmospheric engine.

In the first Otto and Langen engine, the piston had fastened to it a long toothed rack protruding from the open top of the cylinder. The rack meshed with a pinion on the shaft, but because of a ratchet, this gear turned freely on the shaft as the piston moved up. While it did so, gas and air were drawn into the cylinder for half the outstroke. The mix was then ignited, driving the piston to the end of its stroke (but because of the ratchet effecting no motion of the shaft).

By now the gases were cooling in the cylinder and forming a partial vacuum. Atmospheric pressure acted on the top of the piston, pushing it back. The pinion, turned in the other direction by the rack, caught the ratchet and rotated the shaft.

Clumsy and inefficient, the engines were nonetheless marketable. Beginning in 1872, Otto and Langen sold about 5,000 of them, but Otto was dissatisfied. Loath to tinker with a salable product, Langen refused to do further work on a four-cycle engine. Otto tackled it independently, and this time his first effort was successful. A 3 hp engine running at 180 r.p.m., it was so much quieter and more efficient than all preceding ones that it promptly took over the market.

The principle of this first Otto engine and of all four-cycle gas engines since is precisely what Beau de Rochas had proposed in 1862. More properly called the four-stroke cycle (Figure 3) its action is as follows:

1   2   3   4

Fig. 3. The four-cycle Otto engine.

1. Moving out from top dead center, and with the intake valve open, the piston draws air and vaporized fuel into the cylinder for its full stroke.

2. With both valves closed, the piston moves back up to top dead center again, compressing the charge to a fraction of cylinder volume.

3. Ignition occurring at top dead center, the charge explodes, its hot gases driving the piston out. This is the power stroke.

4. With the exhaust valve opening at bottom dead center, the piston returns again to the top of the cylinder, pushing the exhaust gases out.

By 1891, when Otto died, more than 30,000 of his four-cycle engines were popping away, many with more than one cylinder, and some rated as high as 100 hp.

As you can see by following the four strokes through, the Otto engine makes only one power stroke every two revolutions. The flywheel carries it through the three unproductive strokes. You will also realize that each valve opens only once every two revolutions. Therefore the camshaft that lifts the valves is geared at a 1:2 ratio to the crankshaft.

A pressure-volume diagram for an Otto engine (similar to the indicator diagrams Watt made for his steam engines) would be something like that shown in Figure 4. Engineers can plot such diagrams either from test engines or by mathematics, to study or even predict engine performance and efficiency.

The vertical line in the diagram represents pressure inside the cylinder. The horizontal line represents the volume behind the piston (and therefore the position of the piston) as indicated by the drawing below it.

The first stroke of the cycle begins at point 1 with the piston at bottom dead center after taking in a charge of air and fuel. As the piston moves in from right to left, volume decreases while the pressure rises (as is natural when you compress a gas); thus the curve 1–2 is the compression stroke. At point 2 the piston is at top dead center and pressure has risen accordingly. But now ignition occurs (at point 2).

Before the piston can start to move down, pressure rises tremendously from point 2 to point 3. (The line joining these is vertical instead of a curve, because the piston has not moved.) At 3 the piston starts its outward stroke. As the top curve indicates, pressure falls while the piston moves out to bottom dead center (point 4).

Here the pressure is still somewhat above atmospheric (4 is above 1). In the final step, 4 to 1, the exhaust valve opens. (To the thermodynamic engineer, this is equivalent to an instantaneous fall of temperature at constant volume, so the line is vertical.)

We have made only two piston strokes, but these are the important

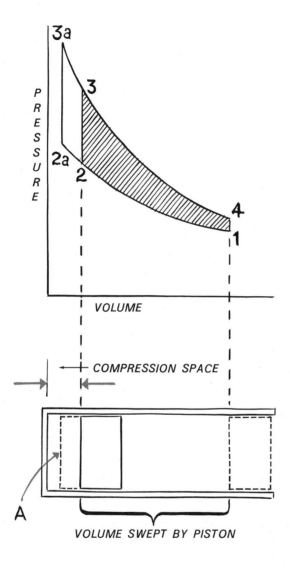

Fig. 4. Pressure-volume diagram for an Otto engine.

ones from the analytic standpoint. We can ignore the intake and exhaust strokes so far as the diagram is concerned.

The wonderful thing about this diagram, if it is carefully scaled, is that the shaded area within points 1 to 4 is equivalent to work done in the cycle. The larger this area, the more of the heat input is doing useful work.

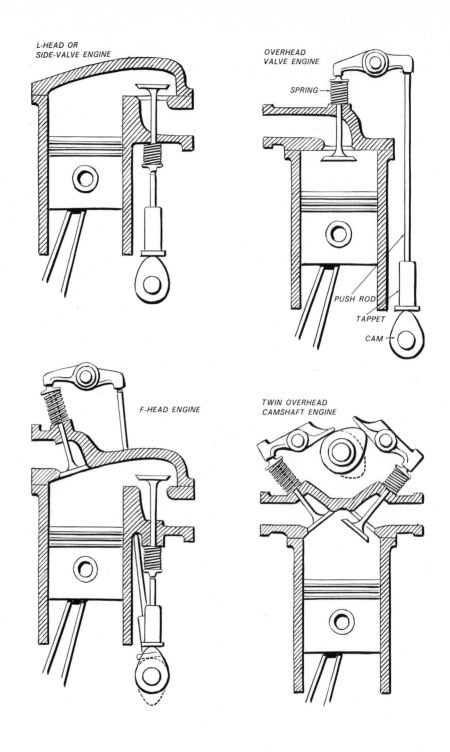

L-HEAD OR
SIDE-VALVE ENGINE

OVERHEAD
VALVE ENGINE

SPRING

PUSH ROD

TAPPET

CAM

F-HEAD ENGINE

TWIN OVERHEAD
CAMSHAFT ENGINE

Fig. 5. Valve arrangements on Otto engines.

176

Suppose now that the piston could move farther back into the cylinder, as shown by its dotted outline (A) in the drawing below the diagram. By decreasing the volume, this would increase compression, so the pressure at point 2a would be higher. On ignition the pressure would rise beyond 3 to 3a. Therefore the shaded area would be larger, more work would be done, and engine efficiency increased.

The two poppet valves of the Otto engine may be arranged in various ways, some of which are shown in Figure 5. At least one car was built with sleeve valves—cylindrical sleeves outside the cylinders that slid up and down to uncover and close ports. In some early engines, the intake valve was not mechanically actuated, but only spring loaded. The light spring snapped it shut, while the suction of the intake stroke sufficed to open it. (This would not serve on high-speed engines, for valve bounce would leave the intake valve open at high revs.)

Some stationary engines had a novel governor arrangement on the exhaust valve. As speed climbed, centrifugal weights would shift the cam operating this valve so as to hold it open. The engine then sucked in only air instead of air and fuel, and would miss a few power strokes until it slowed down.

Being very heavy for their power output, Otto's engines were suitable only for stationary use. But in 1882 Gottlieb Daimler, an engineer employed by Otto and Langen, left that firm to strike out for himself. Within a year he was able to patent the first high-speed gas engine, capable of running at 900 r.p.m., and with a far more favorable power-to-weight ratio than the clumsy Otto engine. By 1883 Daimler had propelled a car, a bicycle and a boat with his new lightweight engine.

TWO STROKES VERSUS FOUR

Not everybody was satisfied with the every-other-time-around power stroke of the Otto cycle. But it was a fantastic notion to cram all four strokes into one revolution—on the face of things, impossible. A Scotsman, Sir Dugald Clerk, was first to achieve this, in 1881, by using two cylinders. Ten years later an Englishman named Day ingeniously used the closed crankcase as an antechamber for the fuel-air charge. How he telescoped the four Otto strokes to get a power impulse every revolution is shown in Figure 6.

This two-stroke engine has no valves. During its travel the piston alternately closes and uncovers three holes (ports) in the cylinder wall to admit fuel and air, to transfer it from the crankcase to the cylinder, and to exhaust

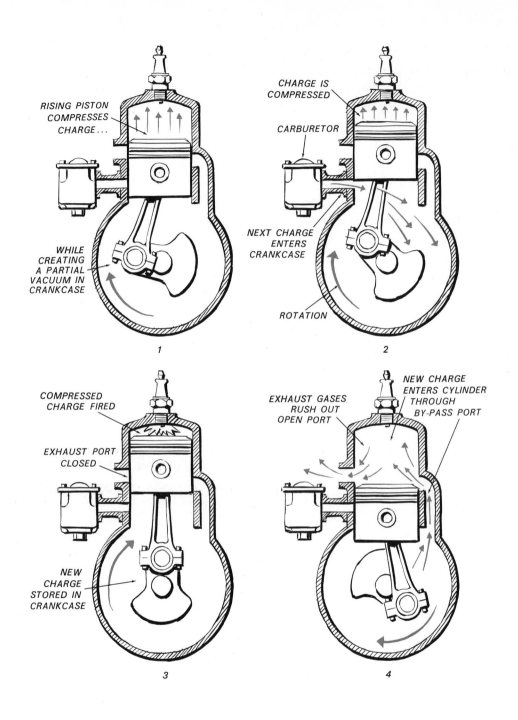

RISING PISTON
COMPRESSES
CHARGE...

WHILE
CREATING
A PARTIAL
VACUUM IN
CRANKCASE

1

CHARGE IS
COMPRESSED

CARBURETOR

NEXT CHARGE
ENTERS
CRANKCASE

ROTATION

2

COMPRESSED
CHARGE FIRED

EXHAUST PORT
CLOSED

NEW
CHARGE
STORED IN
CRANKCASE

3

EXHAUST GASES
RUSH OUT
OPEN PORT

NEW CHARGE
ENTERS CYLINDER
THROUGH
BY-PASS PORT

4

the spent gases from the cylinder. The gears, camshaft, valves and springs of the four-stroke engine are done away with.

In America, the first two-stroke engine may have been a one-lunger built for boats by Ray Palmer, in 1895. As you may have guessed from Figure 6, a two-stroke engine can (if the spark occurs at top dead center) run either way with equal facility. Palmer installed a low-voltage ignition system of his own design that could shrug off salt water without a miss, and aligned the starting knob on the flywheel with the crankpin. Boatmen could therefore cut off the ignition, watch the knob, and just before dead center on its expiring turn, cut in the ignition again—whereupon the engine would lustily restart in reverse.

A similar two-cycle engine is currently being built in Nova Scotia. It has the same make-and-break ignition system and on-the-fly reversing capability as the old Palmer engine. Horsepower is low, but as Walter Hadley, agent for the Acadia engine, points out, "the horses are the kind with big furry feet because power is developed at very low speeds, where most modern engines idle." The 4-hp one-lunger pushes a 20-foot boat at 6 to 7 knots with a slow-turning (650 r.p.m.) 14-inch prop. Downeast fishermen like the old engines because they require no starter, generator or storage battery—only a few dry cells—and because salt spray cannot short out the ignition.

The two-stroke engine was not without problems. One was the difficulty of scavenging—clearing out exhaust gases to make room for a fresh charge of air and fuel. To help do this, the piston head was shaped to give incoming air an upward direction, and much research has been done on the shape of the combustion chamber. A recent development is called loop scavenging. The piston head is flat, but intake and exhaust ports are cunningly designed to give the incoming charge a pretzel-shaped path that scoops exhaust gases out before it.

Fig. 6. Three-port two-stroke engine operates as follows: As the piston goes up, it compresses the fuel-air charge above, at the same time lowering pressure in the crankcase below it (1). Nearing top dead center, the piston skirt uncovers a port leading to the carburetor throat, and a charge enters the crankcase (2). At top dead center the compressed cylinder charge is ignited and starts to drive the piston down (3). On nearing bottom dead center, it uncovers the exhaust port, and then the transfer port. As exhaust gases rush out one side, the fresh charge sweeps up into the cylinder (4). Going past bottom dead center, the piston again starts to rise as in 1, closing the ports and compressing the cylinder charge, as the cycle repeats.

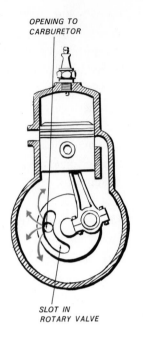

OPENING TO
CARBURETOR

SLOT IN
ROTARY VALVE

Fig. 7. Rotary-valve engine.

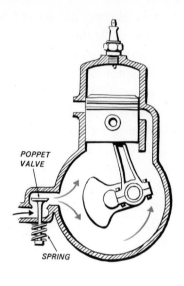

POPPET
VALVE

SPRING

Fig. 8. Two-port poppet-valve engine.

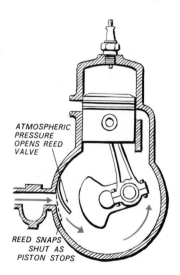

ATMOSPHERIC
PRESSURE
OPENS REED
VALVE

REED SNAPS
SHUT AS
PISTON STOPS

Fig. 9. Reed-valve engine.

Another drawback of the three-port engine in Figure 6 is that the intake port stays closed for much of the upstroke, opening only a few degrees before top dead center. At high speed, the incoming charge has only a few milliseconds to rush into the crankcase before the port closes again. Inventors therefore tried a rotary valve on the crankshaft or on a crank web (Figure 7) that could remain open for a certain part of the piston's instroke.

Though better, this too opened only in relation to the angular position of the crank, and could not respond to other factors such as engine speed or load. Also, the rotary valve was affected by bearing and crankshaft wear.

The next idea was a spring-loaded poppet valve opening to the crankcase. As the piston went up, suction (atmospheric pressure) opened the valve to let the charge into the crankcase (Figure 8). Responding only to the pressure difference between the crankcase and the atmosphere, this valve answered to changes in engine load. The engine started more easily, idled better, breathed more easily and worked harder.

Today's high-performance outboard and chain-saw engines use a variation of this—reed valves between the crankcase and carburetor (Figure 9). These are automatic check valves very much like the old flapper valves, but made of high-quality Swedish steel working on accurately flat surfaces. (A fringe benefit of the reed valve is that, unlike the third port and rotary valve, it snaps shut in case of a backfire instead of letting the flame out to set the carburetor afire.)

Though in theory the two-stroke engine should be twice as powerful as the four-stroke (size for size), this has not been fully attained. Scavenging is one difficulty. Another is that the length of the ports shortens the effective stroke by just that much. Nevertheless, modern design has attained 1.8 times the four-stroke output, and given us such miracles of power as a 5½-hp engine that can be held in the hand.

Two-strokers power motorcycles, tools, mowers, compressors, pumps and dozens of other things, including automobiles. Because each cylinder has one power stroke every revolution, the three-cylinder engines of the Saab and DKW cars have the same smooth power flow as an ordinary six. Furthermore, each of these robust little power plants has only seven or eight moving parts— a crankshaft, three pistons, three con rods, and in the case of the Saab a distributor shaft. (The DKW has its timer right on the crankshaft.) The crankcase of such multicylinder two-strokers is of course divided into separate sealed sections, each drawing in the charge for its own cylinder.

Ray Palmer is credited with the idea of lubricating the two-stroke by mixing oil with the gasoline. Once problems of spark-plug fouling are licked, this system has the advantage of providing fresh oil from the instant of starting and as long as the engine runs. By contrast, your four-cycle car engine gets little lubrication until the oil flows freely; it may wear more in the first few minutes of operation than in the next as many hours. Also, the crankcase oil undergoes slow contamination and dilution, whereas that provided the two-stroke is new at every revolution. The nuisance of mixing oil into the gas has been lessened by self-mixing fuel tanks, and by pumps that inject the proper amount of oil into the gas line.

IGNITING THE FUEL

Lighting a fire inside the cylinder, and doing it 200 to 5,000 times per minute, was a challenge from the first. Early engines that ran on coal gas had an igniting cock—a gas jet burning outside a port in the cylinder. But once compression became part of the cycle, that hole-in-the-wall makeshift no longer served.

Some early engines used hot-bulb or hot-tube ignition. This called for a hollow metal bulb on the cylinder head, or a copper tube that ran through the head, its outer end being closed. Either was heated with a blowtorch to start the engine. When compression rammed the fuel charge back into the hot element, the charge exploded. Once running, the engine kept the bulb or tube hot by itself.

Hot-bolt ignition called for a protruding stem on top of the piston. Being small in cross section, this became red hot after the engine was started by external heat. The charge was fired when its heat of compression, plus that of the hot bolt, added up to more than the flash point of the fuel.

Ray Palmer's make-and-break ignition system consisted of a one-winding coil, six dry cells, and two ignition points inside the cylinder. One of these was a grounded nickel-silver screw. The other, called the flipper, was mounted on a shaft in a mica bushing. A crankshaft eccentric briefly kicked the flipper against the screw. This make-and-break induced a voltage surge in the coil, and a fat spark leaped the points as they opened.

"Six big dry cells would last two or three seasons," recalled an early employee of the Palmer Engine Company. "And if the tripper spring broke, a fellow could make port with a hairpin."

Jump-spark or high-voltage ignition requires a two-winding induction coil, such as you have on your car. Both windings are wrapped around an iron core. One is of comparatively heavy wire, connected through the breaker points to the battery. As the points close, this primary coil generates a magnet-

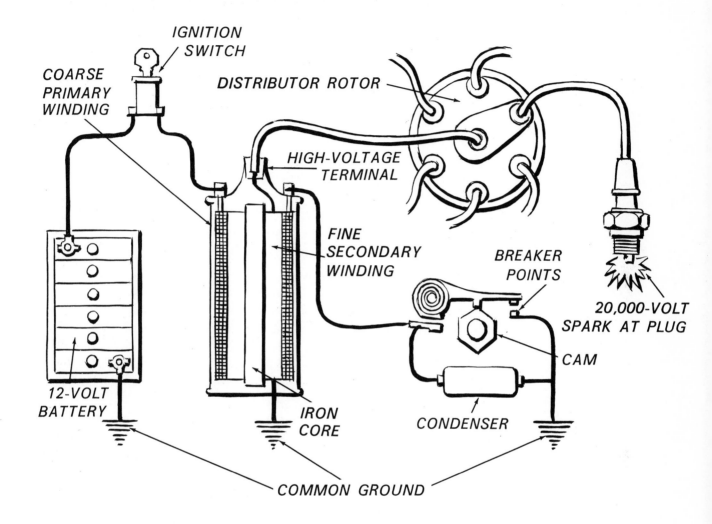

IGNITION SWITCH

COARSE PRIMARY WINDING

DISTRIBUTOR ROTOR

HIGH-VOLTAGE TERMINAL

FINE SECONDARY WINDING

BREAKER POINTS

20,000-VOLT SPARK AT PLUG

CAM

12-VOLT BATTERY

IRON CORE

CONDENSER

COMMON GROUND

Fig. 10. How a modern ignition system works: The ignition being on, current flows through the primary winding, through the breaker points, and back to ground and the grounded battery terminal. As the cam opens the points, the current is interrupted and the magnetic field surrounding the coil instantly collapses. This field collapse induces in the secondary winding a high voltage (20,000 to 25,000 volts). The rotor carries this to one of the distributor terminals, from which it flows to the spark plug whose cylinder is ready to fire. Not shown are the ballast resistor and the centrifugal and vacuum advances that make the spark occur earlier at high engine speeds.

183

ic field that envelops the secondary coil, which has a great many more turns of very fine wire (Figure 10).

When the breaker points open, the primary current is interrupted and the magnetic field instantly collapses (the condenser is necessary for this; it provides a reservoir for the current to flow into, instead of arcing across the points—which would delay collapse of the field).

In falling to zero, the field induces a high voltage in the secondary coil. This current is routed by the distributor rotor to the spark plug of the cylinder whose piston is in firing position.

The Model T Ford had trembler coils, so called because they had a vibrator or interrupter on top. Working much like a buzzer, its points made and broke the primary current hundreds of times per second, so that the coil could deliver a continuous spark. There was a coil for each cylinder, and a simple timer—a roller inside a cage having four contacts—in turn energized each coil as its cylinder was ready to fire.

The Ford had another feature—a magneto, granddaddy of today's alternator (Figure 11). Many horseshoe magnets were fastened to one face of the flywheel. These ran close to an equal number of stationary coils, generating a low-voltage alternating current in them, which supplied primary current for the ignition coils. It took a hefty swing on the crank handle to get a starting spark. (When the Ford T graduated to a battery and starting system, one turned the ignition switch to BAT for starting, then flipped it to MAG for running.)

More sophisticated and compact high-voltage magnetos, incorporating an induction coil, were applied to marine, aircraft and fancier auto engines. Today's one-lung mower and utility engines have powerful magnets built into the flywheel. On passing the poles of the coil unit, they induce a current that is tripped by the breaker points at the instant a spark is desired.

Transistor ignition, available as an option on many modern automobiles, dispenses with the breaker points that are so often a source of trouble. A magnetic pulse in the distributor sends a small current to a transistor, triggering it to cut off the primary current to the coil when it is time for a spark.

But most surprising of all is piezo-electric ignition. The crystal cartridge in certain phonograph pickups, subjected to slight pressure by the vibrating needle, generates a tiny current that is fed to the amplifier to play a record. A similar but far more potent piezo-electric crystal can be used for engine ignition. Encapsulated in plastic, it is about ¾-inch square and a couple of inches long. When suddenly squeezed by a cam on the engine, this crystal generates full sparking voltage—a lusty 20,000 volts—that leaps the spark plug to fire the charge.

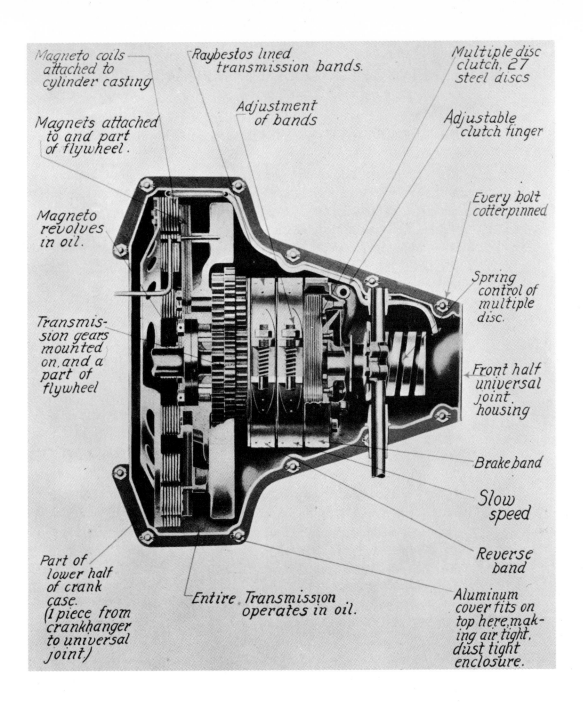

Magneto coils attached to cylinder casting

Magnets attached to and part of flywheel.

Magneto revolves in oil.

Transmission gears mounted on, and a part of flywheel

Part of lower half of crank case. (1 piece from crankhanger to universal joint)

Raybestos lined transmission bands.

Adjustment of bands

Entire Transmission operates in oil.

Multiple disc clutch, 27 steel discs

Adjustable clutch finger

Every bolt cotterpinned

Spring control of multiple disc.

Front half universal joint housing

Brake band

Slow speed

Reverse band

Aluminum cover fits on top here, making air tight, dust tight enclosure.

Fig. 11. Top view of a Model T magneto and transmission.

FEEDING THE INTERNAL-COMBUSTION ENGINE

Coal gas was originally the most suitable fuel, for it was already in gaseous form and widely available. Producer gas, made by passing steam over burning charcoal, was also used. But these fuels tied the engine to a fixed position; for portability, other fuels were needed.

Turpentine and naphtha were tried. Fuel oils and light petroleum met with some success, especially when preheated. Karl Benz, a great name in automotive history, is said to have been first to use the volatile and explosive benzine. In 1886 he patented a carburetor for it.

Other fuel vaporizers were rather less sophisticated than the old fly-spray gun. One, the "mixing valve," was nothing more than a hole in the seat of the poppet valve in Figure 8. Some had wicks from which fuel evaporated into the air stream. Another led an air tube under the fuel in the tank, while the cylinder drew air from the top of the tank. Bubbling through the fuel, the air vaporized some and carried it along to the engine.

The modern float-feed carburetor was invented by Wilhelm Maybach. In it, the fuel is kept at a constant level in a bowl. From this a passage leads to a fine jet set into the carburetor throat. As air rushes past this, it carries out fuel as a spray, which the moving air breaks up still finer. Though many refinements have been added, this remains the principle of most carburetors today.

In modern engine design, the stroke is often very short. Some "over-square" engines have a stroke shorter than the bore. This reduces piston travel per revolution (and therefore wear), while the shorter lever arm of the crank is compensated for by the larger piston area.

Supercharging is a method of ramming more fuel-air mix into a cylinder than the piston could draw in by itself. This of course increases engine power. A supercharger is a blower or rotary compressor that feeds air into the engine at higher than atmospheric pressure.

With the development of higher octane fuels and antiknock additives, compression has been pushed up to 10:1 and even more. But there is a limit to the compression ratio that can be used. Since the charge becomes hotter and hotter as compression rises, it may eventually fire itself before normal ignition occurs. This is damaging both to performance and to the engine itself. The difficulty was of course evident as soon as designers tried to build more efficient engines. Yet one man took advantage of this very drawback to create what was (before the advent of the modern Stirling engine) the most efficient heat engine known.

THE DIESEL ENGINE

Rudolf Diesel, a German, in 1893 published a paper on the theory and construction of what he called "a rational heat motor." He proposed taking in air only—without admixture of fuel—and then compressing it to $\frac{1}{16}$ of its original volume. This would heat it to about 1,000 degrees F., at which point fuel would be injected. It would ignite from the hot air, no spark or other ignition being necessary, and the high compression ratio would greatly boost thermal efficiency. Since there would be no fuel in the air until the moment of injection, preignition would be impossible.

Getting laboratory facilities, Diesel built a one-cylinder model to try out his ideas. Fueled with powdered coal, it blew up, almost killing him. But it had run enough to demonstrate the correctness of his basic reasoning. In 1897 he built a successful engine. Its development made history—and its inventor a millionaire.

The diesel engine may be a two-stroke or a four-stroke machine. Today it powers locomotives, giant earth-moving machinery, generating stations, buses, ships and cars. One small diesel has been applied to bicycles. There are even little diesel outboards, which will run on almost any liquid fuel and greatly outlast conventional outboard motors. Not only are they free of the usual ignition ailments, but they develop twice the thrust of similarly rated gasoline outboards.

For starting, such small engines may operate on a semi-diesel principle. Initial firing is achieved by a glow plug in each cylinder. The element of such a plug is made red hot by an electric current for firing up the cold cylinders. Once the engine is running, current can be cut off and it continues to operate as a diesel engine.

XI

Rotary Power—From the Windmill to the Wankel

Vital as the Newcomen engine and its successors were to the Industrial Revolution, perceptive engineers realized that their reciprocating action was far from ideal. The reversal of a weighty mass at the end of each stroke consumed energy. It took power to stop the piston, its rod, the crosshead and the connecting rod, and still more power to get them moving again in the opposite direction. If the motion of these parts could be made continuous, would not engine efficiency be much greater, and fuel costs less?

The water wheel and windmill offered nostalgic precedent for rotary engines. Persia and Afghanistan probably had the first windmills, dating back to the 7th century, but these were not the familiar Dutch type. According to one description, the windmill of the Near East had a vertical shaft, with flat sails or vanes not unlike a revolving door, and the millstone was fixed on the bottom of the shaft. Flanking the mill were two columns of masonry that funneled the wind to it—to one side of the shaft so that the air flow would drive only the exposed sail, so causing rotation.

These mills were more or less permanently set up to take advantage of prevailing winds. When the European windmill appeared (the oldest of record dating to 1197 A.D.) it had to be oriented to keep working when the wind direction shifted. At first this was done by pivoting the entire mill on a heavy post so that it could be swung facing the wind. Such post mills were very vulnerable to storms, and some time in the 16th century gave way to the turret mill. In this, only the top (carrying the horizontal shaft with its sails) turned to catch the wind. Curved sails, more efficient than flat ones, also appeared about this time.

For its day, the windmill became quite a sophisticated mechanism. Its power was applied to such varied duties as pumping water (including massive drainage projects in the Netherlands), papermaking, grinding up pigments, pressing oil out of seeds, and sawing wood. Probably rotary windmill power was responsible for the invention of the circular saw blade in the 17th century.

Nor did inventors neglect the wind machine itself. In France, someone devised the pantanemone, an affair with two semicircular sails on a horizontal shaft (Figure 1). This would turn with the wind in almost any quarter, except

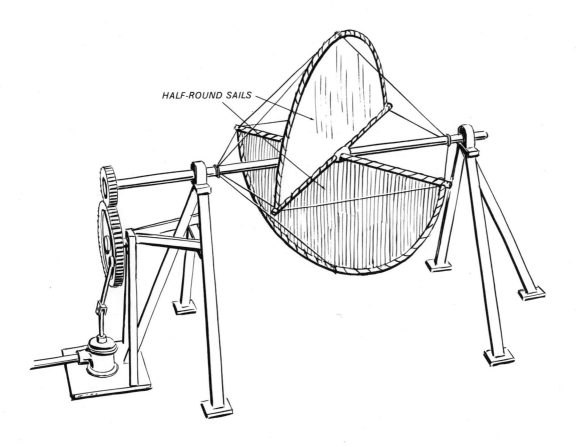

HALF-ROUND SAILS

Fig. 1. French pantanemone.

if it blew directly across (or perpendicular to) the shaft. In this case, the pressure on one sail canceled that on the other.

But the most successful type in common use remained the storybook windmill associated with Holland. Even now, they are not all gone. Tourists may see them not only in the Low Countries, but in the Russian Ukraine. Decades ago American plains farmers built themselves what they called a Kansas windmill (Figure 2). The shaft of this homemade mill being North-South oriented, its canvas sails would turn in almost any wind but one from due east or west.

Before power lines marched across the prairies, thousands of smaller windmills, mounted on towers and automatically steered into the wind by weather-vane tails, pumped water and generated electricity on American farms.

Even more recently, some experiments have been made with large windmills. In October 1941 a wind turbine built on Grandpa's Knob, near Rutland, Vermont, began generating power for the Central Vermont Public Service Corporation. The generator was driven by a two-bladed propeller 175 feet across, mounted on a tower 120 feet above the mountaintop.

Though this structure withstood storm winds up to 115 miles per hour, one of the 8-ton blades snapped off in 1945. The project was phased out, but valuable data had been gained as to kilowatt costs and the selection of locations for such power units.

Even earlier, in 1931, the Soviet Union had a giant two-bladed turbine generating power near Yalta, close to the Black Sea. German and English scientists have also made experiments with modern versions of this classic prime mover. One English design consisted of two semicylinders offset around a common center (Figure 2). The action of the wind on this arrangement is intriguing.

Entering one of the openings between the offset semicylinders, it exerts a force on the inner concave surface. It is then deflected to sweep around in the reverse direction, until it strikes the concave inner surface of the opposite semicylinder. Being on the other side of the axle, this exerts force in the same rotational direction as the first one, and the entire rotor turns.

This wind turbine will work no matter what direction the wind comes from. It powered water pumps sucessfully, but was deemed too costly to build in the sizes necessary for commercial electric power generation. Will it turn if the top cap is left off and an air flow directed straight down, parallel to its axis? The question is hardly pertinent to a large outdoor installation, but experiments with a cardboard model will show that the rotor does turn, presumably due to reaction as the air flows off the curved rotor surfaces.

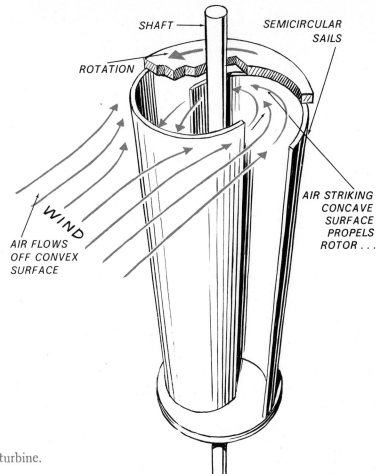

SHAFT

SEMICIRCULAR
SAILS

ROTATION

WIND

AIR FLOWS
OFF CONVEX
SURFACE

AIR STRIKING
CONCAVE
SURFACE
PROPELS
ROTOR . . .

Fig. 2. English wind turbine.

WATER WHEELS AND TURBINES

One type of primitive Middle East water mill resembled the modern water turbine to a remarkable degree. It had a vertical shaft with a vaned wheel at the bottom extending somewhat below ground. Water from a higher level was delivered to this wheel by a duct or pipe, the kinetic energy gained by its fall being imparted to the vanes.

The familiar flat-bladed water wheel set in a stream was driven by the kinetic energy of the flowing water, a much simpler arrangement. The overshot wheel, with its water-holding buckets, derived its power from the falling weight of the water that flowed into these buckets when they were at the top.

A vast improvement over these primitive mills was the Francis turbine, which appeared on the scene about 1855 and was greatly improved in succeed-

191

ing years. About 1910 it was fitted with a propeller-type wheel or runner. In large sizes, the Francis turbine has a vertical shaft, but smaller units may be horizontal in arrangement.

Like other modern hydraulic turbines, it is supplied through a pipe or penstock. The water enters a spiral casing or vortex chamber (Figure 3) surrounding the runner, to which it imparts a certain amount of its kinetic energy. But the water is also under considerable pressure in the casing, and the vanes of the runner are shaped to have a nozzle effect. If the runner were held from turning, the water would issue from it at high speed.

But when the runner is spinning, the water escapes much more slowly, exhausting through the draft tube. The difference in velocity is imparted to the blades by reaction—the same effect that makes a shotgun kick against your shoulder.

The runner blades are adjustable for highest efficiency under various pressure heads, and gates control the flow of water. As much as 95 percent of its energy is converted into rotary motion.

In another reaction turbine, the Kaplan, the angle of the propeller blades is automatically adjusted by a governor to maintain peak efficiency under all operating conditions. It is largely the high efficiency of water turbines that makes them practical in today's pumped storage systems, which put alternating current "on the shelf" to meet peak electrical loads.

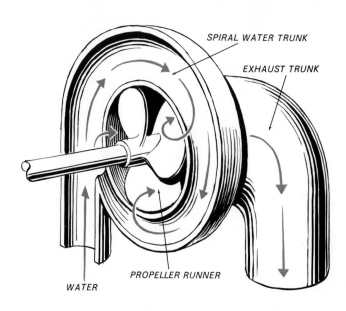

Fig. 3. Francis turbine.

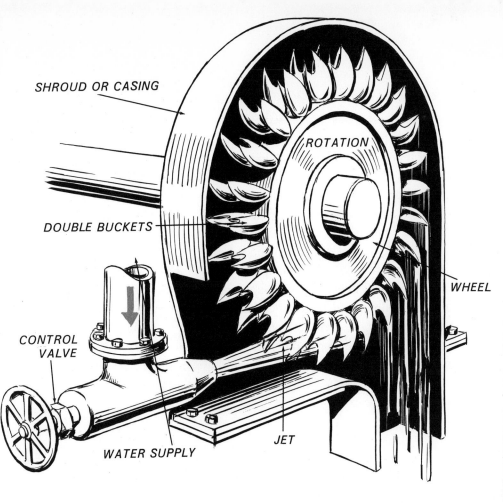

SHROUD OR CASING

ROTATION

DOUBLE BUCKETS

WHEEL

CONTROL
VALVE

WATER SUPPLY

JET

Fig. 4. Pelton impulse turbine.

World's biggest Pelton wheel was built in Switzerland for the American Pacific Gas & Electric Co. It produces 227,000 hp.

An early challenger to the already successful Francis turbine was the Pelton wheel, first built in the late 1870s, and much favored where water was under a high head or pressure. This is a pure impulse turbine. Water issues from a special nozzle as a high-speed jet, striking at a tangent against a rim of double buckets fastened to a wheel (Figure 4).

Aimed at the center ridge between the concave buckets, the jet is divided and reversed, giving up its forward kinetic energy to the wheel. An improved bucket, developed in 1889, is notched on the outside edge. This allows the jet to play through it against the preceding bucket a bit longer, while that one is in the most favored position at the bottom of the wheel. Though a casing is usually fitted to catch and drain off spent water, it does not hold pressure and plays no part in the operation of the Pelton wheel.

193

ROTARY STEAM ENGINES

Dozens of ingenious designs were spawned in the effort to apply the nonreciprocating principle to steam power. Some inventors tried an annular (ring-shaped) cylinder resembling a doughnut, with the piston fixed to a disk. This revolved between the two halves of the casing forming the cylinder. A sliding abutment or partition was to be lifted by a cam to let the piston go by, then fall again to close the cylinder behind it as steam was admitted.

Machining problems, which abound in all rotary engines including today's, were perhaps especially virulent in this one. Not least was that of the piston, which had to be curved—a shape easily obtained by slicing a section out of a doughnut, but difficult to machine from metal with any precision.

Other inventors used a circular casing as the cylinder, with an eccentric or off-center element, or even an oval one, as the piston. The problem of sealing off part of the cylinder as the piston swung around was tackled—more or less successfully—with sliding vanes, pivoted abutments, and great optimism.

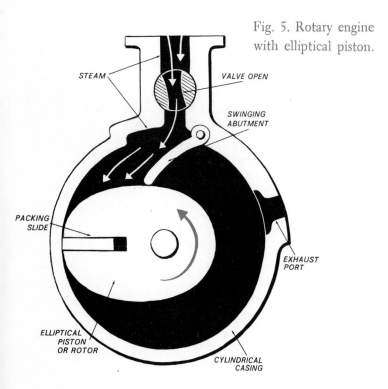

Fig. 5. Rotary engine with elliptical piston.

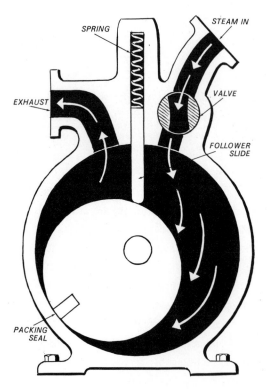

Fig. 6. Rotary engine with eccentric piston.

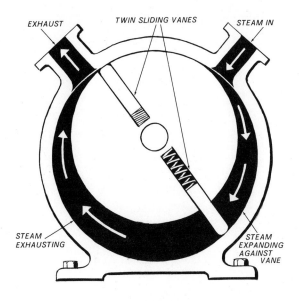

EXHAUST   TWIN SLIDING VANES   STEAM IN

STEAM
EXHAUSTING

STEAM
EXPANDING
AGAINST
VANE

Fig. 7. Rotary engine with concentric piston.

In Figure 5, for example, an elliptical piston keyed to the shaft has a packing slide to seal steam tight against the inside wall of the casing or cylinder. A swinging abutment near the top is held against the piston by steam pressure, so confining steam in the working area to the left. Admitted by a rocking valve in the steam chest atop the casing, steam is cut off by a cam on the shaft (not shown in the drawing) after the piston has made half a revolution. It then expands until the packing slide passes the exhaust port on the right side, after which the piston lifts the pivoted abutment into the recess provided.

Another type of rotary steam engine, which had many complex variations, is shown in its simplest elements in Figure 6. The piston is perfectly round, but mounted off center on the shaft so that it is constantly in steam-tight contact with the casing at one point, which is fitted with a packing slide. (Presumably the sides of the piston also had to be reasonably steam tight.)

The edge of the follower slide at the top is supposed to maintain a seal against the rotating piston at all times, rising and falling as this member makes its round. The steam intake should be controlled by a valve (operated by an external cam) to provide early cutoff and also to prevent blowby at such time as the piston is at its topmost position, when there would briefly be direct communication betwen intake and exhaust ports.

In Figure 7 the piston itself is concentric with the shaft, but mounted off center in the casing. It carries two sliding vanes, on which outward pressure is maintained by steam pressure or by springs. These vanes therefore come out as they sweep around the lower part of the casing, or retract when constrained by the upper part. Steamtightness between the intake and exhaust ports depends upon the fit of the rotating piston against the upper section of the casing, and of course at the sides as well. The two vanes would, all else being well, act like two pistons, steam expanding against one while exhausting from behind the other, as shown in the drawing.

Lest it seem that the packing vane or sliding seals of these engines would fall into the ports and catch on their edges, it should be pointed out that the ports would not have to be full-width slots, but might even be a series of parallel holes, the metal between them providing a surface for the vanes to ride over. But there remained serious drawbacks to such rotary engines. Most of them were far more complicated than the ones shown. Some involved ovoid instead of circular casings, intersecting cylindrical bodies that meshed somewhat like gears, and even rollers working in rubber linings. Undoubtedly some were built, but none left a memorable mark in the annals of steam engineering.

There were those who saw an easier road to a rotary steam engine. Why not a steam windmill? Far simpler than a reciprocating engine, it would have fewer parts, run with little or no vibration, waste no power in reversing reciprocating parts.

But the simplicity of this concept was deceptive. Even low-pressure steam escapes into the air at a speed of over 1,500 miles per hour. Obviously it will spin a bladed wheel. But unless the blades can themselves move at about half the speed of the steam, most of the latter's energy will be lost as it bounces off the blades at high speed.

For reasonable efficiency, steam should flow off the blades at low speed, having given up its kinetic energy to the turbine wheel. But since a steam jet moves so fast, this means the blades would have to have tremendous peripheral speeds—a fact that made someone dub the early steam turbine a tornado in a box.

NOZZLES AND CREAM SEPARATORS

When steam escapes into the air, it loses heat. This heat must, by the laws of physics, be accounted for—that is, it must reappear in some other form. And so it does, as kinetic energy. The steam jet gains an astonishing amount of speed. A heat drop of merely 100 B.T.U. (British Thermal Units) increases the steam's speed by 30 miles per *minute*. That is 1,800 miles per hour. Nor is a British Thermal Unit very large—it is the amount of heat necessary to raise the temperature of one pound of water only one degree Fahrenheit.

Some time in the 1870s a young Swede with an excellent grounding in thermodynamics and engineering was experimenting with steam nozzles—not for turbines, but for sandblasting. He calculated (and proved by experiment) that to let steam expand down from high pressure to high speed most efficiently, such a nozzle should first converge, then flare out at a point in the throat where the pressure drops below a certain critical point.

Having several experimental nozzles set, one day, so that their reactive forces coincided (like the jets on Hero's aeolipile) Carl de Laval was taken by surprise when the setup began revolving. The rotative force developed so impressed him that he remembered the incident, which was to bear fruit years later.

In 1882, having invented a centrifugal cream separator, de Laval sought some means of driving it at the necessary high speed. Gears were noisy, wasted power, and required someone to turn them. Electricity was not yet available on farms. His memory flew back to the incident of the runaway nozzles, and to power his cream separator de Laval invented the single-stage impulse turbine. This was a vaned wheel with de Laval nozzles directed against it (Figure 8).

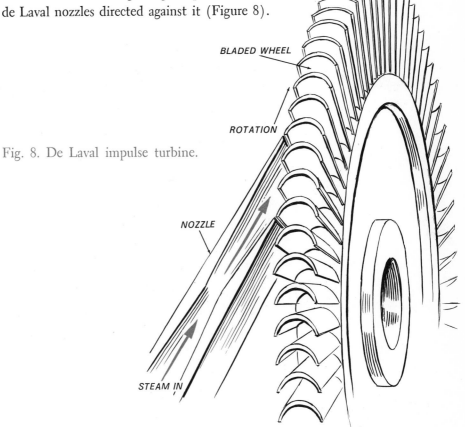

Fig. 8. De Laval impulse turbine.

He got the high speeds he wanted—up to 40,000 r.p.m. Some of his early models flew apart because of centrifugal stresses and vibration. De Laval countered by inventing a flexible shaft that allowed his turbine wheels to find their own center of rotation, and they worked well in his cream separators. (In our own time, very tiny turbines spinning at up to 50,000 r.p.m. have found another use—driving superspeed dental drills.)

Seeking other work for his high-speed turbine, de Laval invented a helical reducing gear to tame it. Some of his machines were put to driving electrical generators. But Charles Gordon Curtis, an American engineer, found a way to slow down the impulse turbine *without* gears.

His method, which he demonstrated in the United States in 1898, was called velocity staging. A Curtis turbine with two velocity stages will have two bladed wheels some distance apart on the same shaft, with a row of oppositely curved fixed blades fastened to the casing between them (Figure 9).

Assuming a steam velocity of 2,400 feet per second (f.p.s.) and a blade velocity of 600 f.p.s. (remember, we wanted a slower turbine), the steam jet is traveling at only 1,800 f.p.s. *in relation to* the first set of moving blades. Its direction reversed on leaving them, the steam will have given up 600 f.p.s. and be moving at only 1,200 f.p.s. in the opposite direction. Now the stationary blades reverse it, so it strikes the second row of moving blades traveling the same way they are, and only 600 f.p.s. faster. Reversed again after it gives up that speed to the turbine wheel, the steam emerges at zero velocity in relation to the turbine casing.

In this way, the two steps of velocity staging have reduced turbine speed to one fourth that of the original steam velocity, yet made use of all the steam's kinetic energy. Up to five velocity stages have been used in Curtis turbines.

DYNAMOS AND THE TURBINIA

Sir Charles Parsons, born in London and educated at Dublin and Cambridge, became interested in turbines for powering dynamos in the newly dawning age of electricity. (He had, incidentally, patented a four-cylinder epicycloidal steam engine in 1881.) Most dynamos, or generators, were belt driven from reciprocating steam engines. Parsons wanted a direct drive, which meant a moderately high engine speed—though nothing like that of the de Laval turbine. There remained the dilemma of high steam velocity versus low blade speed.

But jet velocity depended upon the pressure difference that made the

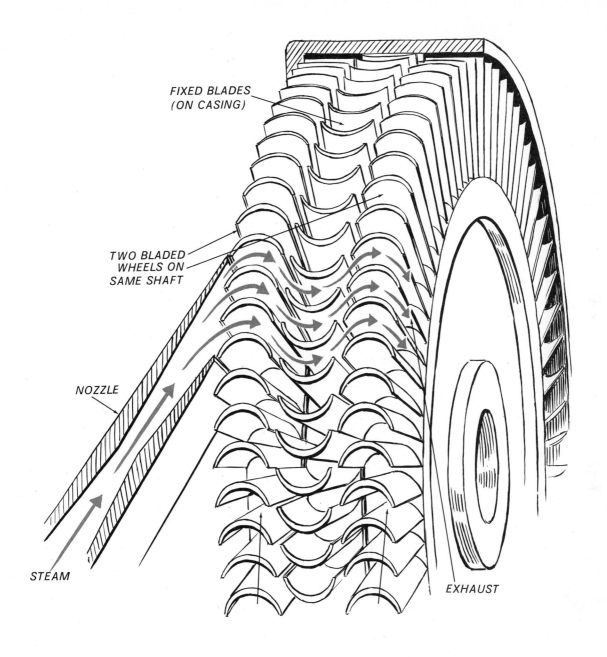

FIXED BLADES
(ON CASING)

TWO BLADED
WHEELS ON
SAME SHAFT

NOZZLE

STEAM

EXHAUST

Fig. 9. Curtis velocity staging.

steam move. What if the steam could be expanded in small increments—that is, pressure be allowed to drop in small steps, each step resulting in a modest steam velocity that the blades could use efficiently while moving at moderate speed? (In a de Laval turbine, the steam expanded from the nozzle all at once, gaining maximum speed then and there.)

Parsons turbines have a cylindrical or drumlike rotor, long enough to accommodate a great number of stages. Fixed on the rotor are spaced rings of blades, and fixed to the inside of the casing between these moving blades are rings of fixed ones much like those in Figure 10 but in greater number. There are no nozzles of the de Laval type.

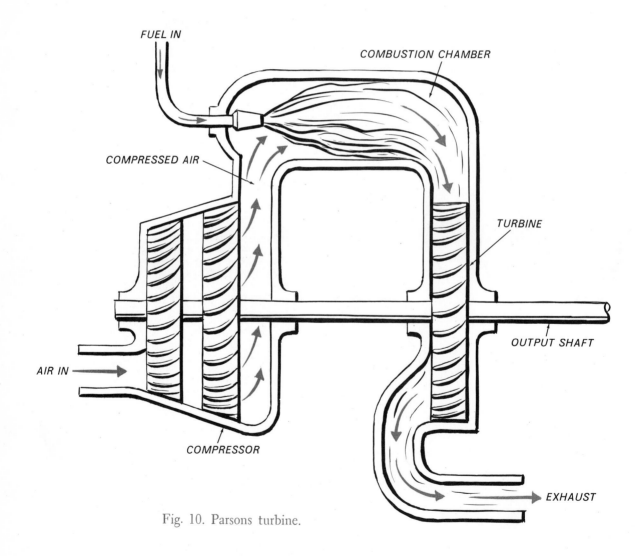

Fig. 10. Parsons turbine.

Steam is admitted at one end of the casing, and drives the first ring of blades partly by impulse as it flows past. But these blades are shaped to act like nozzles as they pass the steam onward. In kicking itself off them, the steam exerts a reactive force on the blades, reinforcing the impulse energy already delivered.

The stationary blades reverse the direction of flow, directing the steam against the second ring of blades. Again these are driven partly by impulse, partly by reaction as they in turn send the steam on. Each stage lowers the pressure, for the steam expands in each ring of vanes. In doing so it also loses some of its heat, and gains speed.

A small amount of steam as measured by weight (3 pounds) will pass through a 13-foot-long Parsons turbine in $\frac{1}{16}$ of a second, its speed increasing fourfold between intake and exhaust ends, and its passage generating a whopping 20,000 hp.

Parsons' genius showed itself in details as well as in the grand concept of the reaction turbine. His first small turbine ran at 18,000 r.p.m., and no dynamo maker would contract to build a generator to operate at that speed. Centrifugal forces alone were prohibitive, amounting to several tons for every pound of rotating metal. But Parsons designed and built such a machine, so successfully that 200 were in use for ship lighting by 1888. Twelve years later he was building 1,000 kilowatt generators for city lighting. Eventually his machines were up to 200,000 kilowatt capacity.

He also applied the condenser to his turbines, expanding steam down to as little as ¼ p.s.i. absolute pressure—actually a vacuum of 14½ p.s.i. To compensate for end thrust, he invented the dummy piston, on which steam pressure counteracts the axial thrust on the turbine vanes. He was also responsible for labyrinth packing—a method of sealing a rotating shaft without a stuffing box (which at turbine speeds would not last). Instead, sharp-edged fixed rings abut the shaft surface just short of touching it. Eddy currents set up as the steam tries to pass these sharp-bordered gaps make it turn back on itself, so acting as its own seal.

But Parsons' most dramatic triumph was in demonstrating his turbine's effectiveness in ship propulsion. In 1894 he built the 100-foot-long, 44-ton Turbinia. Standard propellers, unsuitable for the high speed of its turbine, drove the little vessel at only 20 knots. To get the ship ready in time for demonstration, Parsons mounted three shafts, each with three propellers on it. With this unconventional propulsion system, he took it to the great Naval Review of 1897, on the occasion of Queen Victoria's Diamond Jubilee.

The pride of England's navy being at Spithead that day, Parsons raced his little Turbinia along a line of destroyers at 34 knots—7 more than the fastest of these naval vessels could make. He received a grudging and conditional contract for a turbine-driven destroyer. It proved itself when its 12,000 hp turbines gave it a speed of 37 knots, and the triumph of the steam turbine on the sea was sealed.

Later Parsons developed reduction gear to let his turbines drive big, slow, efficient propellers for cargo ships. He built turbines of 70,000 hp for the Mauretania, the ill-fated Lusitania, and other fast Atlantic vessels. An important factor was his "creep cutting" method of making gears. This distributed any pitch error in the master gear or index plate all around the gear being machined, so equalizing and in effect eliminating it.

Another type of steam turbine, is the radial turbine, on which Parsons worked briefly. In this, steam flows from the shaft outward along the vanes. The most successful radial turbines were those built by two Swedish brothers, B. and F. Ljungstrom, in 1912. Working on the reaction principle, these have two bladed wheels facing each other. Steam passing between them makes them rotate in opposite directions, and each wheel drives its own generator.

As already mentioned, mercury vapor is an efficient if poisonous substitute for steam, having a theoretical efficiency of 60 percent because of its high range of working temperature. The exhaust vapor from a mercury turbine is amply hot enough to generate high-pressure steam, which in turn is piped to a steam turbine, usually in tandem with the mercury unit.

TURBINES AND THE ATOM

A nuclear reactor's energy appears in the form of heat. Although great headway has been made in converting heat directly into electricity, today's giant power plants still use generators. To convert the reactor's heat energy into rotary power for driving those generators, the steam turbine of the Victorian Age has found a place in the Atomic Era.

Figure 11 is a flow chart of a modern nuclear generating station—Consolidated Edison's No. 2 plant at Indian Point, New York, which is scheduled for completion in 1969. The No. 1 plant has been at work since September 1962, having generated at the time of its first refueling late in 1965 more than 2.8 billion kilowatt hours. To do this, it used about 20 tons of nuclear fuel, a pinhead in comparison to the mountain of coal a conventional plant would have consumed—780,000 tons!

The No. 2 plant alone will generate 873,000 kilowatts. Its reactor will be encased in a domed, reinforced, concrete cylinder with walls 4½ feet thick,

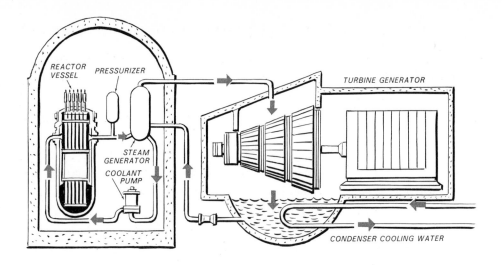

Fig. 11. Flow chart of a modern
nuclear generating station.

lined with welded steel. Pellets of enriched uranium 235 will be packed in
plugged Zircaloy tubes; there will be 193 fuel elements, each consisting of 204
of these pellet-carrying tubes, a total loading of over 215,000 pounds of uranium oxide.

Heat from the nuclear reaction will be absorbed by water circulated
through the fuel elements. This superheated, pressurized water will be
pumped through U-shaped tubes around which other water flows, and will
turn this water into steam. (Such a steam generator is big brother to the
domestic tankless hot-water system, in which a coil immersed in the heating
boiler carries water for the taps.)

Passing to the turbines, the steam delivers its energy to them and then
enters a condenser cooled by river water. The condensate will then be pumped
back to the steam generator to pursue its useful cycle over and over again
(Figure 11).

As the pressurized reactor water will never mix with either the steam
water or the cooling water, there is no risk of radioactive contamination. To
control the power output, the speed of the nuclear reaction is varied by raising
or lowering neutron-absorbing rods into the core, and by changing the amount
of boron (which also absorbs neutrons) in the reactor water.

In a similar way, nuclear-turbine plants power ships and submarines.
For marine use, the great advantage of nuclear power is vastly increased opera-
tional range, free from the limitations of coal and oil supplies. On land there is
the tremendous added advantage that there is no smoke or other effluvia to
add to air pollution. In testimony to this fact, the newest nuclear plants like

Con Edison's No. 2 will not even have a smokestack. As this is being written, there are at least fifty-five nuclear power plants in the United States, and more being built.

THE ROTATING COMBUSTION ENGINE

Any displacement-type internal-combustion engine whose main parts do not reciprocate is called a rotating combustion engine. The rotary displacement concept has such big potential advantages that at least six countries have been developing rotating combustion (RC) engines of some kind or other. Some are already in production.

These engines were given an immense impetus by the success of the Wankel engine, the 1956 home-workshop invention of Felix Wankel of the little town of Lindau, Germany. Wankel sold his idea to NSU, German motorcycle and car makers. In the United States, Curtiss-Wright obtained sole North American license rights and carried on intensive research and development from the early sixties. The vastly improved CW version of the Wankel engine has successfully powered cars, trucks, boats, electric generators and lawnmowers, in sizes from 3 to 1,000 hp. It has been hinted in Detroit that the RC engine is forging ahead of the gas turbine as a candidate for the next breakthrough in mass-produced car engines.

The CW engine has a far better power-to-weight ratio than piston engines. It is much smaller. Having no reciprocating parts, it runs virtually without vibration. Requiring fewer parts than piston engines, it could be mass produced at lower cost.

It also takes in its fuel-air charge for a greater proportion of its shaft rotation, develops torque for a greater part of its cycle than the piston engine, and can buzz along on low octane gas or—with fuel injection—on cheaper combustible fluids. It is little troubled by the "scale effect" that renders small piston engines less efficient than big ones. The casing or working chamber of the Curtiss-Wright engine has an inside contour like a fat figure 8, its waist pinched in only slightly to form what is called a trochoid (Figure 12). The triangular rotor has slightly rounded sides. In each of its three faces is a recess or pocket forming a combustion chamber.

The three apexes of the triangle have sliding seals and the rotor sides also carry seals. Their function is akin to that of the rings on a piston—to separate the displacement areas and provide for good compression. A bore or center hole in the piston is machined smooth for most of its width, but at one end carries a fixed ring gear.

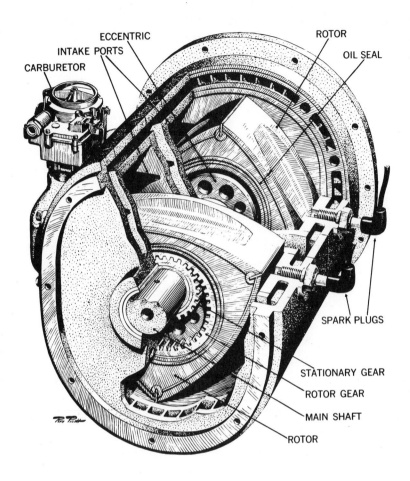

ECCENTRIC
INTAKE PORTS
CARBURETOR
ROTOR
OIL SEAL
SPARK PLUGS
STATIONARY GEAR
ROTOR GEAR
MAIN SHAFT
ROTOR

Fig. 12. Curtis-Wright version of
the Wankel engine.

The machined part of the bore can turn on an eccentric keyed to the
output shaft. But because of the ring gear, the rotor must "walk" around a
stationary gear fixed centrally to one inner wall of the casing. In the engine
shown, this stationary gear has 48 teeth and the ring gear 72. By the curious
logic of planetary gearing, this 2:3 relationship provides a 3:1 ratio between
the output shaft and the rotor.

Revolving around the stationary gear, the rotor bore swings about
eccentrically at three times the rate the rotor itself turns. As the rotor makes

only one-twelfth of a turn, or 30 degrees of a revolution, its bore (and the eccentric it carries within it) moves 90 degrees, turning the shaft a like amount. The best way to convince yourself of this curious action is to try it with an internal gear swung around a fixed spur gear about two-thirds as large.

There are no valves in the CW engine, and only one spark plug per rotor. Intake ports are in the side, where they are uncovered as the rotor lobes sweep past them. The exhaust port is on the periphery of the casing.

As the rotor turns, the face opposite the intake port draws away from the casing wall, like an outward moving piston, so drawing in the fuel-air mix. The other two rotor sides are meanwhile on the firing stroke of the previous charge and the exhaust stroke of the one before that.

As chamber volume reaches its maximum, the rotor closes the intake port. Continuing, it compresses the charge until most of it is squeezed into the combustion pocket. Then the plug fires, and expanding gases drive the rotor about until the forward apex of this face side uncovers the exhaust port.

The almost continuous explosions of the two-rotor CW engine give it a sound somewhere between that of a well-tuned six and (at higher speeds) the whine of a turbine. The two rotors are 3 inches wide and 5.75 inches in diameter, working in separate chambers sealed from each other. Cooling is achieved by passing water back and forth through the casings and the end plates. Lubrication is by pressure-fed oil, which also assists cooling.

Whereas the torque curve of a piston engine drops decidedly past a certain modest speed, that of the CW engine continues to climb at far higher r.p.m.'s. The effect of this flat torque curve is interestingly shown in a test of the 1967 Cosmo sports car. Powered by a Japanese-made 60 cubic-inch, 110-hp twin-rotor engine, the car accelerated from 0 to 60 m.p.h. in 8.7 seconds, and from 25 to 70 m.p.h. in 9. Torque climbs from 65 foot-pounds at 1,000 r.p.m. to 99 foot-pounds at 5,000.

RIVALS OF THE WANKEL

The success of Felix Wankel's brainstorm inspired a number of other inventors, while still others had been at work long before. In 1964 American Motors installed a rotary engine designed by the French Renault company in a test car. This engine has a four-lobed rotor working in a five-cavity casing somewhat like a five-leaved clover. Each cavity had two conventional poppet valves and a spark plug, making the engine far more complicated than the Wankel.

P. R. Mallory and Company, makers of batteries and other electrical products, in 1967 sprang a surprise in the form of a rotary engine having sliding vanes in a slotted rotor. The invention of Wallace L. Linn, and Gianni A. Dotto, the engine as first built lost its load under test and blew apart at something over 18,000 r.p.m. Succeeding models, however, turned in good performance.

Heavy slotted rotor of the Mallory rotary vane engine carries vanes like that at front to the 16 working chambers. Note notches and holes in the circumference of the rotor; they swirl fuel and air to mix it prior to combustion.

The rotor in the Mallory engine is mounted off-center in an elliptical housing. Vanes slide out to form chambers which get smaller to compress fuel.

The rotor is mounted off center, its vanes being held out by a cam on the shaft. These vanes seal off separate working chambers between them, the volume of the chambers becoming greater or smaller as the rotor moves farther or nearer the walls of a slightly elliptical housing. Fuel and air are fed to each chamber in turn through slots in the housing at the five-o'clock position. Maximum compression occurs at the twelve o'clock position, and the single spark plug fires at one o'clock. The exhaust begins at three o'clock.

There is little torque at low speed, but a 185-pound test engine developed 400 hp at 5,000 r.p.m. Made in part of aluminum, the same engine would weigh only 80 pounds, with the fabulous horsepower-weight ratio of 5 to 1. Though at present it screams like a banshee, the engine seems to offer exciting possibilities for helicopters and light planes.

Tschudi engine has four curved pistons running a toroidal track. A pair of diametrically opposed pistons is carried on each rotor. Each rotor also carries two rollers. These rollers bear against two identical cams fixed to the output shaft. The rollers rotate only because of friction against the cams. Power flow is achieved by having one roller push into a cam groove while the other assures positive cam location.

Very different is a curved-piston engine invented by a Swiss engineer, Traugott Tschudi. Each of two rotors carries two such pistons, 180 degrees apart, around a toroidal (doughnut-shaped) track. The pistons have rollers that bear against cams on the shaft, which is off center to the toroids and is turned by the pressure of the rollers against the cams.

Piston action is not continuous. Each rotor actually comes to a stop while the other turns the shaft. Therefore at least two toroids are needed.

Another vaned engine is the creation of Eugen Kauertz, who lives in retirement in Southern Germany. In a circular casing, two sets of vanes approach and draw away from each other to create the necessary displacement action for a four-stroke cycle (Figure 13).

A two-stroke type, the Selwood engine (Figure 14) has curved pistons in toroidal tracks. But these are set around a spider or swash plate, and as the pistons move in their tracks, the entire cylinder block revolves. The output shaft is attached to it, while the main shaft that carries the spider is stationary.

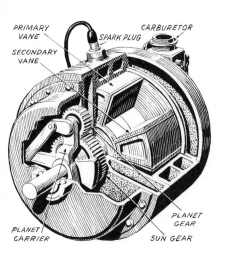

PRIMARY VANE
SECONDARY VANE
SPARK PLUG
CARBURETOR
PLANET CARRIER
PLANET GEAR
SUN GEAR

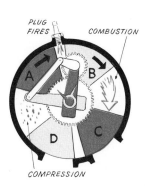

PLUG FIRES
COMBUSTION
COMPRESSION

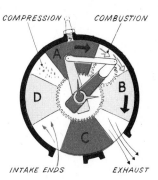

COMPRESSION
COMBUSTION
INTAKE ENDS
EXHAUST

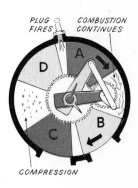

PLUG FIRES
COMBUSTION CONTINUES
COMPRESSION

Fig. 13. Kauertz engine has vane-type pistons in a circular-section working chamber. Two sets of vanes rotate on the same axis but continuously change position relative to each other. This speeding up and slowing down of one set of vanes changes the volume of gas between the two sets. Changes in gas volume produce the pumping action needed for intake, compression, combustion and exhaust. Four effective combustion chambers assure four power phases per output-shaft revolution. Correct phasing of the vane motion is assured by a gear-and-crank system. A 61.6-cubic-inch version of the Kauertz engine has been tested and found to give 213 hp at 4,000 r.p.m. It runs as smoothly as a V-8 piston engine.

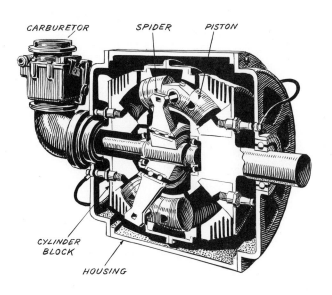

CARBURETOR
SPIDER
PISTON
CYLINDER BLOCK
HOUSING

Fig. 14. Selwood engine is rotary in the sense that the cylinder block revolves, driving an output shaft, while the main shaft, which supports the spider and the pistons, is stationary. As the spider is fixed at a 15-degree angle, it works like a swash plate. The pistons run back and forth in toroidal tracks. Piston travel is possible only by letting the block turn. But the piston doesn't really reciprocate; it orbits around the main shaft and goes through 30 degrees of track travel in half an orbit. The next half-orbit, the piston moves 30 degrees back again. The Selwood works on the two-stroke principle. When one side of a piston begins a power stroke, the other side starts a compression phase. The prototype has six pistons and works as a V-12.

209

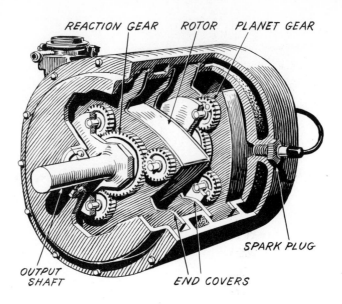

REACTION GEAR · ROTOR · PLANET GEAR

OUTPUT SHAFT

END COVERS

SPARK PLUG

Fig. 15. Jernaes engine is built up around a central output shaft with an integral circular disk. This disk works as the rotor hub. Unlike the Wankel rotor, the rotor has no internal gearing. Instead the disk supports three planet gears running on eccentric shafts. These gears mesh with a stationary reaction gear mounted concentrically with the output shaft and the disk. Each planet gear has the same eccentricity, and they are spaced 120 degrees apart. As the rotor turns, it carries the planet gears along. They are phased to let the output shaft turn at rotor speed (instead of three times rotor speed as in the Wankel). Finn Jernaes claims that his gear mechanism makes for a big increase in torque at relatively low r.p.m. In other words, a four-stroke, single-rotor Jernaes engine produces the same number of power impulses per output-shaft revolution as a six-cylinder piston engine. Rotor side-sealing is ingenious: The end covers revolve with the rotors and are sealed with two simple rings on each side. Intake and exhaust ports are opened by holes in the end covers.

Finn Jernaes, a Norwegian, adapted the triangular rotor and trochoid housing of the Wankel engine to a different kind of planetary gearing (Figure 15). This is claimed to give more torque in the lower speed range. The shaft turns at rotor speed, instead of three times as fast. A single-rotor engine working on the four-stroke principle, the Jernaes provides three power pulses per revolution, the same as a conventional six-cylinder piston engine.

Though some of these highly ingenious machines will probably be abandoned and forgotten, there are strong indications that rotary displacement engines are here to stay, and probably to multiply.

XII

Hydraulic Power and the New Science of Fluidics

Any solid body has a fixed form and size. A gas has neither. It will expand to fill any void, of any shape, until constrained by the walls of the vessel (or, in the case of our atmosphere, by the force of gravity that binds it around the earth). A fluid falls between these extremes, having a fixed volume but no definite shape.

For practical purposes, a fluid is incompressible, determined to fill its own volume. But it will readily move about and change shape to do so. This combination of the flexible and inflexible gives fluids a unique role in the world of mechanics, not only for the transmission of power, but for certain control purposes.

The shock absorbers in your car are one example. Basically they are cylinder-and-piston devices, connected across the springs of the car to control rebound. As the wheel moves up, fluid above the piston is allowed to leave at a controlled rate through a small hole. A violent road impact will cause a popoff valve to open, allowing fluid to pass more quickly. But this closes on the rebound, and fluid can return only through the small orifice. The rebound is thus snubbed harder than the bounce.

Such fluid control has also been applied to a very different field—recording. The stylus that cuts grooves in impressing sound vibrations on the

211

master recording must move inward in a very precise spiral, the spacing between grooves being measured in thousandths of an inch. Ordinarily a precision cut, carefully lapped screw thread is used. But in the Hydrofeed recording lathe, the stylus is mounted on one end of a piston sliding in a hydraulic cylinder. The fluid behind the piston blocks its movement. A needle valve is then adjusted to release the imprisoned fluid at a very slow rate. As it escapes, the piston and stylus move inward at a perfectly controlled speed.

PRESSURE IN FLUIDS

A force exists beneath the surface of any liquid. If you push a glass under water, it will resist and bob up again as soon as it is released. This force buoys up both a rowboat and a battleship, but obviously it must be much greater in the latter case. How large it is depends on two things—the depth of the liquid, and its density. It will be greater in mercury than in water, for example, because mercury is a very heavy fluid.

The effect of depth can be stated this way: the force at any point in a body of fluid is equivalent to the weight of the column of fluid above it. The pressure halfway up a tank of water is less than at the bottom, because there is less fluid above that point. A diver is subject to less pressure at a depth of 30 feet than at 60, for there is less water bearing down on him.

HOW FLUIDS TRANSMIT PRESSURE

From the above facts, the French scientist and mathematician Blaise Pascal (who died in 1662) deduced what has come to be known as Pascal's law: *pressure at any point in a body of fluid is the same in every direction, exerting equal force on equal areas.* If we have a vessel like that in Figure 1, with a neck 1 square inch in area, and through a piston impose a force of 1 pound on the fluid (which will be in addition to the pressure of the fluid's own weight), that force will be exerted in all directions in the whole body of fluid. The total force on the walls of the container will be their total area times 1 pound per square inch (p.s.i.) (disregarding for the moment the fluid's own internal pressure).

Pascal pointed out the possibilities of this hydraulic action. "A vessel full of water," he said, "is a new principle in mechanics, and a new machine for the multiplication of force to any required extent . . ."

Suppose we have a small steel cylinder with a cross-sectional area of 1 square inch, and a larger one with an area of 500 square inches. We connect the two with a sturdy pipe (Figure 2), fill the system with fluid, and insert

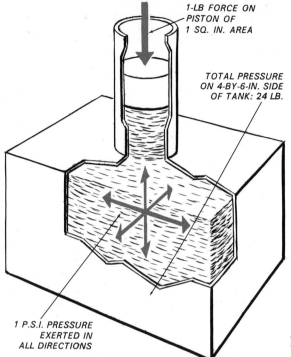

1-LB FORCE ON
PISTON OF
1 SQ. IN. AREA

TOTAL PRESSURE
ON 4-BY-6-IN. SIDE
OF TANK: 24 LB.

1 P.S.I. PRESSURE
EXERTED IN
ALL DIRECTIONS

Fig. 1. Illustration of Pascal's law.

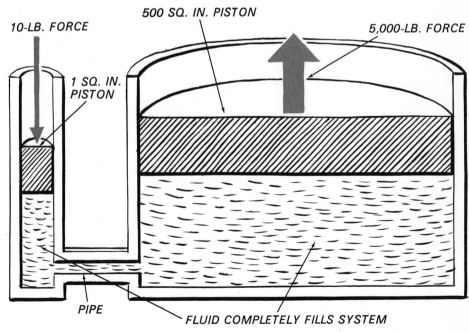

10-LB. FORCE

500 SQ. IN. PISTON

5,000-LB. FORCE

1 SQ. IN.
PISTON

Fig. 2. Pressure of 10 pounds on piston with a cross-sectional area of 1 square inch exerts 5,000 pounds on piston with an area of 500 square.

PIPE

FLUID COMPLETELY FILLS SYSTEM

213

two close-fitting pistons. It will now be necessary to "bleed" the system of air, as your garagemen must bleed the hydraulic brake system of your car at times, for air is compressible and its presence would make the hydraulic action "spongy" and ineffectual.

Having bled the two-cylinder system shown, suppose we press down on the small piston with a force of 10 pounds. The area of this piston being 1 square inch, this means a pressure of 10 p.s.i. is being applied to the fluid. By Pascal's law this is exerted on every square inch of the large piston. But 500 times 10 gives us a total force of 5,000 pounds on the big piston—all as the result of leaning on the little one with 10 pounds of force!

Something for nothing? No. The force is multiplied, but to make it do any work, it must move through a distance. To lift the big piston 1 inch, we must add that height of fluid to the big cylinder. But our small working piston will, in a 1-inch stroke, displace only enough fluid to raise the big piston $\frac{1}{500}$ inch. We will have to move the little piston 500 inches, or make 500 1-inch strokes, to raise the large piston 1 inch. The product of force times distance on the small piston (10 times 500) will be the same as that for the larger piston (5,000 times 1). In practice, there are actually some losses due to fluid friction in the pipes and bends, as well as friction between the pistons and cylinder walls.

THE HYDRAULIC PRESS

Even though we cannot cheat nature, we can make a worthwhile bargain with her. There are occasions when a great force, even though exerted through a small distance, is of immense advantage. Jacking up a truck or a house, compressing material into bales, squeezing oil out of seeds are some cases in point.

We need only add to our two-cylinder arrangement a reservoir to supply extra fluid as the large piston moves out, a one-way or check valve to lock in the fluid already pumped into the large cylinder, and a similar valve to take in more fluid at each stroke of the small piston (Figure 3). Add a rigidly fixed platen above the large piston, and we can squeeze materials with great force. If we push this machine under a load, we can use it to jack up immense weights. The hydraulic truck and garage jack works on precisely the same principle.

In practice, both the hydraulic press and the jack need one more valve, to let fluid bleed out of the big cylinder back to the reservoir, releasing the load and readying the machine for its next job.

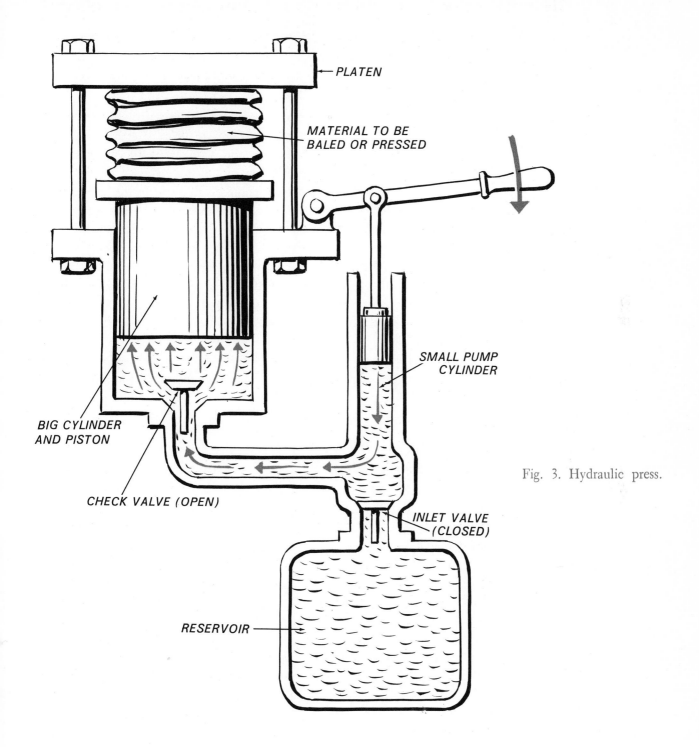

PLATEN

MATERIAL TO BE
BALED OR PRESSED

SMALL PUMP
CYLINDER

BIG CYLINDER
AND PISTON

CHECK VALVE (OPEN)

INLET VALVE
(CLOSED)

RESERVOIR

Fig. 3. Hydraulic press.

215

THE HYDRAULIC ELEVATOR

The car of this now obsolete lift was perched on top of a gleaming column of steel, which slid majestically up and down in the shaft. A counterweight balanced much of the weight of the car and column, so that hydraulic power was expended chiefly in raising the operator and passengers (Figure 4).

The steel column—actually a piston as long as the car's vertical travel—fitted into an equally deep cylinder set into a pit. A seal at the top end allowed the column to slide up and down without undue loss of fluid. Interposed between the pit cylinder and the water supply (which might be the city main or a reservoir on top of the building) was a valve controlled by a counterbalanced rope that passed through the car within reach of the operator.

On being lifted, the valve routed water into the pit cylinder, where its pressure on the bottom of the column raised the car. When the control rope was pulled down, it swung the valve to the exhaust position, shutting off the water supply while instead bleeding fluid out of the pit cylinder to the sewer. As this flow of water was limited by the size of the valve orifice, the car fell at a controlled rate.

Speedier hydraulic elevators used shorter cylinders, placed to one side of the car, and multiplied piston travel by a pulley arrangement, the car being hoisted up by cables. This eliminated the need for a deep pit cylinder.

THE HYDRAULIC RAM

At least 150 years old, this machine is a simple automatic device that makes water pump itself uphill. This is not as surprising as it first sounds, for a good deal of water must flow to a lower level (usually being wasted) to move a smaller quantity to a higher point. Though inefficient, a hydraulic ram is nevertheless a reliable means of pumping water where conditions permit its use. It is unable, however, to pump up water from a source level with or lower than itself, and therefore cannot be used for wells.

Assuming the source is a lake or spring and the ram can be located 10 feet below it, with a 50-foot supply pipe, the device would pump water to a house or tank 50 feet above it (Figure 5).

When water is first admitted through the supply pipe, the delivery valve A is closed and the escape valve B open. But as water rushes down, it fills the chamber and finally snaps valve B shut.

The moving column of water has considerable momentum (which is why the length of the supply pipe is a factor in performance). On the sudden closing of valve B, it surges against the delivery valve A and opens it. Water

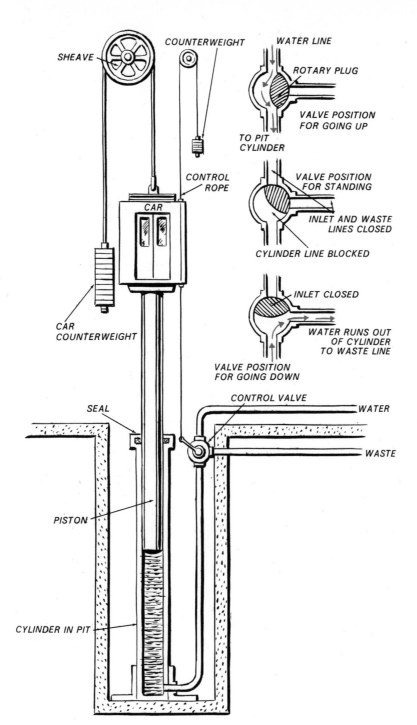

SHEAVE

COUNTERWEIGHT

WATER LINE

ROTARY PLUG

VALVE POSITION
FOR GOING UP

TO PIT
CYLINDER

CONTROL
ROPE

CAR

VALVE POSITION
FOR STANDING

INLET AND WASTE
LINES CLOSED

CYLINDER LINE BLOCKED

INLET CLOSED

WATER RUNS OUT
OF CYLINDER
TO WASTE LINE

VALVE POSITION
FOR GOING DOWN

CAR
COUNTERWEIGHT

SEAL

CONTROL VALVE

WATER

WASTE

PISTON

CYLINDER IN PIT

Fig. 4. Hydraulic elevator.

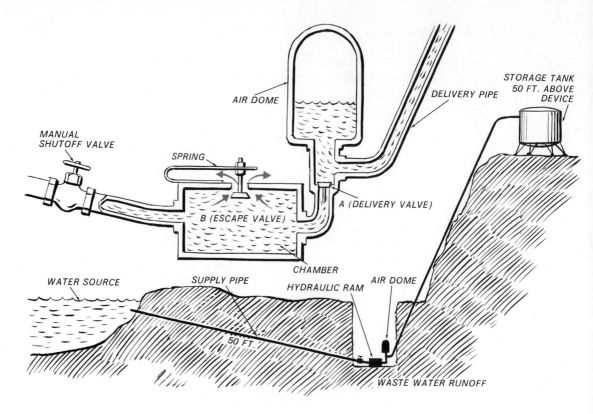

MANUAL SHUTOFF VALVE

AIR DOME

SPRING

DELIVERY PIPE

STORAGE TANK 50 FT. ABOVE DEVICE

A (DELIVERY VALVE)

B (ESCAPE VALVE)

WATER SOURCE

SUPPLY PIPE

CHAMBER

HYDRAULIC RAM

AIR DOME

50 FT.

WASTE WATER RUNOFF

Fig. 5. Hydraulic ram.

rushes through into the air dome and delivery pipe, compressing air in the dome. As the water below loses its momentum, air compressed in the dome exerts pressure on the water in it and on valve A, closing it. Balked by this, water in the dome moves up the delivery pipe.

Meanwhile a back surge in the chamber and supply line occurs, reducing pressure there. Valve B again opens. As the water begins to rush down from its source once more, the cycle repeats, usually 25 to 100 times a minute.

Practical units may have a spring that tends to keep the escape valve open, with stop and tensioning adjustments that limit valve travel and control its resonance rate. These make it possible to "tune" the valve to suit the length and slope of the supply pipe for most advantageous action.

HYDRAULIC AUTO BRAKE SYSTEMS

Fluid is used in automobile brakes to transmit pressure equally to all four wheels at once. The foot pedal moves a piston in a master cylinder, forcing fluid through the lines into brake cylinders at the wheels. There hydraulic pressure pushes out pistons which, through sturdy push rods, squeeze the brake shoes against the wheel drums or disks.

If you release the pedal quickly, the spring in the master cylinder shoves back its piston before fluid can return from the lines. In this case, holes in the piston head let fluid pass from behind it to the front (past the rubber piston cup, which acts like a check valve), keeping this vital space filled just in case you should have to apply the brakes again immediately.

Assuming you do not, the brake-shoe return springs force the pistons in the brake cylinders back in. Fluid is forced out of the cylinders by this action and returns to the master cylinder by overcoming the spring pressure that holds its check valve shut. Excess fluid then goes back to the reservoir through a compensating port uncovered by the master-cylinder piston when it is all the way back.

It takes a pressure of 8 to 12 p.s.i. to open the check valve, which closes as soon as pressure falls below that. This means there is some pressure in the hydraulic lines at all times (though not enough to overcome the brake-shoe return springs). This static pressure prevents the brake-piston cups from leaking and helps keep air out of the system.

As the master cylinder and brake cylinders are not greatly different in area, there is no such immense multiplication of force as in the hydraulic jack or press. Some mechanical advantage is gained from the leverage of the foot pedal, which makes your foot move several inches to advance the master-cylinder piston a shorter way. The great advantages of hydraulic brakes are two: braking effort is automatically equalized, since all the wheel cylinders are the same size; and the hydraulic lines do away with such vulnerable moving parts as rods, cables, clevises and pins.

One disadvantage of hydraulic brake systems is that a break anywhere in the lines will release fluid, dropping hydraulic pressure to zero and making the brakes inoperable. Cadillac, Rambler and Saab have for some time had dual systems to overcome this hazard, and more American cars introduced them in 1967.

The master cylinder in a dual system has a front and a rear piston, both operated from the brake pedal (Figure 6). One piston provides hydraulic pressure for the front wheels, the other for the rear. Should one system fail, the car can still be stopped with the other, a dash indicator light going on to warn that braking pressure has been lost on one pair of wheels.

Power brakes are of two basic types. Both use engine manifold vacuum to apply pressure to a hydraulic master cylinder. One system is a composite unit that combines the master cylinder with a vacuum power unit. The other

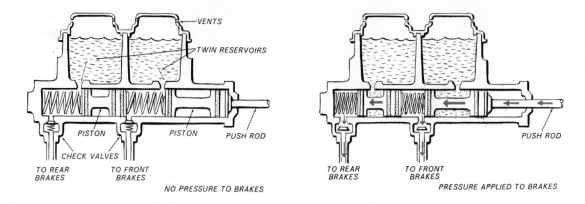

VENTS

TWIN RESERVOIRS

PISTON

PISTON

PUSH ROD

CHECK VALVES

TO REAR
BRAKES

TO FRONT
BRAKES

NO PRESSURE TO BRAKES

TO REAR
BRAKES

TO FRONT
BRAKES

PUSH ROD

PRESSURE APPLIED TO BRAKES

Fig. 6. Hydraulic auto brakes.

has a vacuum unit that assists the driver in applying pressure to a conventional master cylinder. Should the vacuum system fail for any reason, fail-safe engineering makes it possible for the driver still to apply the brakes by exerting more effort.

HYDRAULIC PUMPS AND MOTORS

The oil pump in most auto engines is a gear pump (Figure 7). Two coarse-toothed, relatively wide gears mesh in a close-fitting housing, the intake opening and delivery port being on opposite sides of the area in which the teeth mesh.

What surprises many people about such a pump is the direction of flow through it. Oil is not moved through the meshing teeth, but carried around the outside of both gears in two paths, to join again at the other side and be expelled, as shown by the arrows.

Leakage can occur through the meshing teeth and between the teeth and casing, but if the parts are well machined it is minimal and the pump is quite efficient. Like most other rotary pumps, this one will run as a hydraulic motor if fluid is fed to it under pressure. Its speed will depend upon the rate of flow. Torque is high even at low speed, and the power flow smooth at all speeds, while the direction of rotation (which is the same with reference to the intake side as for a gear pump) can be reversed simply by valving the flow from one side to the other.

Another kind of gear pump, used in some auto power-steering systems, has a smaller gear (or toothed rotor) revolving off center inside a larger, internal-tooth one, which is free to turn. Rotation continuously alters the volume between the teeth, or lobes. Fluid is admitted to the expanding spaces and expelled as these contract, passing through slots in the cover plate (Figure 8).

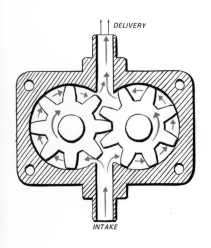

DELIVERY

INTAKE

Fig. 7. Gear pump.

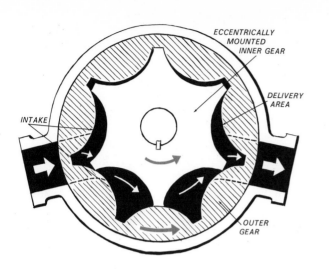

Fig. 8. Internal-external gear pump.

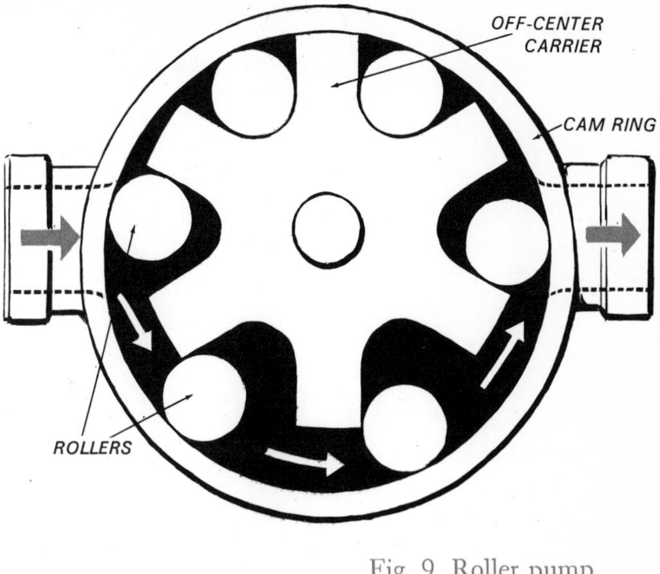

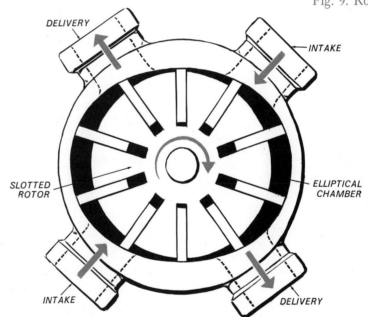

Fig. 9. Roller pump.

Fig. 10. Balanced vane pump.

In another power-steering pump, a six-lobed carrier rotates slightly off center inside a fixed ring. Nestled into the spaces between the lobes are rollers (Figure 9) which seal off each compartment much as vanes would. The volume of each such space increases as it approaches the point of maximum eccentricity, contracting to a minimum 180 degrees later.

A vane pump is shown in Figure 10. A slotted rotor is fitted off center in an elliptical housing. As it spins, centrifugal force keeps the vanes outthrust and in contact with the bore of the housing, while allowing them to slide

221

inward as they pass around the nearer surface. The vanes therefore create as many constantly varying spaces or chambers, which take in fluid as they expand in size and expel fluid as they contract on the outlet side. In the balanced pump shown, pumping action occurs on two sides, increasing output and equalizing the load on the bearing.

PISTON PUMPS AND MOTORS

At first the pump shown in Figure 11 may seem to be another vane pump, but actually it has six reciprocating pistons set in a circular cylinder block. This rotates on a fixed pintle or stud, which has an intake port in one side and a delivery port in the other.

The outer ends of the pistons, fitted with suitable shoes or rollers, ride on the inside of a ring or rotor that is free to turn inside the pump case. The center lines of the rotor and cylinder block are offset slightly (in a variable displacement pump of this kind, the amount of this offset can be varied from zero to a maximum).

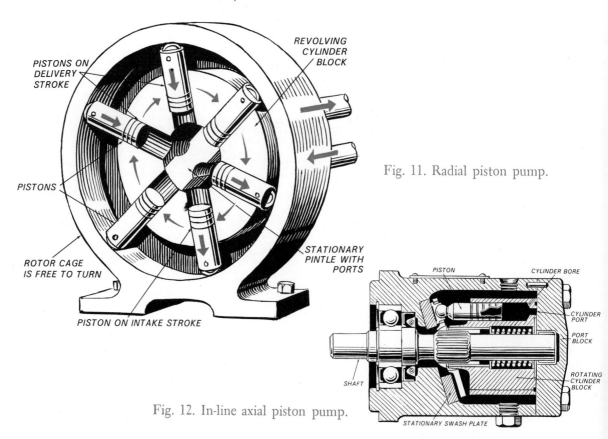

Fig. 11. Radial piston pump.

Fig. 12. In-line axial piston pump.

As the rotor turns, centrifugal force or slight fluid pressure on the intake side moves the pistons out, and the cylinders fill with fluid. On passing the point at which they are fully extended, the pistons are forced back into the cylinders by the eccentricity of the ring, forcing fluid out through the delivery passages in the pintle. If the rotor is moved to zero offset, concentric with the block, the pistons will not reciprocate and there will be no pumping action even though the pump is running.

Axial piston pumps are so called because the cylinders are parallel to a common axis. The simplest of this kind is a fixed-displacement, in-line piston pump, shown in Figure 12. The piston block rotates against a fixed, ported end plate having intake and delivery passages. Ball joints at the ends of the pistons bear against a swash plate set at a fixed angle. As the piston shown at the top swings around to the bottom, it is pushed back into its cylinder by the swash plate, so pumping out fluid. Variable displacement pumps of this type have an adjustable swash plate, which changes the piston stroke and therefore the pumping rate.

Bent-axis pumps have no swash plate, but instead the drive shaft is set at an angle to the cylinder block, which is driven by a universal-joint arrangement. As the cylinders are nearest the drive flange in one position, and farthest when 180 degrees around from that, a reciprocating action is imparted to the pistons (Figure 13). In going around the cylinders communicate successively with intake and exhaust ports in the stationary valve plate.

A variable-displacement pump of the bent-axis type was used to turn aircraft turrets in World War II. The cylinder block had seven bores, and

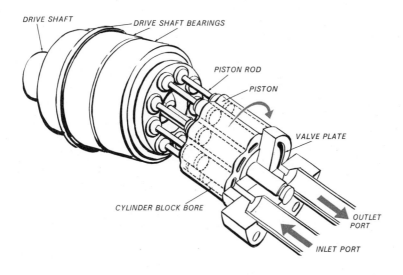

Fig. 13. Bent-axis piston pump.

rotated in a swiveled yoke. Therefore the angle between the drive-shaft flange (in which the piston rods seated) and the cylinder block could be altered to change piston displacement and output. When the yoke was swung to neutral, there was no reciprocating action and no fluid was pumped. Swung to one side, the yoke caused fluid to flow in one direction. Swung to the other, it reversed the flow.

The hydraulic fluid powered a hydraulic motor, the direction and speed of which could thus be controlled by changing the position of the pump yoke. The hydraulic motor in this turret unit was similar to the pump, except that the angle between its cylinder block and drive flange was fixed.

CIRCUITS, VALVES AND ACTUATORS

A hydraulic power system is usually a closed loop, or circuit. Fluid must be pumped under pressure, perform work in a motor or actuator, and return to a reservoir for further use. There must also be a means of bypassing fluid when it is not needed, before excessive pressure can damage the system. This is insured by a relief valve (Figure 14). The spring will hold the ball against its seat, keeping the inlet shut. But if pressure exceeds that of the spring (because the fluid is not being used to operate some device it normally would, for example), the spring is forced back and fluid escapes back to the reservoir through the relief port.

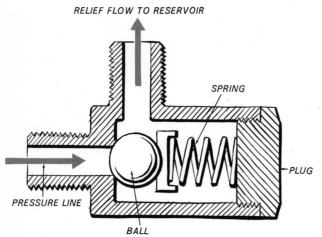

Fig. 14. Relief valve.

Directional controls may be of the poppet type, with a valve or ball that is lifted off its seat to let fluid pass (A in Figure 15), the rotary type (B), or the sliding spool type (C). If the spindle in valve B is turned one way, fluid flows between 1 and 2, and between 3 and 4. But when the rotary valve is turned 180 degrees, the connections are between 1 and 4, 2 and 3.

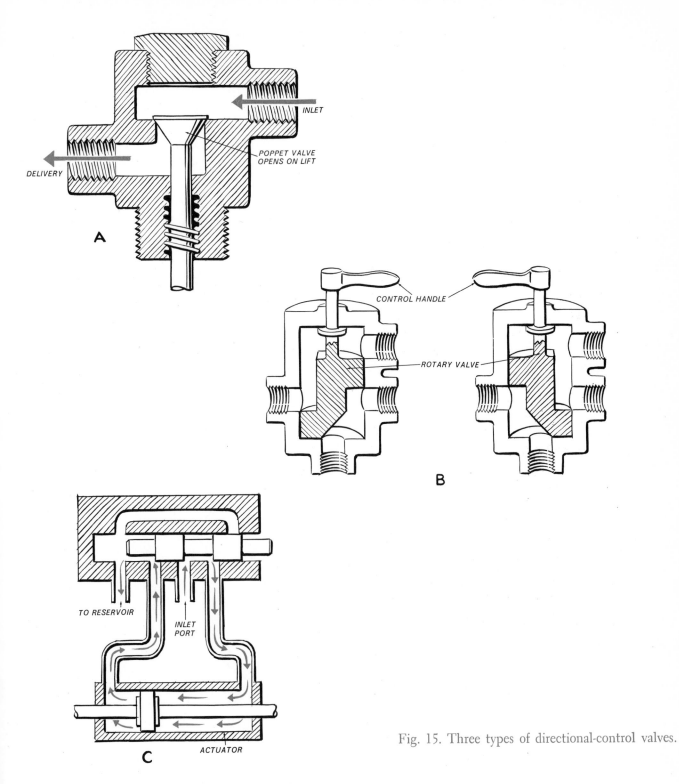

INLET

POPPET VALVE
OPENS ON LIFT

DELIVERY

A

CONTROL HANDLE

ROTARY VALVE

B

TO RESERVOIR

INLET
PORT

ACTUATOR

C

Fig. 15. Three types of directional-control valves.

225

The spool in valve C is admitting fluid from the pressure or inlet port to the right side of the piston in the actuator cylinder. This will move the piston to the left, while fluid from its left side is valved back to the reservoir. In the reverse case, fluid would pass from the right side of the cylinder through the bypass above the spool valve and back to the reservoir, pressure on its left side moving the piston right.

The actuator shown, with its piston rod extending out on both sides, is a double-acting nondifferential type. It can apply power in either direction, and because the piston area is equal on both sides, equal force will be exerted either way.

If the piston rod extended through the cylinder at one end only, this end of the piston would be smaller in area by that of the rod. Hydraulic force would therefore be less than on the other end. Such a differential cylinder provides a slower, stronger stroke when hydraulic pressure is applied to the larger piston area, while the return stroke will be quicker (assuming the same fluid flow rate) but less powerful.

Hydraulic motors are also used as actuators, and include gear, vane, radial piston, axial piston and limited rotation vane motors, the latter making not quite a full revolution (Figure 16).

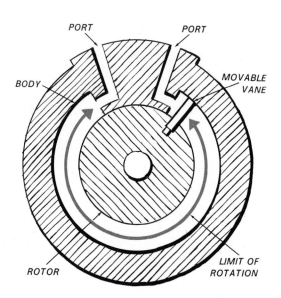

Fig. 16. Cross-sectional diagram of a hydraulic motor.

POWER STEERING

Designed to help steering effort while leaving the driver enough wheel resistance to keep the "feel" of the road, power steering relies on a hydraulic pump that may be a separate belt-driven unit or mounted on the back of the generator. Its function is to maintain a fairly high hydraulic pressure (150 to 900 p.s.i.) ready for instant use. The pump unit incorporates a fluid reservoir and a relief valve. If fluid is not being used to operate the steering gear, the valve opens and routs it back to the reservoir or the intake side of the pump.

The actuator that supplies the steering assist is, in some systems, a long cylinder fitted to the steering linkage under the car. The end of the piston rod may be anchored, and the cylinder itself move, or vice versa. In some systems, the piston and cylinder are built into the steering column. Hydraulic pressure may be applied to either end of the piston, making the actuator assist in either a right or a left turn.

The spool valve normally admits oil to both ends of the piston, so centering it with no inclination to move either way. When the driver turns left, the worm shaft of the manual steering gear shifts axially a few thousandths of an inch (in reaction to the load of moving the ball nut and pitman arm).

This axial movement is transmitted to a pivot lever, one end of which is set in a thrust bearing. The other end of the lever moves the spool valve, cutting hydraulic pressure off the right-turn side of the cylinder, which is instead opened to the return-flow line, so that fluid may escape. At the same time fluid pressure is valved to the left-turn power chamber, pushing the piston downward and turning the wheels to the left.

Simultaneously hydraulic pressure is directed to a "reaction ring" that tends to return the pivot lever to the neutral position. If the driver releases the steering wheel, this pressure will at once bring the thrust bearings and pivot lever back to neutral. The spool valve will again equalize oil pressure on the two sides of the piston, straightening the front wheels.

The more steering effort the driver applies, the farther the spool valve will shift and the more hydraulic power assist will be applied. This action is strictly one-way; though hydraulic power helps turn the front wheels, road shocks that tend to twist them off course are opposed and thereby cushioned by the hydraulic unit instead of being transmitted back to the driver.

Hydraulic power is used for machine-tool feeds and actions, for swiveling and elevating gun mounts, actuating aircraft landing gear and flaps, raising and lowering the scoops and buckets of earth-moving equipment, and on farm machinery and ships. Experimental cars have been built without gears or drive shafts, the engine driving a big pump which powered hydraulic motors in each wheel.

THE NEW SCIENCE OF FLUIDICS

In 1958 the U.S. Army's Harry Diamond Laboratories pioneered a new science—fluid technology. This development has already proved capable of turning a destroyer in its tracks, controlling jet engines, rockets and aircraft, master-minding the operation of pipelines and boilers, and guiding torpedoes.

Though research thus far has been chiefly for military and aerospace applications, fluidics may eventually replace the carburetor on your car with a compact metal-plastic sandwich, stop an assembly line if any part of a manufactured unit is wrongly installed or missing, and cycle the family washing machine.

Fluid technology relates to sensing, logic, power amplification and control devices that have no moving parts, but only moving fluids. The first such devices were fluid amplifiers, an amplifier being something that enables a small control force to trigger or direct a larger force (the classic examples are the vacuum tube and transistor).

The simplest fluidic unit is a block of material having a Y-shaped trio of passages inside, plus two cross passages where the yoke of the Y joints its single leg. This leg is the input end of the power stream. The cross passages are for two smaller control jets (Figure 17).

If the power stream is flowing in leg A of the two branches as shown, a control jet from the upper passage will at once shift it to leg B. Another control pulse from the lower passage would shift it back. Between control pulses, the power stream will keep flowing in the leg to which it was last directed.

This is due to a curious phenomenon, known after the Rumanian who first identified it in 1932 as the Coanda effect. To demonstrate it, direct a thin, fast stream from a hose nozzle near to and parallel to the sleek side of your car. When it is about an inch away, the stream will be drawn against the surface and will stay there until you move the hose away.

The explanation for this wall-attachment effect is that the moving stream drags along—entrains—some air with it (Figure 18). As the stream approaches the side of the car, the air in the narrow space between flows faster than that on the other side of the stream. This faster flow creates a low-pressure region—a slight vacuum—between the water and the car's surface. The higher air pressure on the other side therefore pushes the water stream over.

The same effect holds in the two-state device or fluidic amplifier de-

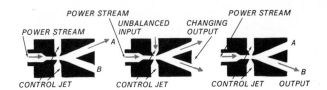

Fig. 17. A bi-stable—or two-state—device.

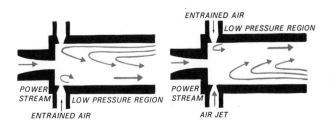

Fig. 18. Cause of wall-attachment effect.

scribed. The jet will hug the wall of either passage until another control pulse moves it over. So long as fluid flows, the device is as stable as a toggle switch. Because the control jets may be much weaker than the power stream, the device amplifies in much the sense a vacuum tube does.

To see the effect, adjust a nozzle on a garden hose to produce a thin, speedy jet of water. Aim this sideways at a heavy stream flowing from another hose or a yard faucet. The thin control jet will divert the heavy stream at a considerable angle.

PROPORTIONAL AMPLIFIERS

The two-state or bi-stable device described is a yes-or-no proposition, like an on-off switch. Though it amplifies, it does not do so quantitatively. The Coanda effect prevents a partial or divided flow. For one type of proportional amplifier, the wall-attachment effect must be destroyed. This is done by widening the main passage before it splits (Figure 19). If now the two control jets are of equal force, the power stream will split equally. But if the control jets are unbalanced, the power-stream output will be greater in one leg than in the other.

Another proportional amplifier is the aerodynamic type (Figure 20). Here the Coanda effect normally makes the power stream flow over a curved surface having the same contour as the tip of an airplane wing. A single control jet will, depending on its force, shift a proportionate amount of the power stream to the upper leg, while a larger control input will divert all of it.

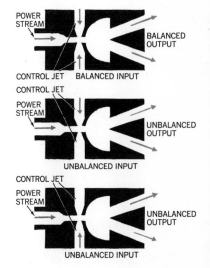

Fig. 19. Proportional amplifier with widened passage.

229

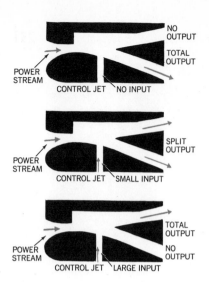

NO OUTPUT

TOTAL OUTPUT

POWER STREAM

CONTROL JET — NO INPUT

SPLIT OUTPUT

POWER STREAM

CONTROL JET — SMALL INPUT

TOTAL OUTPUT

NO OUTPUT

POWER STREAM

CONTROL JET — LARGE INPUT

Fig. 20. Aerodynamic amplifier.

Fig. 21. Vortex amplifier.

FULL OUTPUT

POWER STREAM

CONTROL JET — NO INPUT

POWER STREAM

LIMITED OUTPUT

CONTROL JET — FULL INPUT

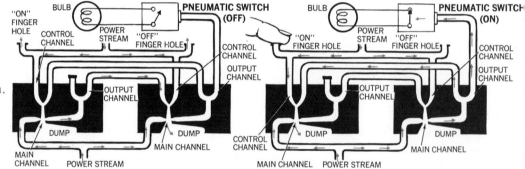

Fig. 22. Fluidic light switch.

A fluidic amplifier made of clear plastic, and operating with water as its working fluid, renders the action of control and power streams visible. *Courtesy Bowles Engineering Corp.*

Here are the innards of a fluidic controller, consisting of nine book-like modules (each holding several integrated circuits) and the necessary actuating hardware. *Courtesy Bowles Engineering Corp.*

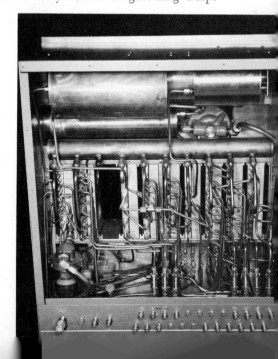

Figure 21 shows a curious fluidic control device called a vortex amplifier. With no control input, the power stream swirls around and rushes out of an axial output tube at the center of the circular cavity. But the control jet sets the power stream spinning much faster, like a tiny whirlpool. Strangely enough, the effect is to greatly reduce the total output of the power stream.

Figure 22 shows two states of a fluidic light switch which is also a yes-or-no arrangement, worked by placing a finger over one of two air holes. When both are uncovered, the power stream passes across a main channel (at left in the drawing) and over to a control channel at the right. Here it deflects the right-hand branch of the power stream, "dumping" it into the atmosphere, and nothing else happens.

But close the "on" hole with a finger, and you channel the upper power stream downward at the left, dumping that side of the lower power stream. The right branch now continues across the main channel on the right (because it is no longer deflected) and flows upward to actuate the pneumatic switch.

This is only a demonstration device; a toggle switch would do the same job. Fluidic devices are in any case no substitutes for millionth-of-a-second electronic circuits. Fluidics operate in the thousandths-of-a-second range. But fluid technology has demonstrated peculiar advantages in some applications. In jet engines, for example, fluidic sensors withstand heat that would threaten electric or electronic sensors.

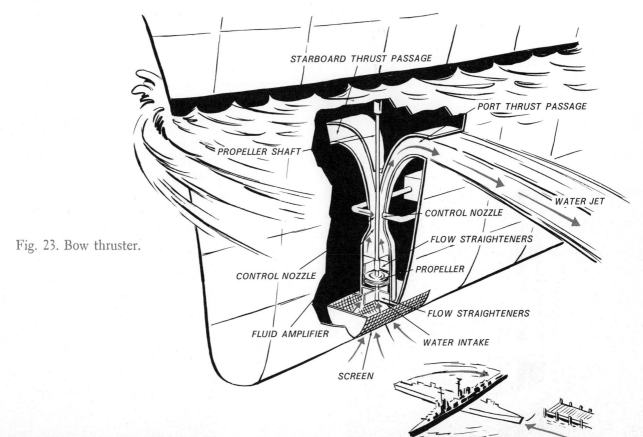

Fig. 23. Bow thruster.

In a test tank, a technician operates a 1/20 scale model of the 50,000-gallon-per-minute bow thruster that can turn a ship on its keel. *Bowles Engineering Corp.*

The working channels can be etched or molded into relatively thin blocks of metal or plastic. Covered with a flat plate and hooked up to a fluid or air flow, they are ready to work. A number of fluidic units can be ganged on a single block the size of a thin book. These "integrated circuit modules" may then be inserted in shelflike racks to build up a computer, a control system, or instrumentation.

Nor is fluid technology limited to the gentle arts of control and computing, though it has already proved itself in both. Honeywell in 1964 demonstrated a fluid roll-control system in the U.S. Army's Test and Instrumentation Missile (TIM). The same company successfully tested a three-axis autopilot for light aircraft, and in 1965 a fluid control system for turbojet engines.

A startling large-scale application of the fluidic amplifier is the bow thruster developed by the Bowles Engineering Corporation (Figure 23). This can literally push a warship around. It consists of a large Y-shaped passage, its bottom open to the sea and the upper two legs opening on the port and starboard sides of the bow below water level.

An intake propeller in the single leg pumps up water taken in under the bow. Control jets divert this power stream to one side or the other, and the ship swings in the opposite direction. To a pilot, this is as handy as a car capable of sliding into a parking space sideways. Such bow thrusters might eventually render ships independent of tugboat help.

Meanwhile, fluidics is at about the same stage of development as transistor technology was in the 1950s. Already a respected and growing science, it commands the research facilities of many large American companies. Among these are Bendix, General Electric, IBM, Honeywell, Bowles Engineering, Sperry Rand, Martin Marietta, and Corning Glass. From these giants and the scientific minds they command, we can expect more surprises in the field of fluid technology.

XIII

Gas Turbines, Jet Engines and Rockets

About the time Watt's steam engines were flexing their muscles throughout the industrial world, a man named John Barber foresaw one of today's most important prime movers. In 1791 Barber obtained a patent for an engine comprising a gas producer, air compressor, combustion chamber and bladed wheel. On paper at least, he had invented the gas turbine.

Other inventors before (and after) him had looked longingly at the possibility of an internal-combustion turbine. But if combustion was to be continuous (as it should logically be to drive a turbine) how could the fuel-air mix be taken in, compressed, fired and exhausted in that sequence which Carnot had shown vital to an efficient heat-engine cycle? The answer, set forth in Barber's patent, lay hidden there for 111 years.

At Cornell University in 1902 a graduate student, S. A. Moss, converted a de Laval steam turbine into a water-cooled experimental gas turbine. Though it ran briefly, its power proved insufficient to operate the compressor necessary to its functioning. A more successful turbine was built in 1905 by two Frenchmen, Armegand and Lemale. Theirs was a two-stage impulse turbine driving a multistaged centrifugal compressor. It worked, but its efficiency was a doleful 3 percent, feeble competition for the highly successful steam turbine of that day.

The gas turbine is a flow instead of a displacement machine, combustion being continuous. Such improvements as intercooling, regeneration and better design have improved overall efficiency to the point where today the gas turbine can in more applications compete successfully with piston engines as a source of rotary power—and surpasses them for other purposes.

Materials have been a severe problem, not only because of high temperatures, but because the turbine blades must withstand these while subjected to great centrifugal stress. The combined effect is like that of hanging a great weight on a thin wire, and then heating the wire white hot. Though maximum temperatures are no higher than in a piston engine, the parts of the latter are subjected to them only momentarily. A four-stroke engine has three strokes in which to cool down from the fury of the firing stroke. Not so the gas turbine, which is firing all the time.

Furnishing excess air—air not burned with the fuel—to cool the combustion chambers and the gases driving the turbine is one solution. Though it violates the Carnot precepts and requires a bigger compressor (so absorbing more of the turbine's energy) it has been successful in some turbojet engines, notably the de Haviland Ghost, which powered the original Comet I airliner.

Materials capable of withstanding higher heat are another solution. Cemented hard carbides, sintered aluminum, fused quartz and porcelain all offer promise in this direction, and space-age technology is opening still other possibilities.

Gas turbines have powered cars, locomotives, Coast Guard cutters, generating plants and propeller-driven (turboprop) planes. In all these there has to be a net shaft output that can be applied to the wheels, generators or propellers. Instead of piping gases between separate units as shown in the schematic drawing, these engines combine the compressor, combustion chambers and turbine in one casing, through which gases flow in more or less of a straight line.

But the most amazing thing about this heat engine is that it can propel aircraft without the intervention of anything as mundane and solid as a propeller.

THE TURBOJET ENGINE

The principle of jet propulsion is based on Newton's Third Law of Motion: to every action there is an equal and opposed reaction. The space-walking astronaut who pushes a hatch shut will simultaneously shove himself away from his capsule. If you throw enough heavy objects backwards from a rowboat in still water, you will impart a small forward movement to the boat.

If you blow up a toy balloon and then let it go, air will escape from the open neck and pressure in that direction will be less than in all others, including that part of the balloon's skin directly opposite (Figure 1). This imbalance of pressure *inside* the balloon, and *not* any effect of the air jet against the outer air, will impel it into flight until the air is gone. *It would do so even in a vacuum*—proof of the fact that the jet does not "push" against anything outside.

In the turbojet engine, air entering the compressor is given higher speed and pressure and delivered to the combustion chamber. (Usually there are several of these in the form of can burners, disposed in a circle between compressor and turbine.) The hot combustion gases drive the turbine (which in turn spins the compressor). But shaft energy ends there; no rotary power is taken off.

Instead, the hot jet stream is hurled out at high velocity. The reaction to the force that ejects it pushes back on the turbine, the engine, and the plane, driving it forward. Because only part of the turbojet's power appears as shaft rotation—and that not applicable to external use—its propulsive ability is not measured in horsepower, but in pounds of thrust. This cannot be equated

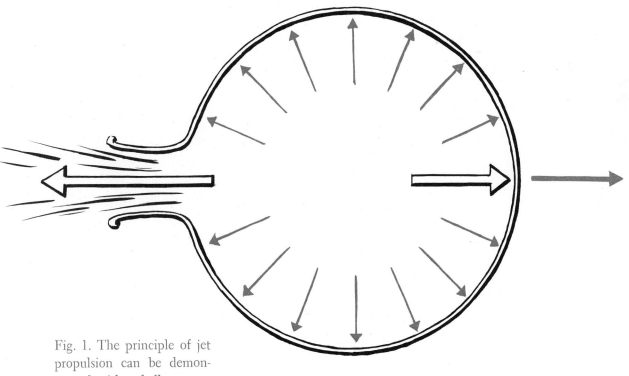

Fig. 1. The principle of jet propulsion can be demonstrated with a balloon.

with horsepower unless the plane is moving, but at 375 miles per hour one pound of thrust equals one horsepower, or one "thrust horsepower." At normal cruising speed, the fan-jet engines in a 707 jet plane each develop about 6,500 hp at an altitude of 35,000 feet.

"Thrust equals mass flow rate times change in velocity" is the engineer's formula for calculating thrust. We have to know how many pounds of air (or hot gases) are flowing per second, and how much faster this mass is moving in the jet than it was when taken into the engine.

Imagine a jet engine that takes in 150 pounds of air per second, and after compression and combustion ejects it (because of the heat energy added) at 1,800 feet per second greater speed. However, the mass flow *rate* must take into account not only the 150-pound figure, but also gravitational acceleration, which is 32.2 feet per second per second.

The engineer's formula above, converted to figures, would be:

$$\text{Thrust} = \frac{150}{32.2} \times 1800$$

Multiplying 150 and 1,800 gives 270,000, which divided by 32.2 gives the answer as 8,385 pounds of thrust.

The power of this engine could be boosted by taking in more air, by increasing the ejection velocity, or both. A strange and wonderful thing about the jet engine, which makes it a superb propulsion unit for aircraft, is that its thermal efficiency goes up as the plane flies faster. This is because the plane's forward motion helps ram air into the compressor, so not only taking in more air, but also lifting some of the burden from the turbine and thus increasing the velocity of the exhaust gases.

This "ram effect" keeps increasing along with speed. It compensates for what would otherwise be a loss of thrust at high speeds, when the plane's own velocity detracts from that of the jet. Increase air speed enough and you can do without the compressor—and therefore also without the turbine. You will then have a ram-jet engine, similar to the ones that power the 1,500 m.p.h. Navajo, Bomarc and Talos missiles of the United States defense system.

THE TURBOFAN OR FAN JET

Straddling the turboprop and the jet engine, the fan jet has certain advantages of economy, a lower noise level, shorter takeoff and more rapid climb than either. The Pratt & Whitney JT3D, a typical fan-jet engine, has two compressors, separately driven by two turbines in the rear section (Figure 2).

Fig. 2. Pratt & Whitney JT3D fan-jet engine.

The first or low-pressure compressor delivers air to the high-pressure compressor, which further compresses it before passing it on to the burners. Heated, it drives both turbines, and the high-speed exhaust provides jet propulsion for the plane.

But the Turbofan engine draws in more air than needed to power its turbines. The extra air, accelerated by a two-stage "fan" ahead of the first compressor, is routed through annular ducts to exhaust around the engine in the same direction as the main jet. This large quantity of unheated air, accelerated to a relatively low velocity, supplies extra thrust like the propeller on a turboprop engine. It provides more power at modest airspeeds and adds to engine efficiency, with an accompanying saving in fuel.

At full power, the JT3D consumes enough air every five seconds to fill a twelve-room house. The heat developed in one square foot of its combustion space is a thousand times as much as that generated in the same space by a household oil burner.

PULSE JETS AND RAM JETS

In 1931 a German engineer flew the first pulse-jet engine. It was this type that powered the V1 flying bombs launched against England in 1944. The engine itself is simple. Just behind the air intake is a grating. Over the holes in this grating are simple spring-steel flap valves, much like the reed valves in a modern outboard, opening toward the inside (Figure 3). Alongside the valves are fuel injection nozzles, aimed into the combustion space behind the air-intake grating. An electric glow plug is fitted in the combustion space for ignition.

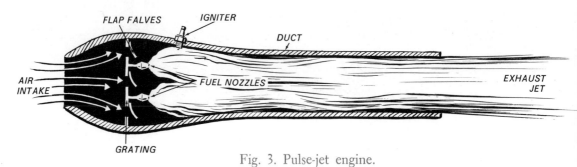

Fig. 3. Pulse-jet engine.

The V1 was launched from a ramp at about 200 miles per hour. This rammed air into the open nose against the flap valves, opening them. Air rushed through, was mixed with fuel, and ignited. The sudden expansion of hot gases behind the flap valves closed them. But as the gases roared out at the tail, creating forward thrust, there was a momentary drop of pressure in the combustion chamber. This allowed air pressure from the front to open the flap valves again, and the cycle was repeated in a series of rapid pulses—over 2,400 per minute, enough to keep the engine firing without further help from the glow plug.

This type of jet engine is also called the resonance duct engine, because the length of the tube must be tuned to the natural frequency of the flap valves for smooth running. It is a fuel-greedy engine; at 300 miles per hour the V1s consumed a gallon of low-grade gasoline for each mile of flight. The engine was fixed on top of a short-winged fuselage having fuel tanks in the wings, air bottles in the fuselage for pneumatic controls, and an autopilot with three air-driven gyros for guidance.

The ram jet or athodyd was fathered by René Lorin, a Frenchman, in 1915. As it has to be brought up to a speed of 350 m.p.h. to start working, his idea had to wait until 1949 for its first test. Then the French launched a ram-jet aircraft from a fast plane, attaining a speed of 450 m.p.h.

Though only for high speeds, this engine develops increasing power at sonic and higher velocities. It could be described as a sky-going blowtorch. If lit while standing still, it will exhaust gas and flame from both ends. But when it is moving through air at high speed, the shape of the entering nozzle compresses the air at some loss in its speed (Figure 4). Rearward the taper of the duct is reversed to boost air speed at the expense of pressure. A fuel is injected and ignited, the expanding combustion gases roar out of the tail at high velocity, generating tremendous forward thrust by reaction on the engine.

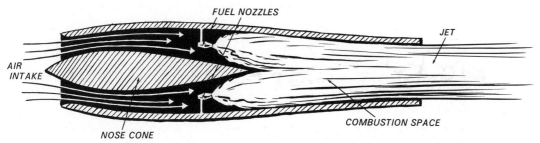

Fig. 4. Ram-jet engine.

ROCKETS AND SPACE TRAVEL

All the jet engines described thus far are earthbound. They must travel in the atmosphere, thin though it is at the heights they attain, to continue running. Their fuel cannot be burned without oxygen, and this is derived from the air through which they travel. For a heat engine that can operate in airless space, we must look to fuels that carry their own oxygen, bound in chemicals aptly called oxidizers. The Chinese discovered the first such fuel some time before 1040 A.D., when the formula for it was first published. It is called gunpowder.

Mix together 75 percent potassium nitrate, 15 percent carbon (such as charcoal) and 10 percent sulphur, and you are living dangerously. If the stuff has not exploded in the mixing (as is all too likely) it will do so enthusiastically when ignited. The potassium nitrate supplies abundant oxygen to convert the carbon to carbon dioxide, and the sulphur to sulphur dioxide. Huge quantities of these gases are generated almost instantaneously, at a temperature estimated to be 2,700 degrees Centigrade (4,892 degrees Fahrenheit).

The Chinese did not confine the use of their gunpowder to firecrackers. They invented rockets, possibly just as fireworks to begin with. But about the middle of the 13th century they used rockets as offensive weapons against the Mongolians. The Chinese also built cannon, first with bamboo and later with bronze barrels.

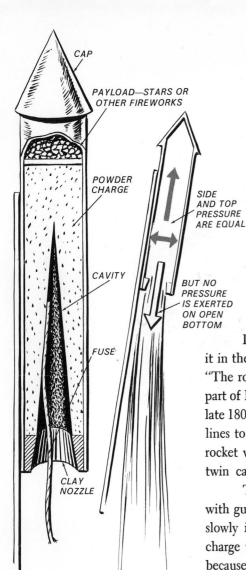

CAP

PAYLOAD—STARS OR OTHER FIREWORKS

POWDER CHARGE

CAVITY

FUSE

CLAY NOZZLE

SIDE AND TOP PRESSURE ARE EQUAL

BUT NO PRESSURE IS EXERTED ON OPEN BOTTOM

Fig. 5. Basic skyrocket.

Little more was heard of the rocket as a weapon until the British used it in the Napoleonic Wars and in the War of 1812 against the United States. "The rocket's red glare" of the national anthem was not mere poetry on the part of Francis Scott Key. Rockets remained part of British ordnance until the late 1800s, then were relegated to the innocuous roles of signaling and carrying lines to stricken vessels for towing or rescue work. But in World War II the rocket was dusted off, examined anew for its war potential, and launched on twin careers as a weapon and a propulsion engine.

The basic skyrocket (Figure 5) has a cardboard casing almost filled with gunpowder (whose composition may vary from that given to burn more slowly instead of exploding). A conical combustion space is formed in the charge to control burning and direct the jet downward. Thrust is generated because the gas pressure—which would be equal in all directions in a closed space—is unbalanced by the open nozzle through which the gases can stream out. This leaves pressure in the opposite direction (against the forward end) unopposed. It is the reactive force that drives the rocket up, not any "push" against the outside atmosphere.

Reaction makes a six-shooter kick up as you fire it, a cannon recoil against its mounting. But a rocket uses that reactive force to propel itself, so there is no recoil on its launching apparatus. This is why big rockets, with fire power equivalent to the guns of a cruiser, could be shot off the deck of small landing craft in World War II. The famous bazooka, a short-range rocket weighing 3½ pounds with a high-explosive warhead, could be fired by a two-man team yet had enough destructive force to demolish a tank. Small war planes carrying rockets have the striking power of much larger cannon-carrying aircraft.

240

The rocket is a high-speed engine. To use it efficiently, the vehicle it drives must attain a respectable fraction of the speed of the rocket exhaust, or jet velocity. To hitch rockets to an automobile (as Opel did decades ago), or to a boat or a rail car is to hamstring them. Most of a rocket's power is wasted at low speeds—and anything less than 300 miles per hour is, in rocket terms, a crawl.

There is some legitimate use for rockets where speedy acceleration from a standstill is worth the cost. The acceleration sleds used for testing aircraft ejection seats and airmen's suits and harnesses are one example. Auxiliary rockets that get planes airborne more quickly are vital to some military operations. With rocket assist, heavily loaded bombers and fighters can take off from carrier decks or short airport runways they could not otherwise use. The propellant for such rockets, which are usually dropped when spent, is cordite; 25 pounds of this explosive develop a 1,000-pound thrust for a few seconds.

SOLID-FUEL ROCKET ENGINES

Gunpowder is far outdated as a rocket fuel. Its jet velocity is low—a mere 1,500 feet per second. Jet velocity being a critical factor in rocket power, fuels with higher velocities make an enormous difference in performance and offer our only hope at present of reaching interplanetary space. In 1918, Robert H. Goddard, then considered a science-fiction visionary, sent aloft the first rocket powered by smokeless powder. Since then, the search for more potent fuels has branched out in two directions—solid and liquid propellants.

In the solid-fuel rocket engine, as in the common skyrocket, the fuel space and combustion chamber are in effect one. The cavity in the fuel becomes larger and changes shape as burning progresses. No control can be exercised once the fuel is alight, so any desired alteration in burning must be foreseen and provided for in the design of the cavity or the use of successive stages. Steering is possible only by swiveling the jet nozzle, by setting adjustable vanes in its throat, or by means of auxiliary steering rockets.

Solid fuels had other drawbacks to be overcome. Some hurled part of their charge out with the jet, so that it was wasted before it could contribute any propulsive effort. Early solid fuels had a tendency to break up as burning portions expanded more than relatively cool unfired parts. This was overcome by the admixture of rubber, which made the fuel mass elastic enough to withstand unequal heating. Great changes in outside temperature or humidity sometimes cracked the "grain," as the shaped fuel charge is called. (A typical grain may look like a cylinder with a starred hole running through its length.)

A big solid-fuel motor would burn out its casing if it burned more than a minute or so. The answer for such long-range solid-fuel missiles as the Polaris and Minuteman, was extra motors or stages.

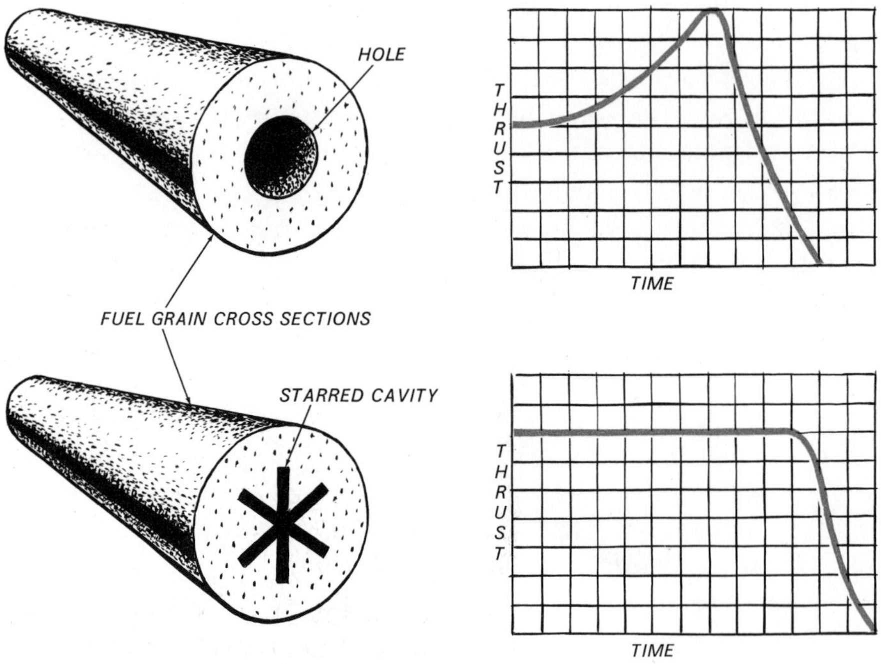

Fig. 6. Solid-fuel sections.

For military uses, the solid-fuel rocket motor has great advantages. One is stand-by readiness. It is always ready to fire, has no moving parts, is readily portable, can be stored for long periods and fired by relatively unskilled crews. By contrast, liquid-fuel rockets must be fueled just before launching, the fuel and oxidizer are hazardous and hard to care for, the motors have a maze of plumbing, and they require highly skilled personnel and elaborate servicing.

By 1963 the chemical industry had developed a number of high-energy propellants that put solid-fuel rockets in a strongly competitive position. These propellants consist of a rubbery binder (vinylpolyester, polyurethane, polyvinyl chloride for example), oxidixing agents (ammonium perchlorate, ammonium nitrate, potassium perchlorate), and sometimes powdered aluminum or other metal additives to provide extra energy.

It is a fact, elucidated under the name of Piobert's Law, that a flame front will always eat into solid fuel in a direction normal (that is, perpendicular) to its surface. Fill a casing completely with solid rocket fuel, light one end, and the propellant will burn straight down the tube like a cigarette.

But if you make a hole all the way through the fuel charge, so that it resembles a thick-walled pipe (Figure 6) and light the fuel all along this tunnel, the flame will eat outward radially from this inner surface. When it reaches the casing wall, all the fuel will have been consumed. As the hole burns larger, the combustion surface increases. Therefore jet-gas volume and thrust will be smallest at the time of ignition and greatest at the instant of burn-out, as shown by the thrust-time curve in Figure 6.

More commonly, you want maximum thrust at takeoff, when the rocket is heavy with fuel and its engine relatively inefficient because it is starting from a standstill. Various cross sections of the grain have been developed to meet this and other conditions. The second one in Figure 6 will hold maximum thrust from takeoff until just before the fuel burns out. Sometimes two or more layers of fuel are used, with different burning rates, to obtain the thrust-time curve desired.

Fuels that can be shipped to remote launching sites, and loaded into rocket casings there, have already been developed. A solid former is lowered into the casing, the fuel poured around it in slurry form (something like a watery cement mixture) and carefully regulated heat applied to cure and solidify it. When the former is pulled out, it leaves the desired cavity or configuration in the grain.

Though not all experts agree, there are some who think the future belongs to solid rocket fuels and that solid-fuel motors could be built in enormous sizes to develop thrust up to 10 million pounds. (A motor 14 feet in diameter puts out 2,400,000 pounds.) Proponents of this idea suggest using liquid-fuel motors only for the upper stages of spaceships. These would be cut in after the bigger solid-fuel stages below have fired, accelerated the spacecraft, and dropped away. The astronauts would then use the more controllable liquid-fuel stage to make final approaches and landings at their destination.

LIQUID-FUEL ROCKETS

For twenty years, beginning in 1923, Dr. Robert Goddard pioneered the search for more powerful fuels and safe, efficient liquid-fuel motors. A typical motor of this kind consists of a combustion chamber (perhaps with a cooling jacket around it), with separate jets for the fuel and oxidizer. An electric igniter initiates combustion, after which the motor continues to function by itself.

Complicating the motor are the tanks, pumps or pressurizing equipment, and metering devices needed to hold and deliver these two liquids to the motor in the right proportions.

Gasoline and liquid oxygen (lox) were used in some early experimental rockets. The German V2 flying bomb, dread successor to the V1, was fueled with lox and alcohol, the latter probably more available than war-scarce gasoline.

The rocket motor, with steering vanes in its throat, was located at the rear. Four external fins also had control vanes on them. These were actuated by electro-hydraulic systems, guided by a gyroscope auto pilot.

Jet velocity of the V2 motor was estimated at 6,000 feet per second, four times that of gunpowder. Before being delivered to the motor, the fuel circulated through a jacket around the nozzle and combustion chamber to cool these. In doing so, the fuel took up heat, which added to its own energy, the process being called regeneration. Mixed with lox in burner cups, the warm alcohol was fired in the combustion chamber.

Steam to power the pump turbine was generated by an ingenious chemical "boiler." Compressed air from a flask forced calcium permanganate into hydrogen peroxide at a metered rate. This produced an exothermic (heat generating) chemical action that provided superheated steam.

The measuring stick of fuel energy is the British Thermal Unit or B.T.U. (the amount of heat needed to raise the temperature of one pound of water one degree Fahrenheit.) Aviation gasoline has 18,500 B.T.U.'s per pound, kerosene and jet fuel 18,000. This is far below the potency of hydrogen, which has 52,000 B.T.U.'s per pound. But for use as fuel, it would

SCOUT

THOR-AGENA D

DELTA

ATLAS AGENA D

ATLAS CENTAUR

Launch vehicles for the U.S. space program of different sizes and capabilities, determined by the weight of the payload they are designed to carry and the flight path they are intended to take. They range in size from the Scout, which is 68 feet high, to the Saturn V, which is 365 feet high with its payload. With the exception of the Scout and the Delta, all the rockets use liquid fuel in all stages. The Scout uses solid fuel in all four stages; the Delta in its third, and last, stage.

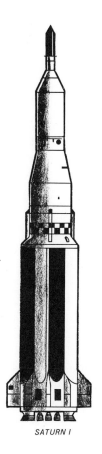

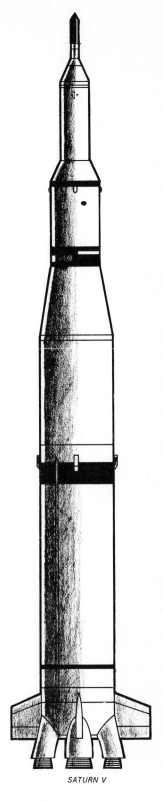

GEMINI-TITAN II   SATURN I   UPRATED SATURN I   SATURN V

245

have to be kept liquefied, which means very, very cold. Nevertheless, the second stage of the huge Saturn rocket, which in 1964 boosted a 19,400 pound dummy payload into orbit, was powered by six Pratt and Whitney liquid-hydrogen engines.

Nature has locked hydrogen into various fuels by combining it with carbon. Petroleum, coal, natural gas are all hydrocarbons. But the carbon itself has a low B.T.U. rating—only 13,000 per pound. For high-energy rocket fuels, chemists searched the list of elements to find those that have a high heat potential in themselves and would combine with hydrogen.

Beryllium, first on the list to be considered, weighs in at 29,000 B.T.U.'s. But it is scarce and also toxic. Alphabetically, researchers did not have far to go. Boron, with 26,000 B.T.U.'s per pound, came next. It is derived from Borax, the kitchen cleanser long associated in the United States with the plodding twenty mule teams that hauled it out of Death Valley. Borax is plentiful, and chemists found that boron could be linked with hydrogen to make very powerful, safe, and reasonably priced rocket fuels. Powdered aluminum, magnesium or lithium is sometimes added. Oxidizers may be liquid oxygen, aniline, nitric acid, hydrogen peroxide, or other chemicals.

To get U.S. astronauts to the moon, it will be necessary to lift 3,000 tons off the surface of the earth—that's the total weight of the Saturn V booster, the Apollo spacecraft with its three-man crew, and propellants. To accomplish the task, space engineers have developed a liquid-fuel engine known as the F-1. Five of them will boost Saturn V toward the moon. Fed by propellant tanks in the booster, the massive turbopump forces three tons of kerosene fuel and liquid oxygen per second into the F-1 engine. Oxygen goes directly from the pump through the injector into the combustion chamber, where flame reaches 5,000 degrees F., but most of the fuel is sent first through cooling tubes making up the wall of the chamber; some fuel goes straight into the injector. The injector sprays propellants through holes—2,600 for oxygen, 3,700 for fuel—into the combustion chamber. Fuel from the cooling tubes flows through 32 radial channels to orifices. Propellant pumps are driven by the turbine powered by hot gases from the kerosene-oxygen mix burned in the elbow-shaped gas generator; the 1,000-degree turbine exhaust is fed around the nozzle to act as a coolant for the hollow-walled nozzle extension before passing through slots into the engine exhaust. Hydraulic actuators, using high-pressure fuel as working fluid, gimbal engine to steer the booster.

LIQUID
OXYGEN

KEROSENE
FUEL

HYDRAULIC
ACTUATORS

INJECTOR

OXYGEN

FUEL

TURBINE

GIMBAL
BLOCKS

COMBUSTION
CHAMBER

GAS GENERATOR

TURBOPUMP

COOLING
TUBES

NOZZLE

TURBINE
EXHAUST

NOZZLE
EXTENSION

EXHAUST
DUCT

THE ATOM IN SPACE

Since atomic fission can yield enormous amounts of energy (and atomic fusion even more) an atomic reactor would seem to be the ideal propulsion engine for rockets and spacecraft. The catch is that so far reactors provide only heat, which in the absence of jetting gases cannot move a rocket. An atomic-powered rocket would have to carry a working fluid. Pumped to the reactor and heated by it, this fluid would be vaporized and expelled from a nozzle as a high-speed jet. Reaction would then drive the rocket or spacecraft forward. Liquid hydrogen, ammonia, methane and even water have been considered as propellant fluids.

The first experimental work on an A-rocket was conducted by the Atomic Energy Commission's Los Alamos Scientific Laboratory before 1958, while NASA's Lewis Research Center worked on the nonnuclear parts of the problem, such as cooling the nozzle and building a turbine-pump combination for circulating the propellant. The first experimental nonflying reactor engine, tested on a railroad car so that it could be moved out of dangerous proximity for testing and decontamination, was aptly named the KIWI-A, for the earth-bound New Zealand bird. The Kiwi tests led to the more powerful Phoebus reactor engines. In June 1965 the first of these ran for over ten minutes at full power, developing 1,500,000 horsepower. In February 1967 the Phoebus 1B developed 2,000,000 horsepower—more than the whole electrical output of Hoover Dam.

As this is written a 55-inch Phoebus is to be scheduled for test. It is designed for an output of 6,700,000 horsepower. Next in the scheduled lineup is NERVA (Nuclear Engine for Rocket Vehicle Application). This flyable nuclear engine would be incorporated in a Nuclear Propulsion Module 33 feet in diameter (Figure 7).

Because the exhaust jet is pure hydrogen, lightest of all gases, the greater the exhaust velocity can be and therefore the more thrust is generated for every pound of propellant exhausted. Thus the nuclear engine promises a larger percentage of payload than chemical rocket engines.

NERVA could for example be the third stage of a Saturn V, nearly doubling that rocket's payload and making manned flights to the moon possible without auxiliary vehicles or an orbital rendezvous. With a different propellant tank, the module could be a shuttle craft between earth and moon orbits. NERVA could also take a crew and supplies for a two-year fly-by trip to Mars and back. More ambitious but still possible is a Mars landing. This would require a cluster of NERVA modules, assembled in earth orbit. Chemical rockets would land the astronauts on Mars, the spacecraft remaining in orbit, while a final NERVA module would return them to earth.

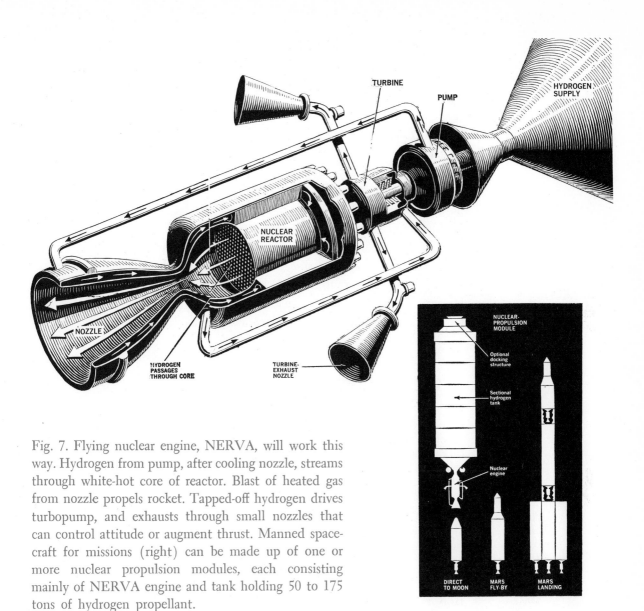

TURBINE PUMP HYDROGEN SUPPLY

NUCLEAR REACTOR

NOZZLE

HYDROGEN PASSAGES THROUGH CORE

TURBINE-EXHAUST NOZZLE

NUCLEAR-PROPULSION MODULE

Optional docking structure

Sectional hydrogen tank

Nuclear engine

DIRECT TO MOON MARS FLY-BY MARS LANDING

Fig. 7. Flying nuclear engine, NERVA, will work this way. Hydrogen from pump, after cooling nozzle, streams through white-hot core of reactor. Blast of heated gas from nozzle propels rocket. Tapped-off hydrogen drives turbopump, and exhausts through small nozzles that can control attitude or augment thrust. Manned spacecraft for missions (right) can be made up of one or more nuclear propulsion modules, each consisting mainly of NERVA engine and tank holding 50 to 175 tons of hydrogen propellant.

NERVA's nuclear engine would be made of graphite, pierced with thousands of tiny channels and impregnated with uranium 235 at its core. The neutron chain reaction generates a continuous heat flow, except when control rods are inserted to damp it out. At operating temperature, the reactor core glows at white heat. The hydrogen propellant, stored in the nose, is circulated by a pump first through the rocket nozzle—a de Laval type—to cool it. Then, delivered to the front end of the reactor at a pressure of a few hundred p.s.i., it streams through the channels in the white-hot core. On being heated to 4,000 degrees, it jets fiercely but without flame from the exhaust nozzle at something like 19,000 m.p.h. A little hydrogen tapped off before the reactor powers the turbine that drives the propellant pump.

In propellant economy, NERVA should be twice as good as the best liquid-fuel rocket engine, three times as good as the best solid-propellant engines. Among the problems still to be solved are nuclear shielding for passengers, how to regulate the reactor in proportion to the amount of hydrogen passing through, and what safety features to build in to prevent a nuclear accident on earth or in space.

Also proposed (and perhaps tested by now) are nuclear ram-jet missiles to be launched by rocket boosters. Air passing through the reactor would be instantaneously heated just as it is now by burning fuel, but to a higher temperature.

The most advanced idea for nuclear propulsion in space is the ion rocket, but work on this is still in the laboratory stage. The nuclear reactor would produce a jet of ionized particles as the result of nuclear fission. These ions—atoms that have either gained an extra electron, or are short one of their normal complement—are electrified and therefore can be set in motion by electric charges. Expelled at tremendous speeds, they would propel the spacecraft somewhat as the gas stream does a conventional rocket.

BUCK ROGER'S FLYING BELT

Some time after World War II, Colonel Charles Parkin, of the Army's Engineering Research and Development group, strapped a tank of compressed nitrogen to his back with the nozzle down, suddenly opened the valve, and simultaneously jumped off the ground. Repeated trials convinced him that he was jumping higher with the jet boost than he could unaided. He asked several companies to submit proposals for a jet-assist jump belt.

A firm named Reaction Motors, now a division of Thiokol Chemical Company, was first to do so, about 1958. Ray Wiech of that company strapped on the first test model—two big flasks of compressed nitrogen venting through nozzles on a bar above his head. When he pressed the control button, hissing jets lifted him, held him for a moment, and let him down softly.

Onlookers urged Wiech to try again, with an assist from his legs this time. Jumping up as he punched the button, Wiech set a new world's high-jump record for that time. Research on nozzle placement and controls began in earnest.

It was found that the jet nozzles had to be set low, not overhead but near the wearer's center of gravity. One nozzle on each hip, aimed outward and downward, worked well. Next came the dangerous step of testing a solid-fuel rocket system, pound for pound thousands of times more powerful than a car engine. Canisters of fuel, which could be cut in singly or all at once, powered twin jets. In the first test they were so effective that the wearer panicked and shut them off. He immediately fell, but was not injured. Further tests were successful.

As often happens, another man had been thinking along similar lines. Since 1953 Wendell F. Moore, an aeronautical engineer working on small hydrogen peroxide rockets for Bell Aerosystems Company, had been fascinated by the idea of a rocket jump belt. In 1960 he succeeded in interesting the Army's Transportation Command in the idea. Since then, spectacular results have been achieved.

The Bell rocket belt flies on jets of steam. Its fuel is 90 percent hydrogen peroxide, similar to the drugstore product but more concentrated and costly. The fuel tanks are pressurized from a nitrogen bottle, which feeds the peroxide through tiny silver screens behind the nozzles. The silver is a catalyst, mysteriously acting on the peroxide without itself being affected. It decomposes the chemical into free oxygen and water. This action also generates intense heat, which instantly vaporizes the water into high-pressure steam. The twin jets develop 300 pounds of thrust—more than enough to fly a heavy man.

Visible only in cold weather, the steam lifts the rocketman like a swift elevator. To travel forward, he merely leans ahead, so tilting the jets backwards. To stop forward motion he need only straighten up. Up and down movement is governed by increasing or decreasing jet power. Yawing, or skidding sideways, is counteracted by a control that deflects the jets to either side by means of small tilting vanes set into the nozzles.

With this rig, rocketman Harold Graham has jumped 368 feet (500 is considered possible), skimmed through the air at 35 miles per hour, and leaped over buildings. Maximum performance figures are classified.

A soldier wearing such a belt could jump off a cliff and use the jets to float himself safely to the ground, leap across a 300-foot wide river, jump up to a third-floor window and lob in a grenade or crash through ready to attack, or fly across rough country faster than any wheeled vehicle could travel there. Improved belts may lift the rocketman to a height of half a mile, from which he could descend by parachute. With wings added, he might instead glide down to reach distant objectives.

If the cost can be brought down (it is about $100 per flight now) the belts might find civilian applications as well. They might be used for spotting and fighting forest fires, carrying rescue lines to the tops of burning buildings, lifting policemen above snipers, carrying steeplejacks up TV towers and high chimneys, and perhaps whisking space explorers from place to place on worlds not our own.

XIV

Wheels That Remember—
Gyroscopes and Inertial
Guidance Systems

Possibly the last thing space probes and guided missiles bring to mind is the wheel. Yet without a handful of rapidly spinning wheels in each, our military and space hardware would be so much expensive junk. The wheels know where rockets and missiles are to go, and stubbornly correct any deviation from course.

We accept the fact that records, tapes and computer innards can store facts. But that a spinning wheel can remember anything seems at first incredible. Nevertheless it can, and by purely physical means, though electronic, hydraulic computer devices may be used to enforce its orders.

True, a wheel remembers only one thing—its position in space. But it does this supremely well, far better than the human senses—which as airplane pilots know sometimes cannot tell up from down.

The wheels are, of course, gyroscopes. Simple enough to make a toy of, they are today the subject of perhaps the most demanding disciplines in the history of technology. They are more precise, and more difficult to manufacture, than the finest watches. They may spin on the smallest of ball bearings, on tiny jewels, or even on a thin film of air or gas. Some whiz about in a vacuum, electrically suspended so that they touch nothing at all.

Yet the highly sophisticated gyro obeys the same laws as the ordinary toy top. These closely follow Newton's three fundamental laws of motion, although those of angular (or rotary) motion were not clearly set forth until 200 years after Newton. The first and most important of these laws is that a rotating mass will keep turning about its axis (the imaginary line around which it revolves) unless acted upon by some angular torque—that is, a single force that produces a twisting rotation. In other words, a spinning mass wants only to keep spinning forever in the same way, at the same speed, on the same axis.

In practice, of course, air and bearing friction conspire to slow it down and eventually stop it, unless power is applied (in the form of an angular torque!) to keep it going.

Gyroscopic inertia, a result of the law above, is the ability of a spinning wheel to maintain its position unless an outside force shifts it. This was the first of the gyroscope's properties to be exploited. The second, *precession*, is the response of a spinning mass to any force tending to change the position of its spin axis. This result is both mysterious and dramatic. Before going into it, let us see how the gyroscope came to be, and take a look at early attempts to apply the law of precession.

STEPS TO THE GYROSCOPE

Once more the Chinese are credited with a first—the spinning top, probably used by jugglers and as a toy. The easiest way to set a top spinning is with a thumb and finger. In Europe, children literally flog the top into a faster spin by whipping it with a cord whip. The cord-wound top long has been the favorite in America. Also powered by a wound cord was the sedate but colorful singing top of the 19th century nursery.

Spin a top on a tray, and it will remain upright whether you carry the tray around, shake it, or tilt it. The top will slide downhill, but it will remain vertical until it hits the edge of the tray.

An Englishman named Serson, noting this ability of a top to remain erect, about 1740 made one in the form of a metal disk with an axle under it (Figure 1). As the disk would always remain horizontal while spinning, he

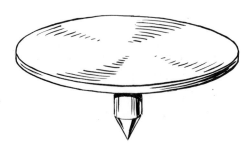

Fig. 1. Serson's artificial horizon.

suggested its use as an artificial horizon aboard ship, for taking sextant readings when the real horizon was invisible. In 1744 the British Admiralty tested the device and agreed to development of it. But when Serson took a new instrument to sea for further testing, he and all hands were lost.

In the 19th century a Frenchman invented another form of this device, said to have been used by the French navy and named after Admiral Fleuriais. It was the first to be continuously powered. The wheel overhung its pivot (Figure 2) and was spun by air jets aimed at buckets in its rim—a surprisingly modern means of propulsion used for many thousands of gyros since. A lens was fitted for reading the wheel's top surface against a sextant, but the instrument proved difficult to use and not very accurate.

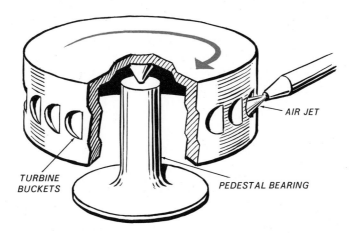

AIR JET

TURBINE
BUCKETS

PEDESTAL BEARING

Fig. 2. Fleuriais' air-spun artificial horizon.

The first gyroscope to resemble the familiar toy gyro was made about 1810 by G. C. Bohnenberger. Instead of a wheel it had a heavy ball. Apparently it was only a scientific curiosity, with no practical application.

In 1851 the French scientist Léon Foucault set up the first visible proof of the earth's diurnal (twenty-four hour) rotation. He hung a very long, heavy pendulum from a high support by a torsionless wire. Its great mass kept the pendulum swinging in the same plane, while the earth majestically turned under it—a phenomenon visible from hour to hour as the direction of swing seemed to shift inside the building. Some museums, and the United Nations building in New York City, have a Foucault pendulum visitors may see.

But Foucault wanted corroborative proof by some means even more independent of the earth. Knowing that a freely mounted rotating wheel would maintain its position in space, he put one in a supporting ring or gimbal frame. Cranked up to high speed on a separate hand-powered machine, this

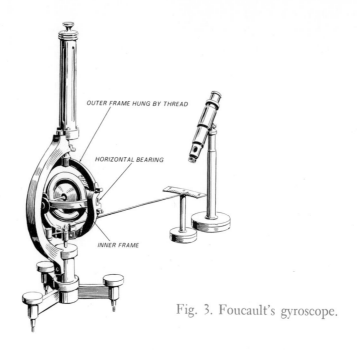

Fig. 3. Foucault's gyroscope.

was quickly placed in a second ringlike frame suspended on a silk thread (Figure 3). A long pointer on this frame extended over a small scale on which a microscope was trained.

That delicately suspended spinning wheel remained fixed while all the world circled around it. For the duration of its spin the wheel was the center of its own universe, its only law its own inertia. The microscope showed definite movement of the pointer, proving that the earth turned.

Foucault named the wheel the gyroscope, from two Greek words— gyros (revolution) and skopein (to see). Built to see the revolution of the earth, the magic wheel has retained its name (usually shortened to gyro) while its uses have far outstripped that first purpose. Foucault himself saw beyond it; he predicted that the gyroscope would eventually be used as a compass.

But it was almost fifty years before a new application was found. In 1898 an Austrian, Ludwig Obry, patented a torpedo steering mechanism. This too was based on gyroscopic inertia. A little bronze wheel weighing only 1½ pounds was spun by an air jet. Its spin axis was horizontal, normally in line with the torpedo's axis. But the frame carrying the wheel could pivot around a vertical axis on bearings fixed in the torpedo body (Figure 4). Also mounted on this frame was control-valve linkage that remained neutral so long as the spin axis was aligned with the torpedo.

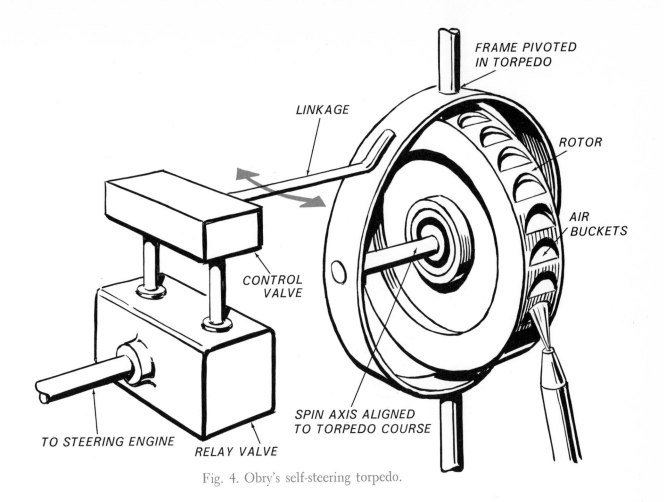

FRAME PIVOTED
IN TORPEDO

LINKAGE

ROTOR

AIR
BUCKETS

CONTROL
VALVE

SPIN AXIS ALIGNED
TO TORPEDO COURSE

TO STEERING ENGINE

RELAY VALVE

Fig. 4. Obry's self-steering torpedo.

If the torpedo shifted course even a fraction of a degree, the rotor remaining stationary in space, the angle between the linkage and valve would shift. The control valve then actuated a relay valve big enough to power the steering engine. As the rudder brought the torpedo back on course, the rotor frame was once more aligned with the torpedo and the valve linkage returned to neutral.

Other inventors also worked on steerable torpedos, among them Louis Brennan, inventor of the monorail car. Also about the end of the century a German, Otto Schlick, invented a roll stabilizer for ships. A rotor weighing more than half a ton was mounted with its axis vertical, in a gimbal having bearings athwartship (Figure 5). The rotor could tilt fore and aft, but not sideways, and so resisted the roll or beam-end movement of the hull. This lengthened the period of roll so that it no longer coincided with wave frequency and its effect was greatly damped. In a test on a German torpedo boat, the Schlick stabilizer reduced a 30-degree roll to 1 degree.

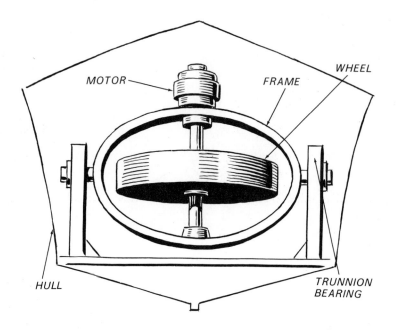

Fig. 5. Schlick's ship stabilizer.

From this it may be seen that gyroscopic inertia is of considerable magnitude. A 6-inch gyro, housed in a case and standing on knife edges as it spins, can be hit a solid blow with a fist. Instead of toppling over, it merely shudders—and twists around a little on the knife edges. This action is the second of the gyro's surprising properties—precession.

THE MYSTERY OF PRECESSION

Suppose a simple top is turning clockwise and you manage, without slowing its spin, to apply a tilt force away from you in what we will for convenience call a northerly direction (Figure 6). Instead of obediently heeling over toward the north, the top tilts to the right or eastwards instead. It has precessed—turned your effort around a corner, or 90 degrees from its original direction.

258

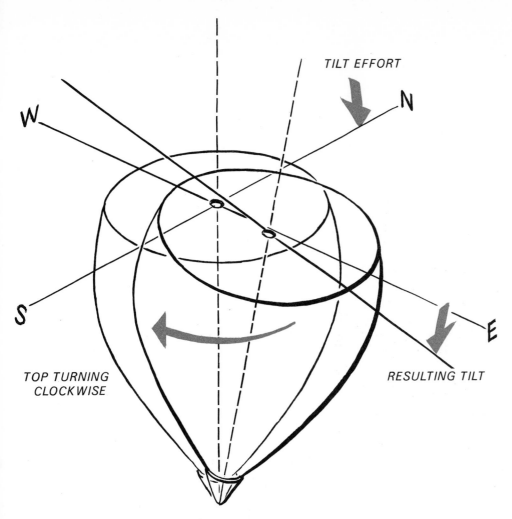

TILT EFFORT

N

W

S

E

TOP TURNING
CLOCKWISE

RESULTING TILT

Fig. 6. How a top recesses.

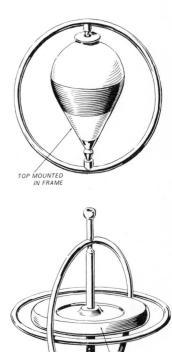

TOP MOUNTED
IN FRAME

HEAVY-RIMMED
ROTOR

Fig. 7. A top in a frame
would be a simple gyro. A
wheel is better.

If your tilt effort were in a southerly direction, the top would precess to the west, while if the top were spinning the other way (counterclockwise) the direction of precession for each tilt would be reversed.

Place the top in a frame (Figure 7), and you have the basis of the gyroscope, for now you can tilt the wheel axis without slowing its spin. Better still, instead of the turnip-shaped top, use a wheel having most of its mass concentrated in its outer rim, like an engine flywheel.

It is better if all gyroscopic actions are seen as movements about certain axes rather than a push against the rim of a wheel or the end of a shaft. Taking another look at Figure 6, the northerly push we applied is really a torque around the west-east axis, while precession occurs around the north-south axis. (Remember that the compass points are used only for identification in this example. As yet they have no real reference to the gyro's behavior.) But in all

259

cases, precession makes the spin axis tend to align itself with the torque axis—not with the *direction* of your push, but with the *axis* around which the push is applied, 90 degrees around!

To understand *why* precession occurs, imagine two particles on opposite sides of the wheel rim, which are of course actually one with the solid wheel and its axle (Figure 8). Let these particles be momentarily on the north-south axis, at 90 degrees to the torque axis around which we are going to try to tilt the wheel. At any instant the particles have momentums tangent to the wheel as shown by the long arrows. (Remember that a stone whirled around at the end of a cord will, if the cord is cut, not continue in a circle but instead fly straight out.)

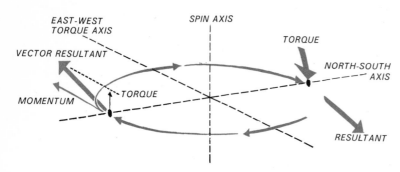

Fig. 8. Why gyros precess.

The torque or tilt effort we apply by pushing down on the particle at the north is in Figure 8 shown as a short vertical arrow downward. But as this takes place around the east-west axis, it becomes an upward force on the opposite side of the wheel, and so is shown there by another short arrow upward.

The two forces shown—momentum and torque—result in a vector force being applied to each of our two rim particles. We show this, by the parallelogram method outlined in Chapter 5, as a sloping arrow—upward for the particle nearer us, downward for the opposite one. Both particles must follow vector courses. But they are one with a rigid body, so the entire wheel tilts around the north-south axis, which is at 90 degrees to the torque axis. The tilt we tried to apply has literally been made to turn a corner.

Anyone who has to roll a tire some distance soon learns that it cannot be steered by turning it in the desired direction. In fact, that tends to make it fall over. Yesterday's children, who enjoyed rolling hoops, knew that the way to steer them was to apply a little tilt to the top of the hoop (or tire) in the direction you wished it to go. If you tilted it to the left, it would not fall over but instead *turn* left. Any effort to tilt it to the right made it turn right. Once more the applied torque turned a corner, as a result of precession.

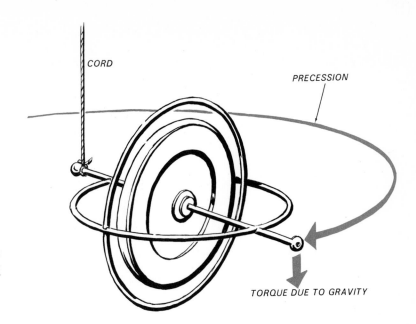

Fig. 9. Toy gyroscope hung on a string while it's spinning will precess continually.

A rolling coin often travels much farther than expected before falling over. When it starts to tip, precession occurs and turns it on a new path. At the end of its roll, when its spin is weak, it rolls in a tightening circle until it falls flat.

The common toy gyroscope demonstrates precession in another way. While it is spinning, hang it by a cord loop on one end of its spin axis (Figure 9). Though it remains level, apparently defying the law of gravity, earth's attraction is nevertheless trying to tilt the free end of the spin axis downward. But precession translates this torque into one 90 degrees around—that is, about the vertical suspension axis instead. The gyro turns on that, and because gravity is continuous, it keeps right on turning around its supporting string. If you hang the gyro from the other end of its spin axis, it will precess in the opposite direction.

There are three strange things about precession besides its odd basic behavior.

1. It stops the instant the torque producing it stops, as if a brake were applied.

2. If the torque continues, so does precession. But it does not accelerate. Precession simply reaches a certain angular velocity or speed (which depends on that of the torque) and maintains it. (Actually, precession can continue only for 90 degrees, because at that point the spin axis coincides with the torque axis, and torque applied around that is ineffective.)

3. Either of the two axes at 90 degrees to the spin axis can be the torque axis, the other becoming the precession axis.

261

TWISTING A GYRO'S TAIL

Another strange thing happens if, while a gyro is precessing, we interfere and try to speed up precession. Instantly the precession axis becomes the torque axis. But that causes precession at right angles to it—a full 180 degrees around from the first torque. A powerful force is created in exactly the opposite direction to the original torque.

As an example of how this *enforced precession* might be useful, consider the primitive little gyro car in Figure 10. A toy gyro is mounted in gimbals crosswise of the car, like Schlick's boat stabilizer. (It must be said that this is not a very stable little car, and no answer to high-speed monorail transport, for it is sensitive to curves and hills. But it will ride along a straight track or a wire for some distance.)

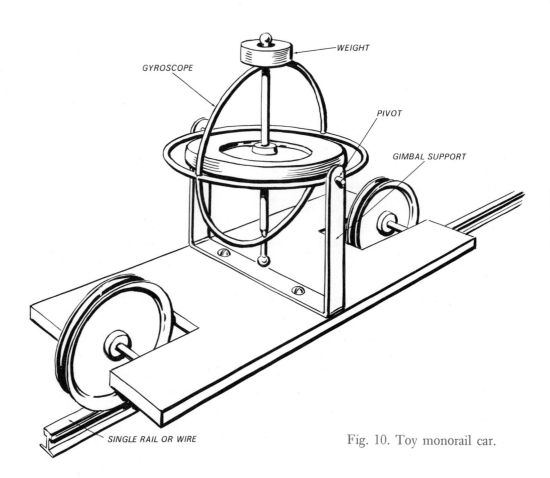

GYROSCOPE

WEIGHT

PIVOT

GIMBAL SUPPORT

SINGLE RAIL OR WIRE

Fig. 10. Toy monorail car.

A gyroscope stabilizes this three-wheels-in-line "gyro-carrier" used by the U.S. Forest Service on narrow trails. The vehicle is propelled at 5 m.p.h. by an 18 hp engine which drives both wheels and gyro. *U.S. Forest Service.*

If the gyro is wound up and spun, it tries to hold the little car upright on its single rail. But almost at once the gyro begins to oscillate violently, and soon it tips over, taking the car with it.

Now we do a strange thing. We add a small weight to the top of the gyro, making it more unstable than ever. In fact, it takes a steady hand to set it upright while spinning. But now (if we have just the right weight) the gyro stands fairly steady. The whole car seems remarkably stable. When the gyro begins to run down and oscillations begin, they are of modest amplitude at first. What makes the difference?

The instant the car starts to heel over, the gyro begins to precess either forward or backward. But that brings the weight over center, so that it tends to hasten the precession. In doing so, it creates a new precession counter to the original torque (that is, to the heeling over of the car). It is as though an invisible finger tilted the car back to straighten it!

Experimental monorail cars have used electric or hydraulic power, triggered by the original precession, to enforce precession and so maintain equilibrium. In 1909 Louis Brennan demonstrated a monorail car in England, carrying forty passengers around an experimental track. Brennan, the inventor of a successful steerable torpedo, in at least one of his experimental cars used two gyros with their spin axes horizontal. These precessed around vertical axes while tilting around a common center. Friction between the gyro axles and projecting shelves on the sides of the car enforced precession. According to a writer in McClure's magazine for February, 1910, the car was remarkably stable and able to negotiate sharp curves and hills, besides remaining upright for a considerable time after gyro power was shut off.

Others stated that Brennan's car could not take unlimited curves. A German and a Russian also built such cars, apparently with little success. Evidently there is room for research in this direction, though the monorail idea remained dormant for decades until the need for swifter urban transport became evident recently.

Dr. Elmer Sperry of the United States in 1913 demonstrated a ship stabilizer of his own design. To Schlick's trunnion-mounted gyroscope he added a small control gyro. Sensing the very start of a roll, this signaled an electric motor that promptly enforced precession of the big gyro, so creating a counter-precession that resisted the ship's roll, much as in our little gyro car.

Though successfully tested in a U.S. Navy ship, Sperry's stabilizer was not adopted for navy use. Instead it was installed on a number of passenger vessels, among them the Italian *Conte di Savoia*. In this liner Sperry installed three rotors, each 13 feet in diameter and weighing 108 tons, because a single rotor capable of doing the job would have had to be 18 feet in diameter, too difficult and costly to make.

The size, weight and cost of the large rotors impelled Sperry to patent a completely different kind of ship stabilizer in 1927. The Gyrofin Ship Stabilizer has large underwater fins, controlled by gyro sensors. Sensing the rate, acceleration and angle of roll, these sensors signal corrective measures to hydraulic actuators that tilt the fins accordingly.

Because of the ship's forward movement, each fin can exert as much as 3,000 foot-tons of lift to counteract the roll. But the fins, which fold back into the hull when not needed, are effective only when the ship is moving. The Gyro-Stabilizer, on the other hand, can operate whether the vessel is under way or lying to. An improved 1959 version of this spinning-rotor stabilizer, designed for nuclear subs, has more sensitive anti-roll control by reason of a variable-speed precession drive, which replaces the fixed-speed drive used in earlier Sperry models.

By switching the control connections, a Gyro-Stabilizer can be run in reverse, so causing a roll while the vessel is in calm waters. This curious inversion finds good use in the Great Lakes. Since 1914 icebreaker ships there have reversed their stabilizers to induce a heavy roll that helps shatter the ice about their hulls.

MODERN GYRO SYSTEMS

It is in control and guidance systems that the gyro has made the greatest advances. Engineers call the rotation of the rotor the *spin*, the torque

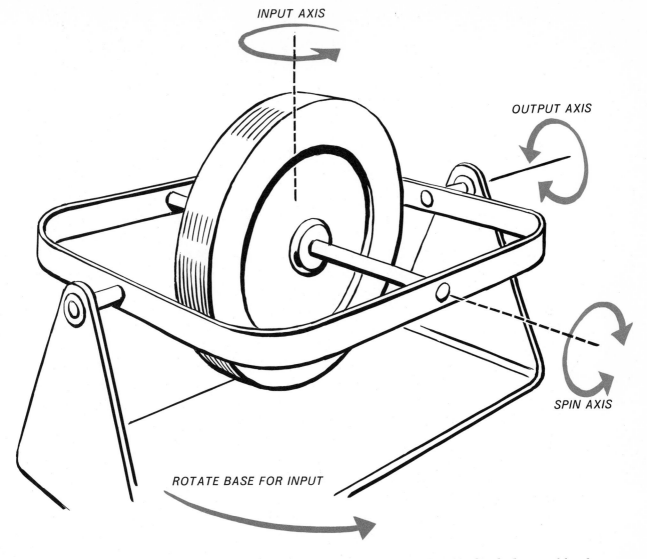

INPUT AXIS

OUTPUT AXIS

SPIN AXIS

ROTATE BASE FOR INPUT

Fig. 11. Single-degree-of-freedom gyro.

applied to twist it out of position the *input*, and the resulting precession the *output*. Thus they speak of the spin axis, the input axis and the output axis, as shown in Figure 11.

The gyro in this drawing has a single pair of gimbal bearings, which enable it to tilt freely about one axis. Engineers call it a single-degree-of-freedom gyro. But where, you may ask, is the input axis? It is vertical, and to apply torque around it you would have to rotate the entire unit—twist the frame. This is exactly what would occur if the whole thing were mounted in a fixed position in a ship or plane. The turning of the vessel or aircraft would impress an input torque on the gyro.

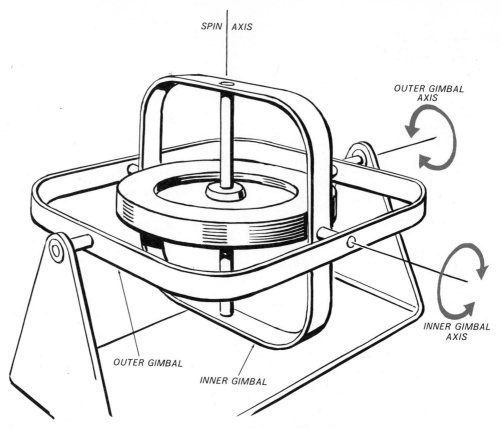

SPIN AXIS

OUTER GIMBAL AXIS

INNER GIMBAL AXIS

OUTER GIMBAL

INNER GIMBAL

Fig. 12. Two-degrees-of-freedom gyro.

If the gyro gimbal is mounted in a second ring or frame on suitable bearings, we have a two-degrees-of-freedom gyro, or a free gyro (Figure 12). The rotor will remain in one position no matter how the base, ship or plane moves around. It is free of all outside influences. Usually the free gyro makes use of gyroscopic inertia to perform its function, rather than precession. For that reason there is rarely any designation of input and output axes.

An important application of the free gyro is the Attitude Gyro Indicator, developed by the Sperry Gyroscope Company in 1944. As shown in Figure 13, it tells the pilot almost pictorially what the attitude of his plane is at any and all times, through a full 360 degrees of roll and pitch. This makes aerobatic maneuvers possible even under blind-flying conditions.

The rate gyro. Today's jets and missiles fly so fast that corrections must be made almost instantly to avoid disaster. A tiny change in attitude quickly pyramids to a major change in position. Therefore the rate of change becomes

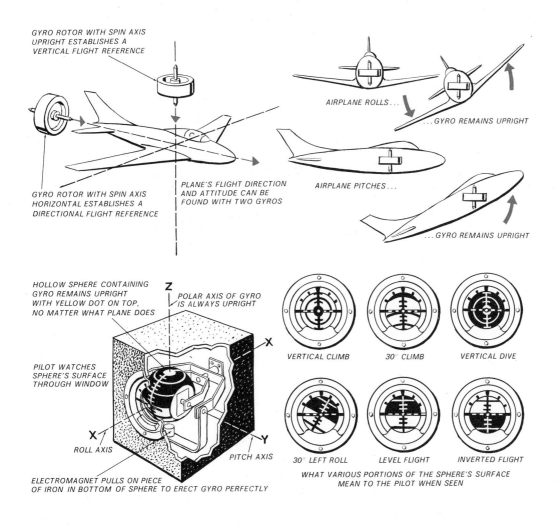

GYRO ROTOR WITH SPIN AXIS UPRIGHT ESTABLISHES A VERTICAL FLIGHT REFERENCE

AIRPLANE ROLLS...

...GYRO REMAINS UPRIGHT

GYRO ROTOR WITH SPIN AXIS HORIZONTAL ESTABLISHES A DIRECTIONAL FLIGHT REFERENCE

PLANE'S FLIGHT DIRECTION AND ATTITUDE CAN BE FOUND WITH TWO GYROS

AIRPLANE PITCHES...

...GYRO REMAINS UPRIGHT

HOLLOW SPHERE CONTAINING GYRO REMAINS UPRIGHT WITH YELLOW DOT ON TOP, NO MATTER WHAT PLANE DOES

Z

POLAR AXIS OF GYRO IS ALWAYS UPRIGHT

X

PILOT WATCHES SPHERE'S SURFACE THROUGH WINDOW

X

ROLL AXIS

Y

PITCH AXIS

ELECTROMAGNET PULLS ON PIECE OF IRON IN BOTTOM OF SPHERE TO ERECT GYRO PERFECTLY

VERTICAL CLIMB

30° CLIMB

VERTICAL DIVE

30° LEFT ROLL

LEVEL FLIGHT

INVERTED FLIGHT

WHAT VARIOUS PORTIONS OF THE SPHERE'S SURFACE MEAN TO THE PILOT WHEN SEEN

Fig. 13. Attitude Gyro Indicator.

important. Besides that, a single-degree-of-freedom gyro will, if an input torque continues, eventually precess 90 degrees or against its stops, if such have been fitted. In either case, it can provide no more significant information.

In its place, engineers have developed the rate gyro (Figure 14). The single gimbal movement of this is restrained by springs, which normally hold the spin axis in a horizontal plane. But if the aircraft this instrument is mounted in makes a turn, this input torque causes precession, stretching one of the springs. Precession continues, however, only until the output torque and

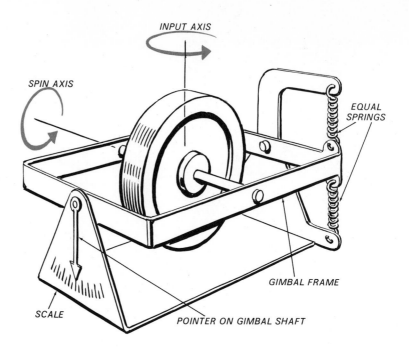

INPUT AXIS

SPIN AXIS

EQUAL SPRINGS

GIMBAL FRAME

SCALE

POINTER ON GIMBAL SHAFT

Fig. 14. Rate gyro.

spring tension are equal. Fixed to the gimbal frame is an indicator that can swing to either side of its zero position. With the right gyro mass and spring tension, a pointer on the gimbal shaft will read proportionally to the rate (or suddenness) of the aircraft's turn.

A gentle turn will provide a weak input and a low rate reading, a fast turn a strong input torque and a correspondingly high reading. Rate gyros are also used in some automatic pilots. Three of them provide output signals (instead of indications) to make the elevators, ailerons and rudder counteract pitch, roll and yaw to just the right degree.

The rate gyro added deadly accuracy to Allied antiaircraft fire in World War II. Planes were attaining new and higher speeds, and if a gunner sighted on one directly it would be long gone when his bullets reached the spot. Gunners were of course trained to fire ahead of such rapidly moving targets, but how much to "lead" them to make aircraft and bullet coincide in some other part of the sky was a decision depending on individual experience and skill.

A rate gyro changed that. It closely estimated the required lead and aimed the gun accordingly. As the gunner swung optical sights to stay on the target, this movement put an input torque on a rate gyro (Figure 15). Precessing against spring tension by a proportionate amount, the gyro-con-

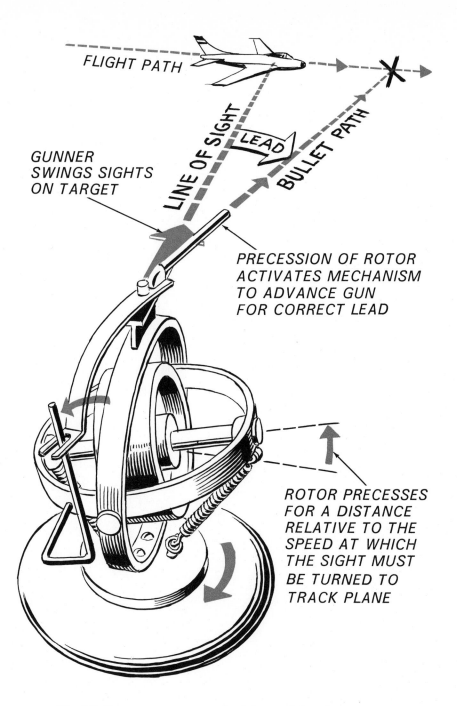

FLIGHT PATH

LINE OF SIGHT

LEAD

BULLET PATH

GUNNER
SWINGS SIGHTS
ON TARGET

PRECESSION OF ROTOR
ACTIVATES MECHANISM
TO ADVANCE GUN
FOR CORRECT LEAD

ROTOR PRECESSES
FOR A DISTANCE
RELATIVE TO THE
SPEED AT WHICH
THE SIGHT MUST
BE TURNED TO
TRACK PLANE

Fig. 15. Rate gyro computes lead for antiaircraft guns.

trolled mechanism swung the gun barrel ahead of the sight line—just the right amount to make target and bullet arrive in fatal coincidence.

The wheel that points north. It has been said that if man had always lived inside the earth, with never a glimpse of the outer world, the gyro could have told him three things: 1) that the earth rotates; 2) the direction of true north: 3) the latitude of the observer.

Foucault's experiment proved the first point, and it was he who foretold the gyro's use as a compass. Although a toy gyro will not spin long enough to align itself in a north-seeking mode, you can use one to show this action by analogy.

Saw off both of the frame projections at the ends of the spin axis, and find a glass or cup in which the frame can rest while free to turn in any direction. This makes your toy gyro a simple free gyro.

Wind it up for a good spin and place it in the glass or cup. It will simply buzz there, perhaps precessing slowly because of poor balance. But now place the glass on a swivel chair, piano stool, or phonograph turtable and slowly turn this. In just a few revolutions the gyro will have shrugged itself about and settled with its spin axis straight up, *parallel to the spin axis of the stool or turntable*.

Now assume the turntable is the earth, and you can see the possibility of a gyro compass. For a workable and reliable instrument, there must be means of compensating for friction, latitude, and the speed of the ship or plane on which the compass is used. Dr. Herman Kaempfe of Germany patented a gyro compass in 1908. Dr. Elmer Sperry of the United States tested his version on the U.S.S. Delaware in 1911. In Great Britain S. G. Brown devised an ingenious gyro compass about the same time.

Figure 16 shows the principle of the Sperry instrument in schematic form. Sperry added a mercury ballistic to the gimbal-mounted rotor, shown in the drawing as a U-tube with enlarged ends, partially filled with mercury (a liquid at ordinary temperatures). As the earth turns, the rotor tries to keep its axis in its original plane (east-west in the drawing). But as the gyro moves around earth's curvature, this eventually makes one leg of the U-tube lower than the other. Mercury flows into this lower leg. The unbalanced weight on the gyro tries to pull that end of it down. The gyro naturally precesses. The unbalance and precession continue as the earth carries the gyro farther around, until the gyro axis is parallel to the spin axis of the earth—whereupon it is of course pointing true north. As the U-tube is now also oriented north-south, the mercury levels out and precession ends.

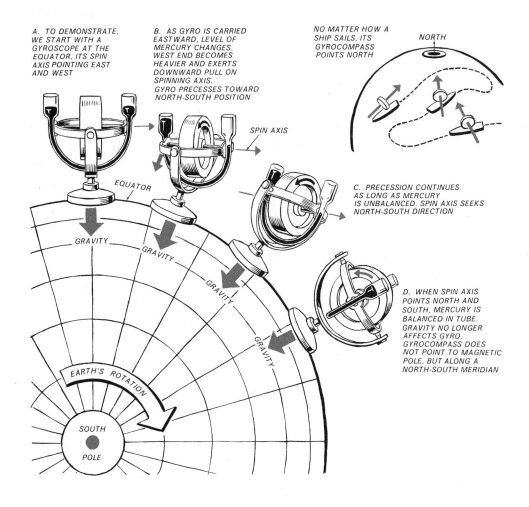

A. TO DEMONSTRATE, WE START WITH A GYROSCOPE AT THE EQUATOR, ITS SPIN AXIS POINTING EAST AND WEST

B. AS GYRO IS CARRIED EASTWARD, LEVEL OF MERCURY CHANGES. WEST END BECOMES HEAVIER AND EXERTS DOWNWARD PULL ON SPINNING AXIS. GYRO PRECESSES TOWARD NORTH-SOUTH POSITION

NO MATTER HOW A SHIP SAILS, ITS GYROCOMPASS POINTS NORTH

NORTH

SPIN AXIS

EQUATOR

GRAVITY

GRAVITY

GRAVITY

GRAVITY

EARTH'S ROTATION

SOUTH POLE

C. PRECESSION CONTINUES AS LONG AS MERCURY IS UNBALANCED. SPIN AXIS SEEKS NORTH-SOUTH DIRECTION

D. WHEN SPIN AXIS POINTS NORTH AND SOUTH, MERCURY IS BALANCED IN TUBE. GRAVITY NO LONGER AFFECTS GYRO. GYROCOMPASS DOES NOT POINT TO MAGNETIC POLE, BUT ALONG A NORTH-SOUTH MERIDIAN

Fig. 16. How the gyro compass operates.

Being nonmagnetic, the gyro compass is unaffected by changes in the earth's magnetism, a ship's own metal, or land masses containing iron ore. In 1922 Sperry introduced the Gyropilot, known as "Metal Mike," an automatic helmsman guided by the gyro compass. This steers the straightest course possible, using minimum rudder, until disengaged to let a human helmsman take over.

True north does not coincide with compass north, and the deviation varies from month to month and year to year. But the north-seeking gyro is a valuable adjunct to marine and aerial navigation, and indispensable to inertial guidance systems. It might be thought that the gyro compass would be most effective at the equator, and useless near the poles. But today's instrument is so far perfected that the navigating officer of the nuclear submarine Nautilus reported, after that craft's journey under the North Pole in 1958, that the Mark 19 Sperry Gyro Compass stayed on the true meridian at least to 88 degrees north.

In 1944 Sperry introduced the Gyrosyn compass, a useful hybrid. Slaved to a magnetic detector that senses a plane's orientation to the earth's magnetic field, and to a magnetic compass, a gyro is synchronized with the earth's magnetic lines of force. Its signals can be relied on for accurate heading information at any time, with no allowance for drift or need for resetting, as is frequently necessary with gyro compasses.

Mechanics of a gyro. The rotor may be driven by air jets against its rim, though in practice the gyro casing is usually hooked to a vacuum line. As a result, air is drawn in through orifices aimed at the rim buckets (Figure 16). This is the same way vacuum windshield wipers operate.

Many gyros are electrically driven, being built like an inside-out electric motor, the wire-wound stator fixed inside the revolving rotor, which is driven by induction (Figure 17). In the Gyrosyn, for example, the 12-ounce rotor is driven by 400-cycle, three-phase current at 22,000 r.p.m.

Some gyros that have only a short use period, such as those in a missile booster, may be spring wound.

Though some rotors turn on miniscule ball bearings, and others on tiny jewels, new developments surpass even these delicate mountings. There is the gas bearing, which supports its load on a micro-thin film of gas or air. (To take an extreme case as an example, Honeywell has built a spacecraft simulation platform weighing nine tons, that is free to turn in any direction on a spherical air bearing. The steel ball of this bearing—and the platform's full weight—rest on a cushion of pressurized nitrogen seven ten-thousandths of an inch thick.)

Northrop Nortronics developed one of the first electrostatically suspended gyros (ESG). Honeywell's has a ball-like rotor of beryllium. Electrical forces hold ESG rotors suspended in a vacuum. Neither air nor bearing friction can slow them or introduce errors.

Some gyros are sealed inside cans containing helium or other light gas. Others rest on jeweled gimbal bearings in cans filled with a viscous fluid, of

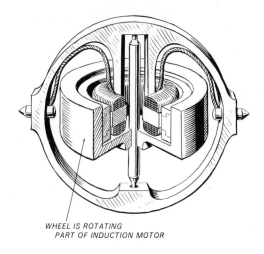

WHEEL IS ROTATING
PART OF INDUCTION MOTOR

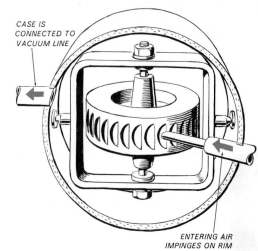

CASE IS
CONNECTED TO
VACUUM LINE

ENTERING AIR
IMPINGES ON RIM

Fig. 17. Powering the gyro.

such a density as to just balance the weight of the suspended parts, so that the bearings are actually not loaded. The viscosity also damps precession, making these a special kind of rate gyro called integrating gyros.

Other gyro applications. The gyro is now used in helicopter flight controls. The Sperry Flight Director processes gyro and instrument information, then delivers correct flight instructions to a pilot on a single indicator. A reliable gyro horizon, and even a special Gyrosyn that can be unslaved from its magnetic partner for navigating airliners over the Pole, are other examples of gyro applications to air travel.

On land, the gyro finds other difficult jobs to do. A track recorder that takes over the work of human trackwalkers records differences in rail elevation, depressions, rail spreads and rough spots under actual operating conditions—since the recorder is in a railroad car as it works. A tiny gyro lowered with oil-drilling equipment keeps a photographic record of the course of the drill and elapsed drilling time, so avoiding the embarrassment and expense of drilling under a neighbor's or competitor's property.

Another interesting gyroscope application is a camera stabilizer, introduced by Kenyon Products Inc. about 1960. A small metal cylinder contains two gyro wheels spun by self-contained batteries at about 20,000 r.p.m. On top of the case is a camera tripod screw. With the gyros running, a photographer can hold his camera rock steady even if he is subject to the vibration of a helicopter or the pitching of a boat deck. Pictures taken from such an unstable

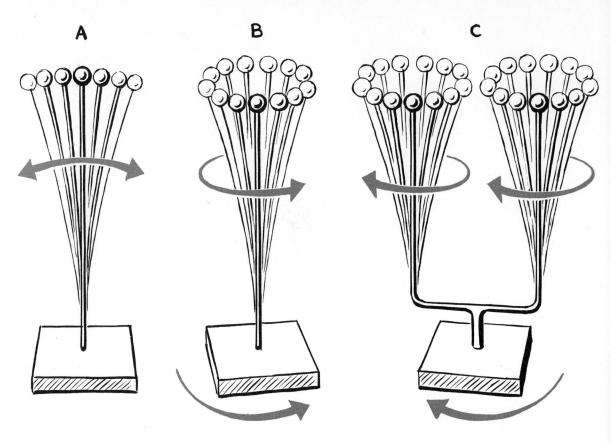

Fig. 18. How vibrating rods precess.

platform are much sharper when the camera is steadied by the gyroscopic inertia of the Kenyon unit.

The vibratory gyro. Just when we were well on our way to taming the magic of the spinning wheel, an American named Joseph Lyman asked in effect, "Why spin a rotor? Use a tuning fork." In 1953 the Sperry Gyroscope Company unveiled the results of this brand new concept in the form of the Gyrotron Vibratory Gyroscope (vibragyro for short). Its active element is not a wheel, but a stunted tuning fork about the size of a king-size cigarette, and it does not revolve, but vibrates.

An oscillating mass can be compared to a pendulum, which wants to keep swinging in whatever plane it is started—the same inertial property Foucault used to demonstrate the rotation of the earth. So a weight on a flexible rod (A in Figure 18) will vibrate to and fro in a straight arc. But if you turn its support about, that straight path becomes an ellipse (B). Like precession in the wheeled gyro, the amplitude of this change—the breadth of the ellipse—is proportional to the rate of turn applied.

274

Fig. 19. The fly's vibragyro.

With two vibrating masses as in a tuning fork (C) this effect results in a twisting action where they join at the stem. Again this is proportional to the applied torque. (The necessary vibration can be produced mechanically, or more conveniently by oscillating electromagnetic fields.)

Having its own built-in springs, the vibragyro is a natural rate gyro. It is superior in some ways to the spinning-rotor gyro. Test models made for the U.S. Navy Bureau of Aeronautics in the 1950s survived shocks 200 times the force of gravity, were capable of a wide range of measurement, and had remarkable freedom from drift and false responses, in part because the vibragyro has no spin bearings and therefore is not subject to bearing friction. In time it may replace the spinning wheel in some gyro applications.

After the first models had been successfully tested, Sperry experimenters were amazed to be told that the idea was pretty old—a few million years old at least. Two winged flies, including the common house pest, have a pair of vibrating appendages behind their wings (Figure 19). Entomologists, who called these *halteres*, claim they are organs of balance—not heavy enough for direct stabilization, but acting as sensors that send corrective control commands to the wings.

To resolve the natural doubts of Sperry's engineers, entomologists pointed to work done at Cambridge University. There J. W. S. Pringle cemented the halters in place so that they could no longer vibrate. Released, the flies proved to be as unstable as a flying shingle, and tumbled helplessly to the ground.

INERTIAL GUIDANCE

The first guided missile in the United States was an aerial torpedo made for the Navy in 1915. Guided by gyro equipment designed by Elmer Sperry, the device is said to have scored "accurate bullseyes at 50 miles." Later Sperry devised still more accurate equipment making use of radio command signals from the ground.

But as radar and other electronic systems were developed, it became evident that missiles required a guidance system that could not be jammed, fooled or otherwise subverted by enemy equipment. Therefore it could not depend upon electromagnetic waves, infrared detection, sound waves, or any combination of these. Ideally it should be governed only by its own inherent properties, but how then could it relate to the rest of the earth or any position on it?

The answer was in that property of matter called *inertia*—the tendency of a mass to remain at rest or in uniform motion unless acted upon by an outside force, which is Newton's First Law. Systems based on this are therefore called inertial guidance (I.G.) systems.

In 1945 U.S. investigators found German documents relating to research on such a system for the V2. These were sent to Redstone Arsenal, but it was at the Massachusetts Institute of Technology three years later than Dr. C. Stark Draper built the first star-tracker inertial navigator. It weighed 4,000 pounds. In 1953 Dr. Draper flew a huge inertial system, lightened to 2,800 pounds, from Boston to Los Angeles on a B-29.

From then on things moved quickly. The year 1958 saw the U.S. nuclear submarine Nautilus navigate under the North Pole by an inertial system, as well as the first delivery of such systems for the Jupiter IRBM.

The first Polaris submarine, the *George Washington*, itself guided by an inertial system, in 1960 launched the first similarly equipped Polaris missile from beneath the sea. That same year an Atlas missile made the first full ICBM flight from the Atlantic Missile Range guided by I.G. equipment, and the *U.S.S. Triton* circumnavigated the globe in eighty-four days, entirely under water, its eyes an inertial guidance system.

In 1964 Pan American Airways bought its first I.G. system and announced plans to use them on its entire fleet of 707s. Northrop Nortronics in the fall of 1967 announced it would study the feasibility of a ball-shaped platform only 4 inches in diameter for I.G. systems. In midsummer of that year Honeywell had a record of 272 hours of flawless operation of its inertial measuring unit during ten manned Gemini missions. The same year Honeywell could boast of the first successful flights of a strapdown sensor block instead of a conventional gimballed system. An "electronic gimbal" in the digital computer of the system determines position even more reliably and at lower cost than a gimballed sensor block.

I.G. systems are basically a refinement of the centuries-old concept of dead reckoning. If a sailor knew his ship's speed and direction, and how long it had sailed, he had a fairly close idea of his location with respect to his starting point, even without sextant readings.

But you cannot throw a long line out of a plane or missile, nor bounce sound or radio waves off the ground to measure your speed, if you want an interference-free guidance system. What is needed is an inertia-actuated instrument called an accelerometer. This does not actually measure the speed or distance covered. It can sense only *changes* in velocity, and it does this by measuring the resistance of a small body to such changes—its inertia, in fact.

Teamed with a good clock, the accelerometer can tell us how far and in what direction a vehicle has traveled, taking into account every deviation and change in speed.

Basically, the accelerometer is a relatively heavy chunk of material mounted on low-friction guides so that it can move back and forth (Figure 20). The *seismic mass* is held centered by springs of equal and carefully calibrated tension. A sensitive electric contact or pickoff that slides on a resistance wire signals the position of the mass at all times to other components of the system.

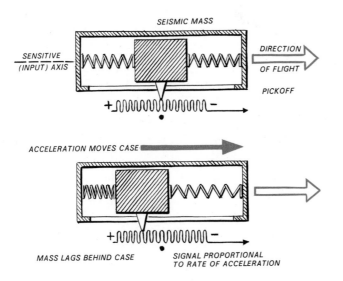

Fig. 20. An accelerometer is actuated by inertia.

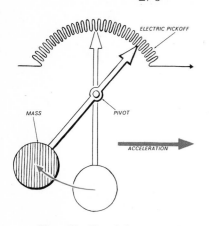

Fig. 21. Pendulous accelerometer in simplest form.

As the plane gains speed in the direction of the solid arrow, the inertia of the mass will make it lag behind, stretching the forward spring as shown. When the engines are throttled back and the plane settles to a constant speed, the spring will draw the mass back to center. It will remain there unless head winds reduce the speed, the engines are slowed, or the flaps lowered. The resulting deceleration in any of these cases will again make the mass lag behind the movement of the rest of the instrument (and the plane), but this time in a forward direction. Again a signal will be sent to the guidance system.

In some accelerometers the springs themselves support the seismic mass, while in one design the mass is kept centered by a magnetic field. To keep it from overshooting, it is sometimes immersed in water or a more viscous fluid.

The pendulous accelerometer is shown in its simplest form in Figure 21. A floated one makes use of an off-center mass mounted on gimbals—in effect a sidewise mounted pendulum (Figure 22). Acceleration causes the mass to turn, the heaviest part of it swinging backwards. The pickoff signal is amplified and fed back to a torquer coil that returns the mass to neutral, the amount of current necessary to do this being measured as an acceleration reading. Honeywell is working on electrically suspended accelerometers and also on cryogenic units (including gyros) which make use of the strange properties of metals that are cooled to almost absolute zero.

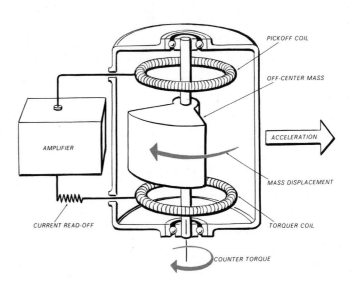

Fig. 22. Floated pendulous
accelerometer.

The 3,963-mile pendulum. If you tilt an accelerometer forward, the weight will slide that way—and inform you of a false acceleration. The instrument must be kept absolutely level with respect to the earth. Gyros will do this—but too well. As the vehicle moves around the earth's curvature, the platform kept stable by gyros will remain parallel to its former position—which means it will be tilted in its present location.

Accelerometers on such a platform will build up intolerable errors, and the guidance system will fail. The platform must be tilted progressively to stay perpendicular to a line drawn from the vehicle to the center of the earth. You cannot hang a pendulum on the platform to keep it so, for the pendulum would be affected by acceleration and deceleration. Dr. Maximillian Schuler, a German professor, in 1923 pointed out that only a pendulum as long as the radius of the earth—3,963 miles—would be unaffected by anything the supporting vehicle might do. Its weight already being at the center of gravity of the globe, it would stay at rest no matter how you moved the string.

Such a pendulum is impossible, but Schuler calculated that its back-and-forth swing would take 84 minutes. Therefore, he said, any undamped physical system oscillating naturally at an 84-minute period would swing uniformly either side of the true vertical. He suggested that this fact might be used to make an artificial horizon.

Instead it proved to be the answer to an inertial platform. Though not a pendulum, it is made to act like one with a closed-loop feedback in its gyro and servo systems. The platform tilts too far first in one direction and then in the other, but when the factors are rightly selected the system acts like a Schuler pendulum with an 84-minute period, and errors cancel out.

How inertial guidance works. Suppose your vehicle were to travel on a flat surface from A to B in Figure 23. Accelerometer X is positioned to read acceleration changes parallel to the desired course, accelerometer Y to indicate such at right angles to the course. The compass keeps these instruments oriented in their proper directions.

When the vehicle starts off, X sends its computer a running account of applied acceleration. (When acceleration stops, the computer assumes the vehicle is moving at the speed last attained. Should it slow down, the accelerometer would report a deceleration and the computer would take account of that.) The clock feeds elapsed-time information into both computers.

So long as the vehicle remains on course, accelerometer Y will have no output. But any drift off course in either direction, toward A or C, will actuate Y and send a signal to the second computer. From this and elapsed time the computer will calculate the amount of deviation, and feed back a course correction to insure the vehicle's arrival at B instead of A or C.

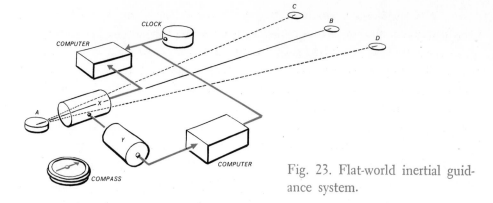

Fig. 23. Flat-world inertial guidance system.

But the world over which we travel is round, subjects us to a mysterious force called gravity, rotates at a terrific speed (17.4 miles per minute at the equator) and has an erratic magnetic field that varies so much as to make a magnetic compass useless for orienting the accelerometers. And, as already mentioned, these must be kept level to the local perpendicular at all times.

The instruments must therefore be mounted on a platform kept level by the Schuler pendulum effect and held stable by three gyros of superb quality (Figure 24). It is also necessary to compensate for the earth's equatorial bulge and for the fact that, because the earth is turning as it moves in orbit, we have to take a curved course in space to follow a straight one over the globe.

The gyros are rate integrating gyros, of a quality deemed impossible twenty years ago. Usually the rotors are mounted in jeweled pivots, then floated to zero buoyancy. The actual platform has at least four gimbals, to permit even a 90-degree displacement with no risk of gimbal lock.

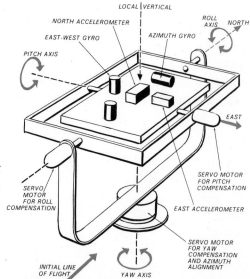

Fig. 24. Simplified accelerometer platform shows leveling and stabilizing devices.

The latitude and longitude of the starting point are fed into the system's computer and the platform aligned north. From then on, the system has a reference point in space and can measure all motion away from it very precisely. The computer adds all accelerations, deducts decelerations, figures in all deviations, calculates elapsed time, and comes up with exactly how far and in what direction the vehicle has moved from its launching point.

Inertial guidance platforms range from small ones weighing only a few pounds to one for supersonic bombers that is about 1½ feet long and weighs 80 pounds. But complete aircraft navigation systems may weigh as much as a ton, and those for naval use much more. Firmly established in military and space applications in the 1950s, inertial guidance is now being applied to civilian aviation.

Fantastic accuracy is necessary in the instruments of such systems. Rotor tolerances, for example, must be held to less than a millionth of an inch. Perhaps it is a modest price to pay for landing a spacecraft on a selected spot after a 250,000-mile flight to the moon.

Ring Laser Inertial Guidance. Another guidance system being used in a number of aerospace applications is the ring laser inertial sensor. Announced publicly by Sperry Gyroscope Company early in 1963, this system measures angular velocity of the vehicle it is guiding by means of two laser beams. These are highly coherent and oppositely traveling light waves generated by laser action moving along a closed path. The waves travel at a constant velocity, and rotation of the vehicle changes the frequency (or, inversely, the wavelength) of the light, thus altering, through a computer system, the vehicle's path.

The first unit of the ring laser sensor was a square device with a perimeter of about 4 yards. Four gas laser tubes were used, one at each side. Triangular units have been developed which are much smaller in size and require only one laser tube to generate the dual light waves. An even more recent system has a laser beam going in one direction, and stability is achieved with a system of mirrors. These are some of the many systems that are bringing all-electronic and all-digital operation with high accuracy and reliability to aerospace vehicles.

INDEX

Index

INDEX   289

War, impetus to, invention, 5
War of 1812, 240
Water, boiling temperature of, 143
Water Wheel, 188, 191–193
Watt, James, 7, 10, 37, 61, 108, 110, 139, 140
Watt's steam engines, 233
Watt, unit of power, 10
Wedge, 2, 54
Wedge, as small inclined plane, 60–61
Wedge, mechanical advantage of, 60
West Point Foundry, 155
Wheel and axle, 2, 28
Wheel, and axle, as lever, 31–32
Wheel, and rotary power, 27–44
Wheel and separate axle, 28
Wheel, Assyrian Six-spoked, 29
Wheel, bronze, 29
Wheel, converting rotary to reciprocating motion, 34–44
Wheel, Greek improvements on, 29
Wheel, inclined animal on, 30, 31
Wheel of pots, 29, 31
Wheel, pegged, 41
Wheel, Persian water, 30, 31
Wheel, potter's, 29
Wheel, primitive, 27
Wheel, ship's, 33
Wheel, solid, 28

Wheel, spoked, 28
Wheels, friction and, 75
Why water explodes, 143
Wich, Ray, 250, 251
Wilkinson, John, 139
William H. Vanderbilt (locomotive), 152
Winch, 130
Windless, adaptation of, 33
Windless, Chinese, 52–53
Windless, principle of, 32
Windmill, 34, 188–190
Windmill, steam, 196
Windshield wiper, vacuum, 159
Wine press, ancient, 25
Work, definition of, 5
World War II, 162, 223, 240, 250
Worm drives, 64, 102, 103
Worm gear, 63
Wright, W. L., 169

York (locomotive), 155

"Zero-reaction," tool of astronauts, 6
Zircaloy tubes, 203